The Student Engineer's Companion

41
£8.95

The Student Engineer's Companion

J. Carvill

Butterworths

LONDON–BOSTON–DURBAN
SINGAPORE–SYDNEY–TORONTO–WELLINGTON

First Published 1980
reprinted 1985

British Library in Cataloguing in Publication Data

Carvill, J
The student engineer's companion
1. Mechanical engineering – Equipment and supplies
I. Title
621.8 TJ153 79-42954

ISBN 0 408 00438 X

Typeset by Butterworths Litho Preparation Department

Printed in England by Page Bros Ltd, Norwich, Norfolk

Preface

This book has been compiled with the intention of providing all those interested in engineering, whether as a profession or as a hobby, with easily understood and clearly illustrated descriptions of a large number of basic machine elements, tools, processes and materials.

With an increasing number of pupils studying technology and engineering drawing and design at school, there is a need for a single inexpensive volume containing a comprehensive range of the 'hardware' of engineering. I hope that this book will satisfy that need and incidentally yield much good material for engineering drawing exercises. It should also prove to be invaluable to students embarking upon engineering courses many of whom will have had little or no practical experience, and especially to students outside the United Kingdom who are studying engineering in the English language, wherever they may be, and have difficulty with the often archaic and confusing terminology. The book should also find a place in the drawing office and workshop as well as the layman's library.

The Student Engineer's Companion describes about 800 concepts presented in four sections, Basic Engineering Components, Power Transmission Elements, Workshop Equipment, and Engineering Materials, which are accompanied by nearly 550 illustrations. Most of these are in the form of engineering drawings, often with two views in third angle projection, and a comprehensive index allows easy cross-reference. As far as possible the alternative American terminology has been given.

The first section describes about 450 basic components including, for example, 90 under the heading of Fasteners such as bolts, nuts, and rivets. In the second section a wide range of power transmission elements is given including, brakes, clutches, shaft couplings and cams. The most commonly used hand and machine tools, together with metal joining and forming equipment, appear in the third section. The final section deals with the more important metals and their alloys, plastics and other materials used in engineering.

I would like to thank my colleagues at Newcastle-upon-Tyne Polytechnic and friends at Thornhill Comprehensive School, Sunderland, for checking the drawings and scripts and for their constructive suggestions. Finally, I would like to thank my wife, Anne, for her patience and assistance in producing this book.

J.C.

Contents

1. BASIC ENGINEERING COMPONENTS

1.1 Fasteners 1
1.2 Screw threads 13
1.3 Springs 15
1.4 Gears 19
1.5 Fluid seals, joints and gaskets 23
1.6 Pipes, pipe fittings, ducts and valves 29
1.7 Shafts and rods 38
1.8 Bearings 42
1.9 Engineering design features 47
1.10 Stock materials 57

2. POWER TRANSMISSION ELEMENTS

2.1 Brakes and clutches 60
2.2 Shaft couplings 66
2.3 Belt, rope and chain drives 70
2.4 Mechanisms 74

3. WORKSHOP EQUIPMENT

3.1 Hand tools 82
3.2 Machine tools 95
3.3 Soft-soldering, brazing and welding equipment 107
3.4 Metal-forming equipment 112

4. ENGINEERING MATERIALS

4.1 Metals 118
4.2 Plastics and other non-metallic materials 120

1. Basic Engineering Components

1.1 FASTENERS

BOLTS

The bolt is widely used in engineering to fasten machine parts together, often in conjunction with a nut, to form a non-permanent connection between the parts. It has a head (usually hexagonal but which may also be square or round) and a shank of circular cross-section which is screwed with a V thread for part of its length. When the shank is screwed for its whole length it is often called a *screw* or *machine screw*.

Bolts are available in a wide range of shank diameters and lengths with various thread pitches.

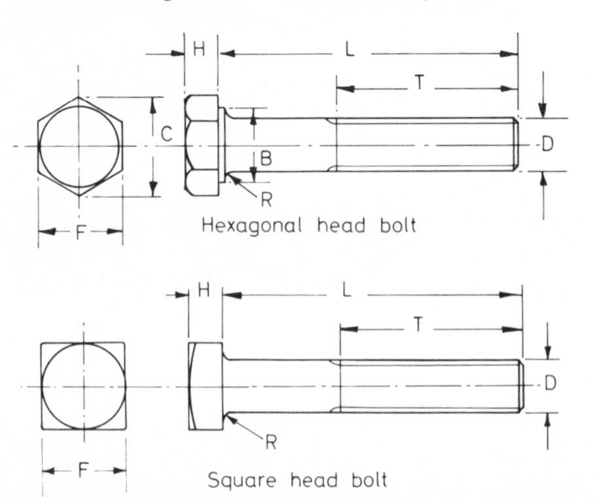

Figure 1.1 *Types of bolt*

Materials Most bolts are made of low or medium carbon steel by forging or machining, and the threads may be cut or rolled. Forged bolts are termed 'black' and machined bolts 'bright'. They are also made in high tensile steel (HT bolts), alloy steel, stainless steel, brass and other non-ferrous metals and alloys. In some cases they are protected from corrosion by galvanising or plating.

Types of thread In Britain metric bolts (ISOM) have largely replaced Whitworth (BSW) and British Standard Fine (BSF). For small sizes British Association (BA) threads are used. In the U.S.A. the most common threads are 'unified fine' (UNF) and 'unified coarse' (UNC).

Dimensions and proportions British and U.S. bolts have fractional inch sizes, e.g. ¼ in., ½ in., 1 in., with standard lengths, e.g. 1 in., 2½ in., etc., and metric bolts are made with diameters of integral numbers of mm, as shown in Table 1.1.

Table 1.1
EXTRACT FROM TABLE OF METRIC BOLT SIZES (mm)

Nominal Size	*D*	*H*	*F*	*Thread pitch Coarse*	*Fine*
M10	10	7	17	1.5	1.25
M12	12	8	19	1.75	1.25
M16	16	10	24	2.0	1.5
M20	20	13	30	2.5	1.5

D = Outside or major diameter of thread
L = Length of shank
T = Length of thread
H = Height of head
F = Distance across flats
C = Distance across corners
R = Radius of fillet under head
B = Bearing diameter

The main dimensions of bolts are: outside or major diameter of thread, length of shank, length of thread, height of head, hexagon size across flats and across corners. In addition, the pitch of the threads is given and sometimes the diameter at the bottom of the threads. The expression 'length of bolt' refers to the shank length.

Loading The total load on a bolt is the sum of the initial tightening load and the load imposed by the machine parts fastened by the bolt. The tightening load is often controlled by the stipulation of a limiting tightening torque and special torque spanners are available for this purpose.

Bolted joint A bolt may be used with a nut and washer to fasten parts together. The washer prevents damage to the surface of the part adjacent to the nut when the nut is tightened. In this case the bolt is referred to as a *through bolt*.

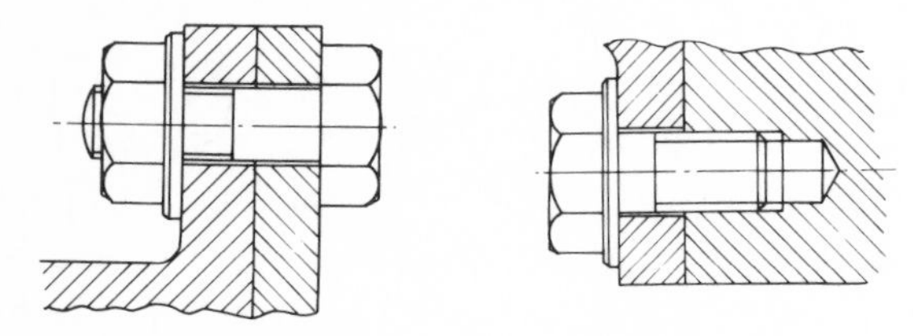

Figure 1.2 *Bolted joint (through bolt) application*

Figure 1.3 *Tap bolt application*

Tap bolt In circumstances where a nut cannot be accommodated it may be replaced by a threaded hole in one of the machine parts connected by the bolt. Passing through a clearance hole in the first part, the bolt is screwed into the threaded hole in the second part. Closer spacing of the bolts is achieved by the use of socket-head screws which are described later.

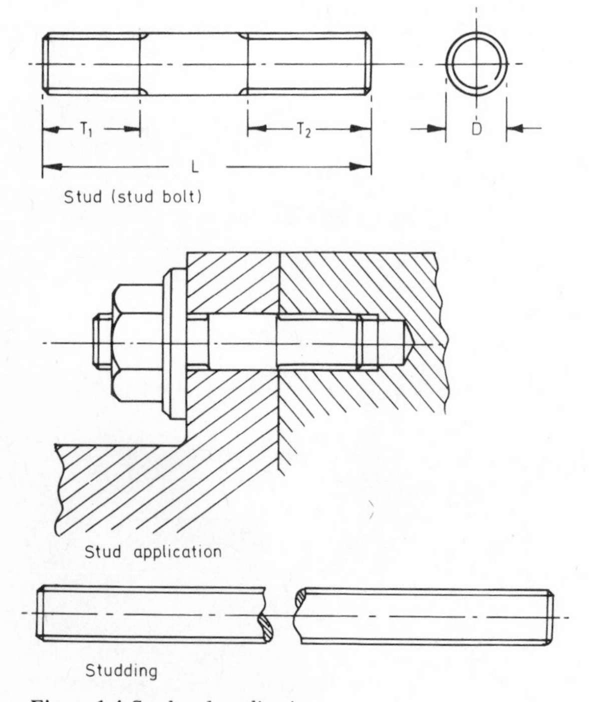

Figure 1.4 *Stud and application*

Stud (stud bolt) In cases where a tap bolt may have to be removed and replaced at frequent intervals, damage to the thread in the hole may occur. In such situations it is advisable to use a stud or stud bolt.

A stud consists of a piece of round bar threaded at each end with a plain middle section. The threads may have different pitches or be of opposite hands, i.e. one right hand and the other left hand. One end of the stud is screwed into the threaded part using two nuts or a special *stud box*, and the other part fastened by means of a nut and washer. The stud is left in place when the parts are dismantled.

Lengths of screwed rod known as *studding* are available for use as studs.

Uniform strength bolt Bolts under high impulsive load have a tendency to break at the bottom of the threads where the cross sectional area is smallest, and the V shape tends to produce cracks.

In a uniform strength bolt part of the shank is reduced in diameter to that at the bottom of the thread. Under high shock loads this part stretches and relieves the stress in the threads.

Alternatively, the shank may be drilled to reduce the area of cross section.

Uniform strength bolts are used for big-ends of connecting-rods in petrol and diesel engines.

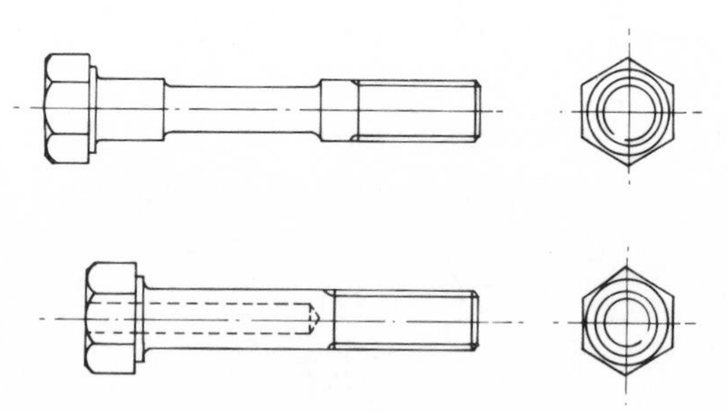

Figure 1.5 *Uniform strength bolts*

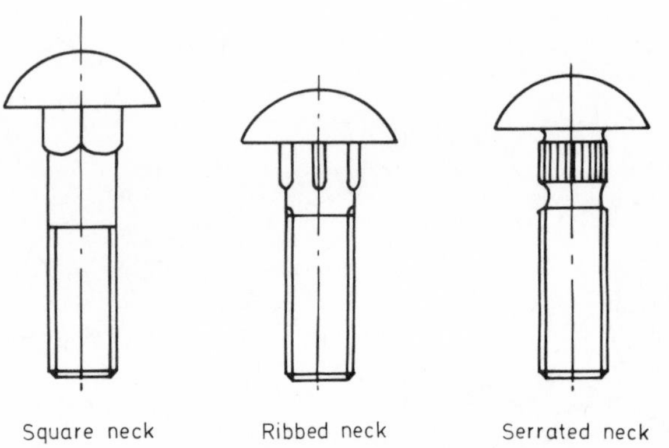

Figure 1.6 *Coach bolts (carriage bolts)*

Coach bolt (carriage bolt) Coach bolts, or carriage bolts, usually have round heads and are black bolts made of low carbon steel with coarse threads. They are used to fasten metal parts to wood. Ribs, fins or a square on the neck under the head act as locking devices. Square nuts are used with coach bolts.

Hexagon socket head screw (or bolt) A wide variety of screws (or bolts) are available which have a hexagonal recess or socket in a circular head requiring a special key or wrench for tightening. The head has many forms: cap, countersunk and button. These screws are invariably made of high tensile steel and have a coating of black oxide due to heat-treatment.

Socket screws are mostly used as tap bolts and the heads are often located in a recess for a neat appearance.

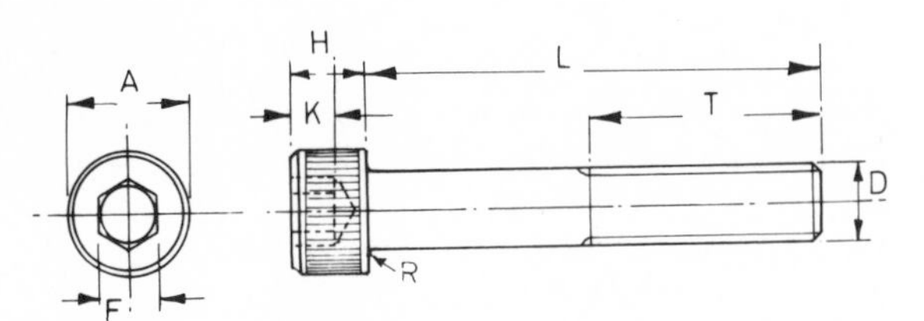

Typical metric sizes (mm)

D = 10.0 R = 0.6
A = 16.0 F = 8.0
H = 10.0 K = 5.5

L/T according to application

Figure 1.7 *Hexagon socket head screw*

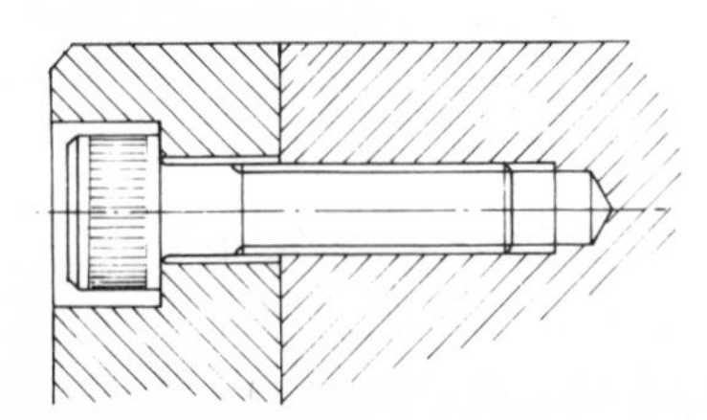

Figure 1.8 *Hexagon socket head screw application*

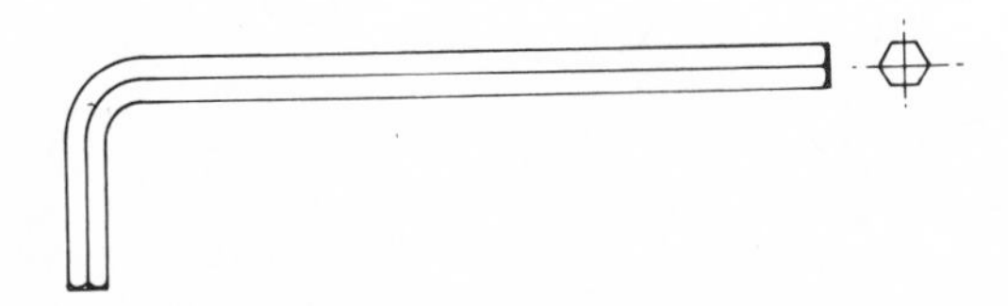

Figure 1.9 *Hexagon socket wrench (Allen key)*

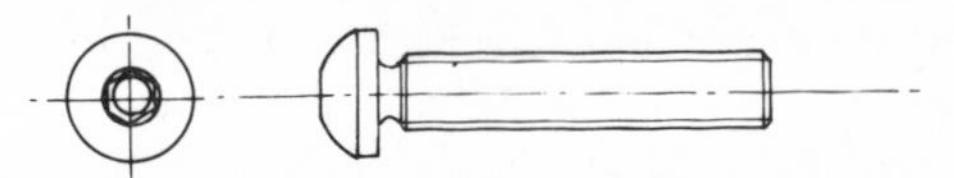

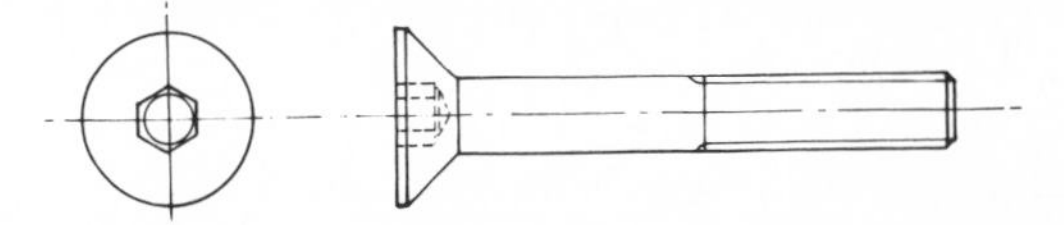

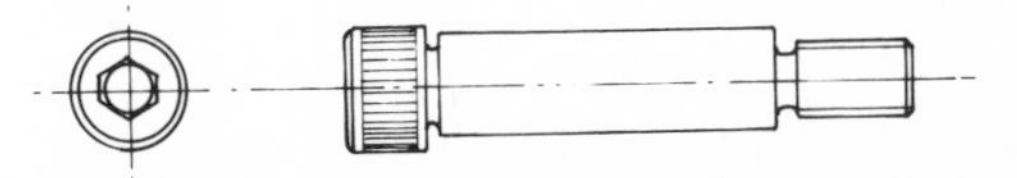

Figure 1.10 *Types of socket head screws*

T bolt The T bolt has a specially-shaped head which suits the T slots in bedplates and machine-tool tables and allows the bolt to slide in the slot without rotating.

It is used extensively for holding down work to be machined and is available in mild steel and high tensile steel.

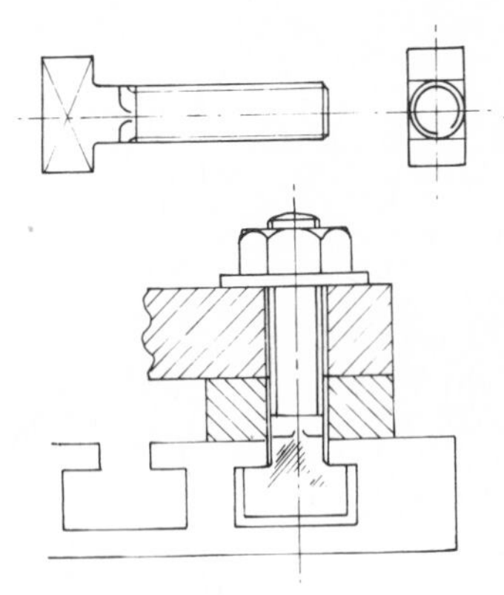

Figure 1.11 *T bolt and application*

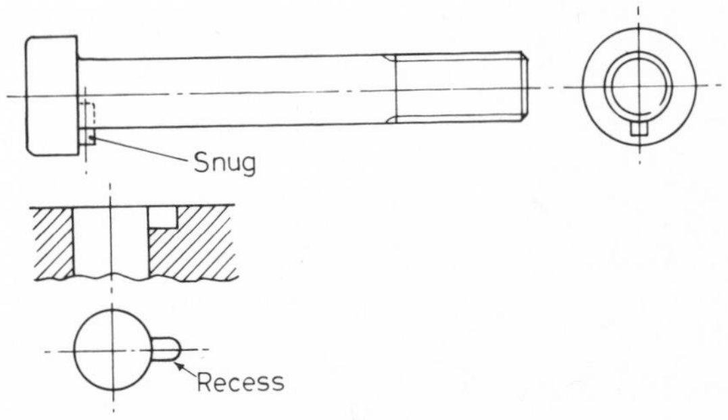

Figure 1.12 *Cheese head bolt*

Cheese head bolt Large bolts are often made with a circular head known as a *cheese head*. This shape eliminates the necessity for a hexagon. To prevent rotation of the bolt when being tightened, a pin or *snug* driven or screwed into the shank, just below the head, engages with a recess in the face of the adjacent part.

Rag bolt (foundation bolt) Rag bolts, or foundation bolts, are used for attaching machinery etc. to concrete or masonry.

Made of steel or iron, the rag bolt has a flat, tapered and roughened head which ensures a good bond when grouted into concrete.

The *indented foundation bolt* has a round body with indentations.

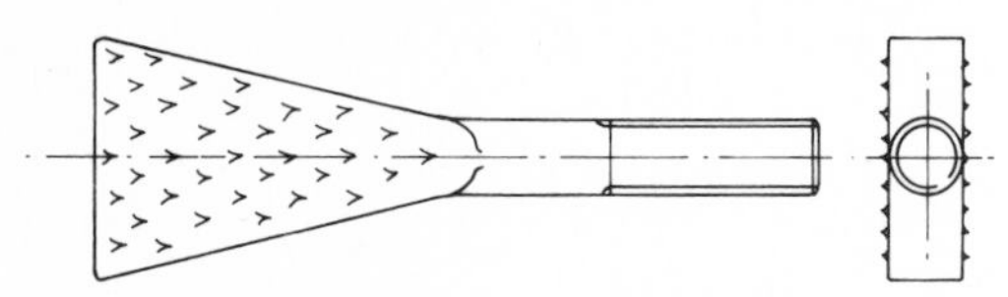

Figure 1.13 *Rag bolt*

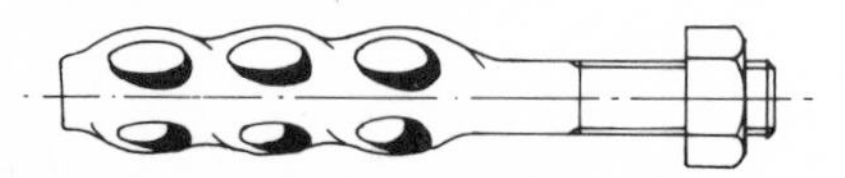

Figure 1.14 *Indented foundation bolt*

Rawlbolt (anchor bolt) A proprietary bolt for anchoring machinery to a floor or wall. A hole is drilled and the bolt inserted. When tightened, the segmented shell is expanded by a cone on the screw to give the bolt a tight fit in the hole.

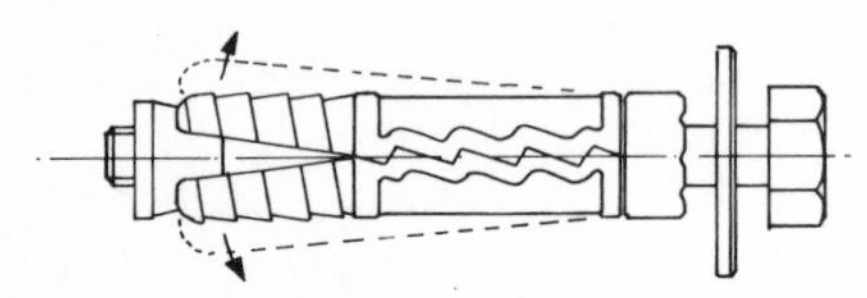

Figure 1.15 *Rawlbolt*

Eye bolt An eye bolt consists of a steel ring to which a screwed shank is attached, and it is usually permanently fitted to heavy machinery to provide an anchorage point for a rope, chain or hook used for lifting purposes.

The proportions and material used are controlled by strict standards.

Fitted bolt In most cases through bolts are fitted into holes slightly larger than the bolt diameter which are known as 'clearance' holes. Sometimes, however, the shank of the bolt is accurately machined and fitted into a reamed or bored hole with a very small clearance and this results in an exact location of the parts bolted together. Fitted bolts are often used in solid bolted and flanged shaft couplings, e.g. for a ship's propeller shaft. An alternative method of location is to use dowels in conjunction with bolts.

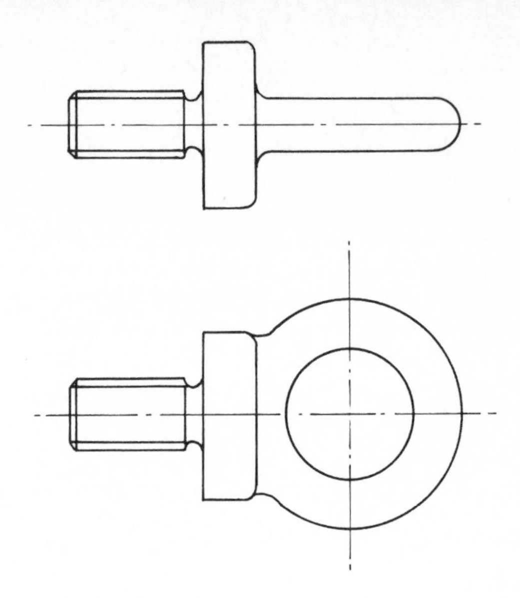

Figure 1.16 *Eye bolt*

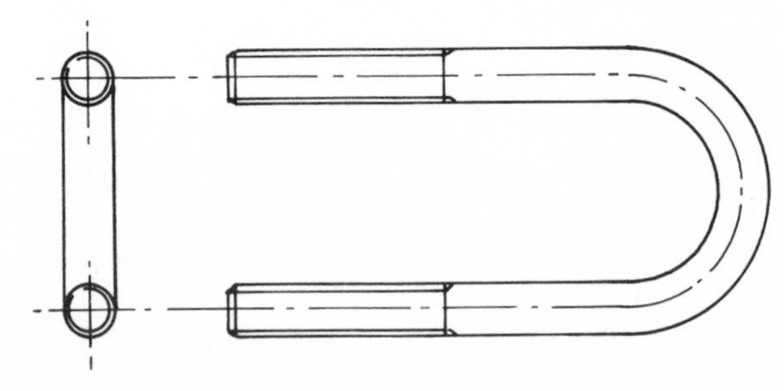

Figure 1.17 *U bolt*

U bolt This consists of a piece of circular bar bent in the form of a U and with the ends threaded. It is used for fastening round, or half round, objects such as pipes and shafts to flat surfaces.

SCREWS

This name is given to a wide variety of threaded fasteners with various types of head used with metal, wood, plastics, etc.

The name is sometimes used instead of bolt, as in the case of socket screws, but usually refers to small screwed fasteners used for light assemblies.

Most screws employed in engineering are made of steel or brass, sometimes plated, using British, metric or American threads. For small screws ranging in size from about 1.5mm to 6mm British Association and metric threads are used.

Special threads are employed for wood screws and self-tapping screws.

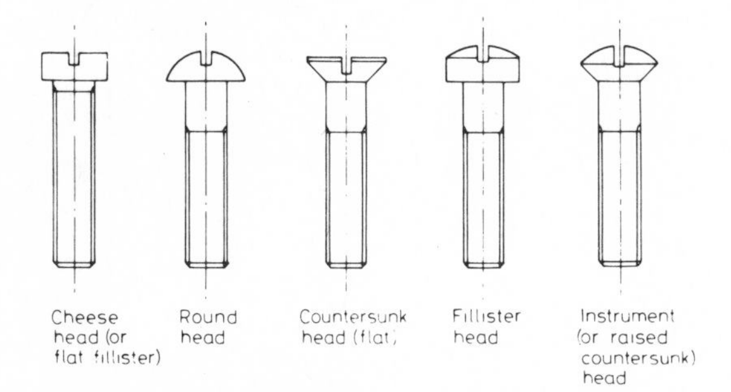

Figure 1.18 *Slotted head machine screws*

Slotted head machine screw This has a rectangular-section slot cut in the head to suit a screwdriver. There are many types of head, including round, cheese (flat fillister), fillister and countersunk or flat.

They are available in various threads and in both steel and brass which may be either cadmium or chromium plated.

Set screw Set screws are used to prevent relative motion between machine parts and often they take the place of keys on shafts where the transmitted torque is small. Most set screws do not have heads but have either a slot or a hexagon socket, and these types are known as *grub screws*.

Hardened steel is used in most cases and a variety of points is available.

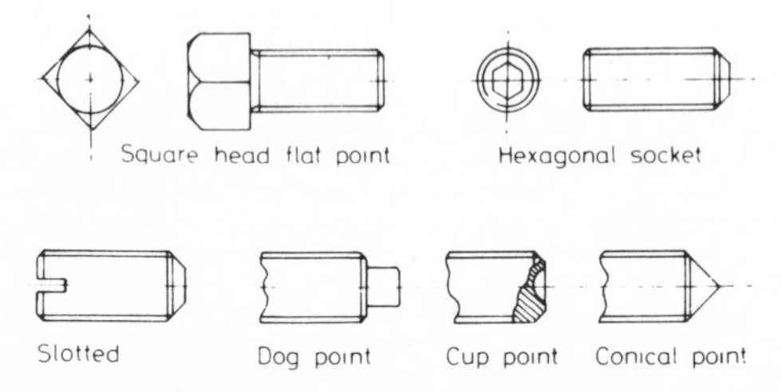

Figure 1.19 *Set screws*

Self-tapping screw (thread-forming and cutting screw) Self-tapping screws have a coarse screw thread on a tapered shank and are made of hardened steel.

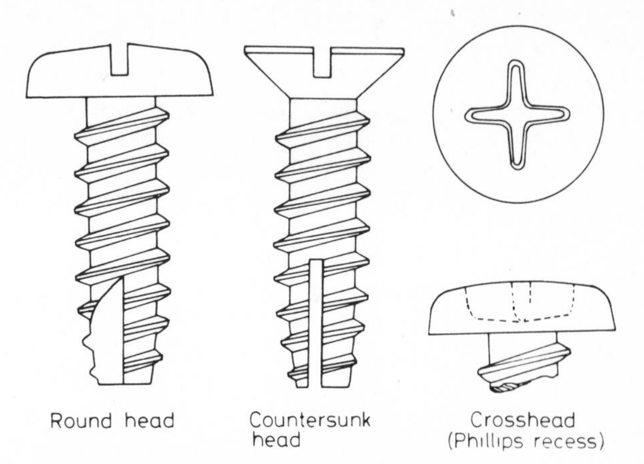

Figure 1.20 *Self-tapping screws*

They eliminate the necessity for a threaded hole or nut by cutting a thread in the material into which they are driven.

The shank may have either a blunt or a pointed end and it sometimes has longitudinal grooves which help to cut the thread in the manner of a screw tap. The heads are round, button or countersunk and have either slots or cross-shaped recesses, the latter requiring the use of a cross-head screwdriver.

These screws are used extensively for the assembly of sheet metal parts, soft castings and plastics.

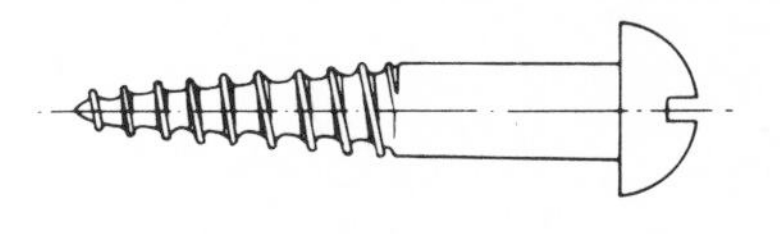

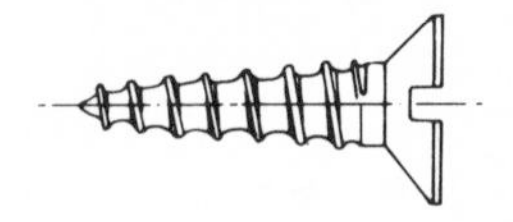

Figure 1.21 *Wood screws*

Wood screw This type is often used in engineering to attach sheet metal to wood. Wood screws are made of steel, brass, gunmetal and copper, and may be painted or electroplated. The heads are round or countersunk with either slots or star recesses.

Wood screws are available in a wide range of diameters from 2–10mm and in many lengths.

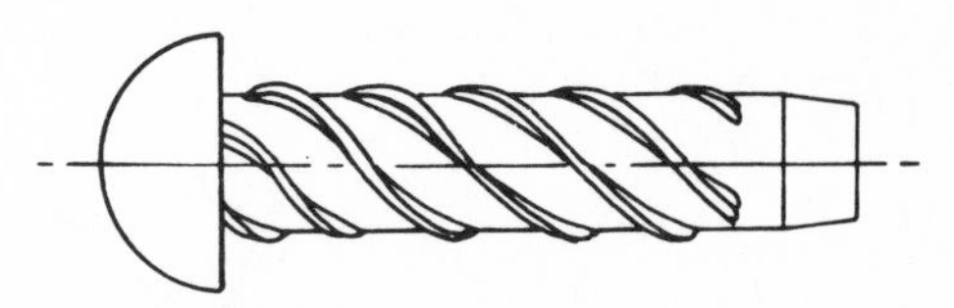

Figure 1.22 *Drive screw*

Table 1.2
ISO METRIC PRECISION HEXAGON NUTS AND THIN NUTS (mm)

Nominal size and diameter	*Thread pitch (coarse)*	*Width across flats*	*Width across corners*	*Thickness of nut Normal*	*Thin*
d	p	s	c	m	t
M5	0.8	8.0	9.20	4.0	–
M6	1.0	10.0	11.50	5.0	–
M8	1.25	13.0	15.00	6.5	5.0
M10	1.5	17.0	19.60	8.0	6.0
M12	1.75	19.0	21.90	10.0	7.0
M16	2.0	24.0	27.70	13.0	8.0

Drive screw Drive screws are hardened steel pins with very coarse pitch multistart screw threads. They are hammered or pressed into unthreaded holes in which they rotate to form a mating thread.

They are used for the rapid attachment of parts such as nameplates to castings, clips, etc. (Figure 1.22).

NUTS

A nut is a collar, usually made of metal, with a threaded hole into which is fitted a bolt, stud or screwed bar. Together with a bolt it provides the most widely used means of fastening parts together.

Nuts may be hexagonal, square or round in shape. Steel nuts are available in either black or bright condition and may be forged or machined. Black nuts may be machined on one or both faces and bright nuts have one or both faces chamfered.

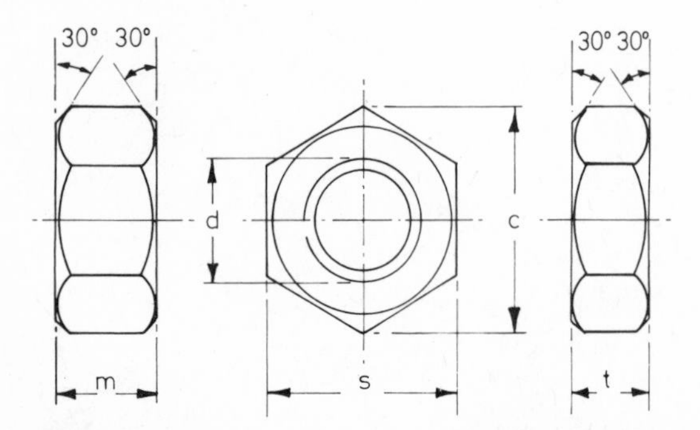

Figure 1.23 *ISO metric precision hexagon nut and thin nut*

Square nut Square nuts are usually obtained in the black, or unmachined, state and provide a cheap alternative to hexagon nuts.

Round nut (ring nut) These are often used for attaching parts to shafts and have slots or holes so that they may be tightened by using a special key.

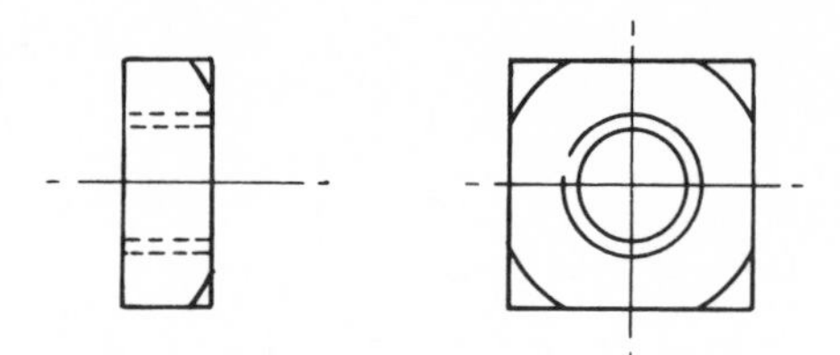

Figure 1.24 *Square nut*

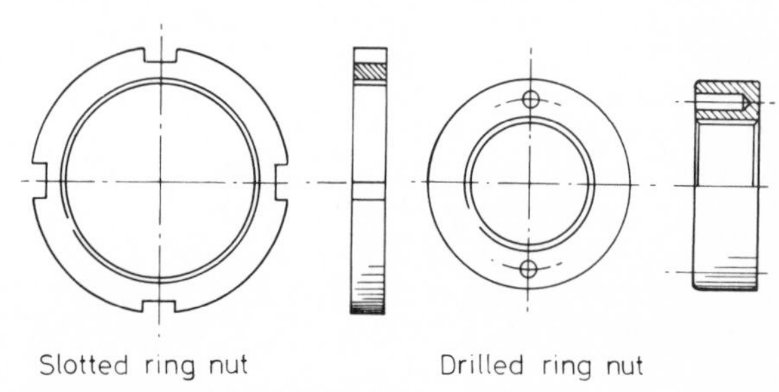

Figure 1.25 *Ring nuts*

Cap nut (crown nut, dome nut) In these one end of the threaded hole is closed and rounded to protect the end of the bolt or stud and give a neat appearance. They are made in steel or brass and are usually chromium plated.

Wing nut These nuts have wing-like projections for hand tightening. They are made in steel and brass and are used where frequent removal and replacement of parts is required.

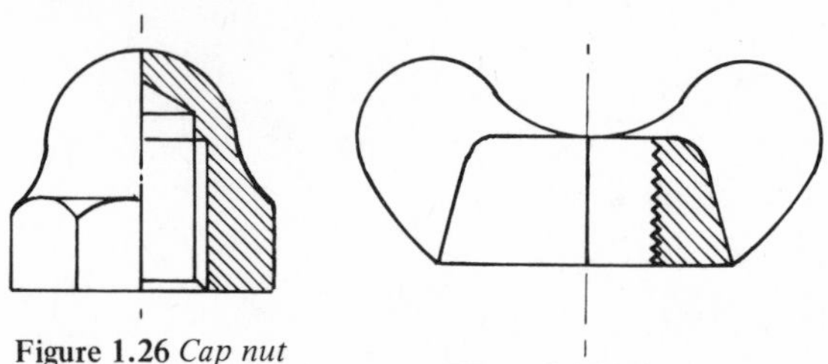

Figure 1.26 *Cap nut (crown nut, dome nut)*

Figure 1.27 *Wing nut*

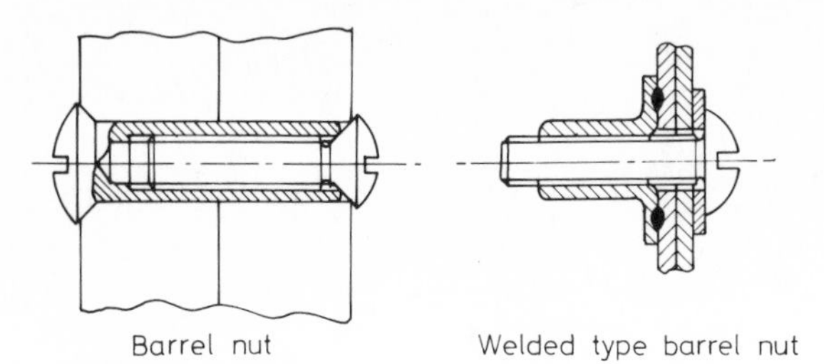

Figure 1.28 *Barrel nuts*

Barrel nut This nut has a tubular form. One type has a slotted head similar to that of the mating screw, while another has a flange which is welded to sheet metal.

Captive nut A nut which is loosely fastened to a machine part so that it is held in position until a bolt or screw is fitted.

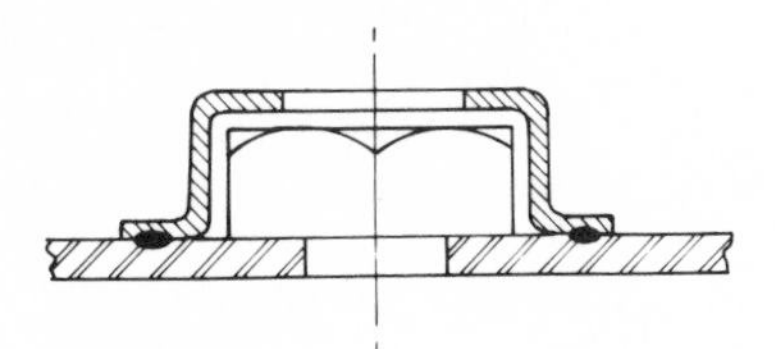

Figure 1.29 *Captive nut*

Locking nuts Nuts subject to shock loads and vibration have a tendency to work loose and cause damage or failure in machines. A wide range of locking devices is available including special nuts, lock washers and adhesives.

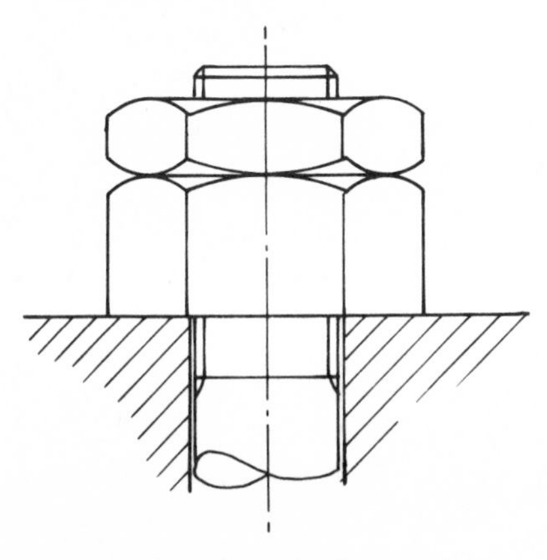

Figure 1.30 *Locked nuts (jam nuts)*

Locked nuts (jam nuts) A nut can be locked by tightening another nut against it and for this purpose a thin nut is used for the sake of economy. Ideally this should be situated below the normal-sized nut although this necessitates the use of a thinner spanner. Two spanners are required when locking the nuts.

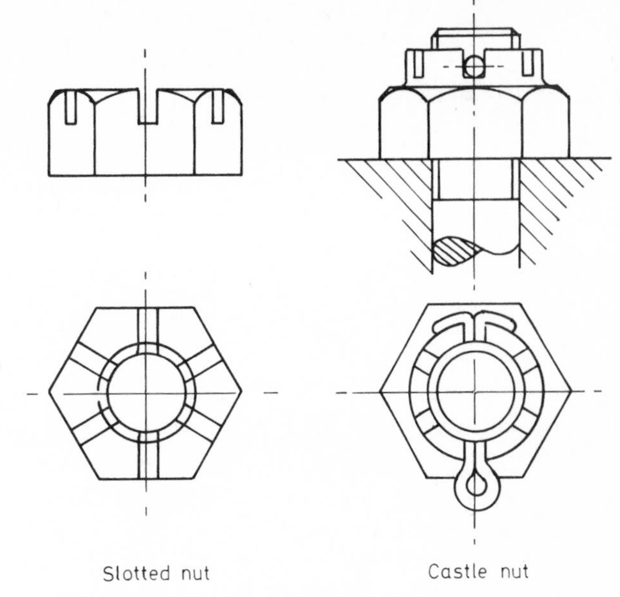

Figure 1.31 *Slotted and castle nuts*

Slotted nut and castle nut A slotted nut is a hexagonal nut with six radial slots cut in the top face two of which line up with a hole in the bolt so that a split pin may be passed through to lock the nut. Alternatively, wire can be used to lock a group of nuts.

In a castle nut the slots are cut in a circular section of the nut above the hexagon.

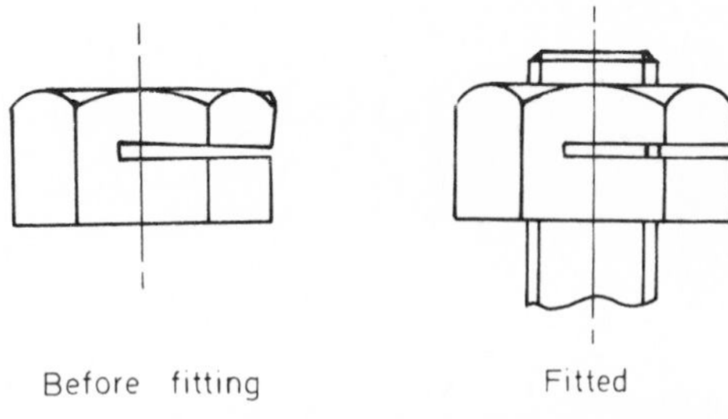

Figure 1.32 *Split nut*

Split nut A slot cut in the side of a hexagon nut is closed before fitting. The bolt forces the slot open with a resulting high frictional force which reduces the tendency for the nut to loosen.

Spring lock nut (compression stop nut) This is a hexagonal nut similar in appearance to a castle nut but the slots in the top of the nut form tongues which are initially pressed down to apply a frictional force on the bolt when fitted (Figure 1.33).

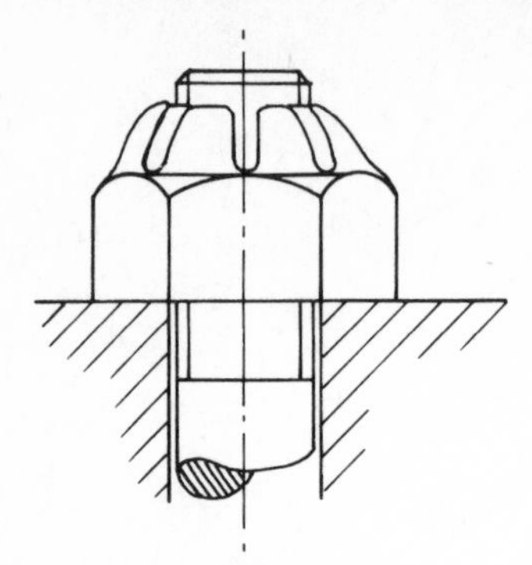

Figure 1.33 *Spring lock nut (compression stop nut)*

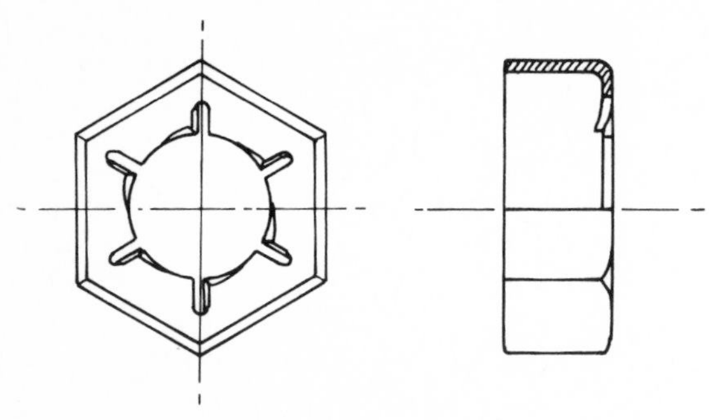

Figure 1.34 *Stamped spring nut*

Stamped spring nut This is stamped out of spring steel sheet in a variety of patterns with a hexagonal form and projections which engage with the bolt thread to give a high degree of friction.

Elastic stop nut (Nyloc nut) A ring of material such as fibre or nylon is inserted into a groove in the bore of a hexagon nut to provide a high frictional force when the nut is fitted.

The Nyloc nut is a proprietary type with a nylon insert.

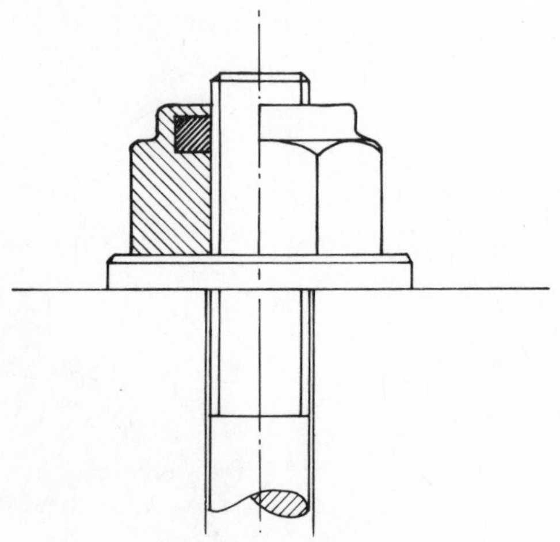

Figure 1.35 *Elastic stop nut (Nyloc nut)*

WASHERS

A washer is an annular disk of metal, plastic, rubber, etc., usually flat, which is placed either under a nut or between the surfaces of a joint to distribute the load when the nut or joint is tightened.

Most washers are made of steel but brass is used in conjunction with brass screws and nuts. Washers of copper, aluminium, fibre and leather are used extensively for sealing fluids.

Plain washer (flat washer) This is a flat washer, usually made of steel, and used under a nut to prevent damage to the face and to distribute the load. Cheap washers are punched out of black plate but more expensive ones are machined and have a bevelled edge for improved appearance. In addition to washers of 'normal' proportions, 'narrow' and 'wide' varieties are available.

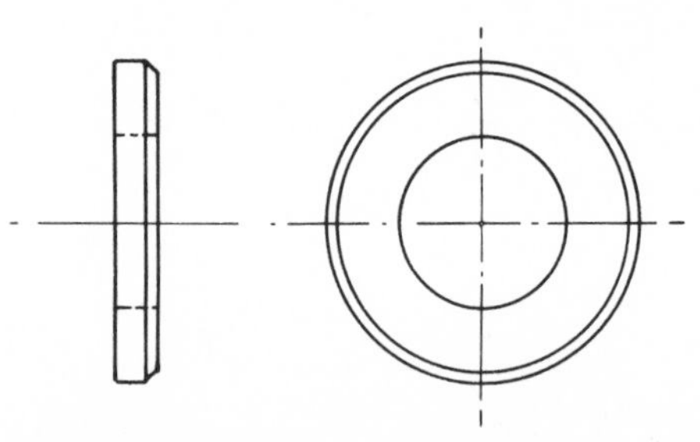

Figure 1.36 *Plain washer (flat washer)*

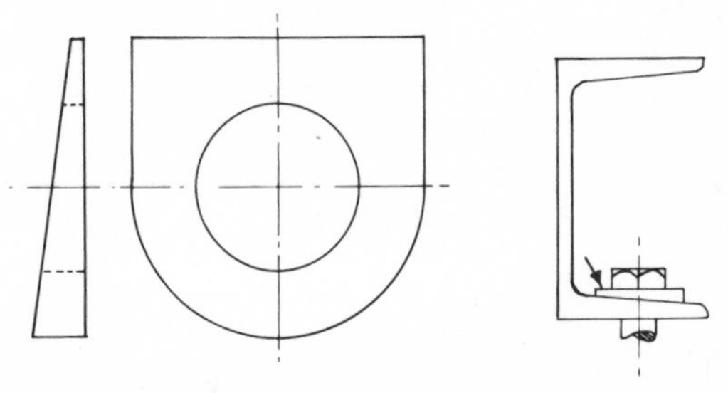

Figure 1.37 *Taper washer and application*

Taper washer A washer where the thickness varies from one side to the other to allow for the taper on the flanges of rolled steel sections such as channel and I beams.

Lock washer To prevent the loosening of nuts due to shock and vibration, lock washers are used extensively as an alternative to locknuts. There are two main types, those which rely on increased friction between the nut and the face, and those which use the faces of the nut to give a positive fixing.

Helical spring lock washer This consists of one or more turns of a helical spring made of rectangular section spring steel wire. When the nut is tightened the washer is compressed to cause a large friction force between the nut and the face. This is aided by sharp ends on the washer which cut into the faces to give positive locking.

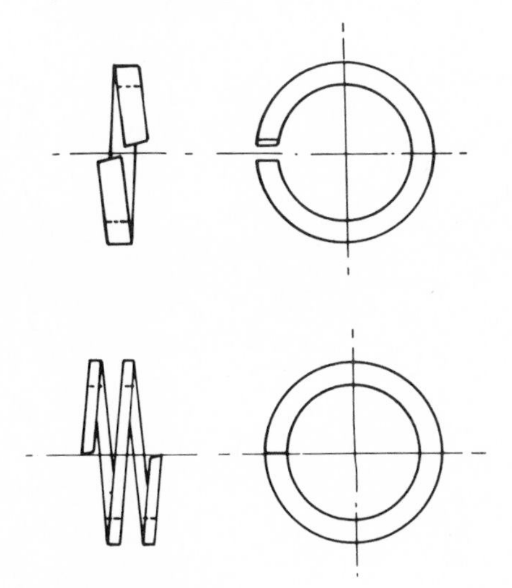

Figure 1.38 *Helical spring lock washer and two-coil spring lock washer*

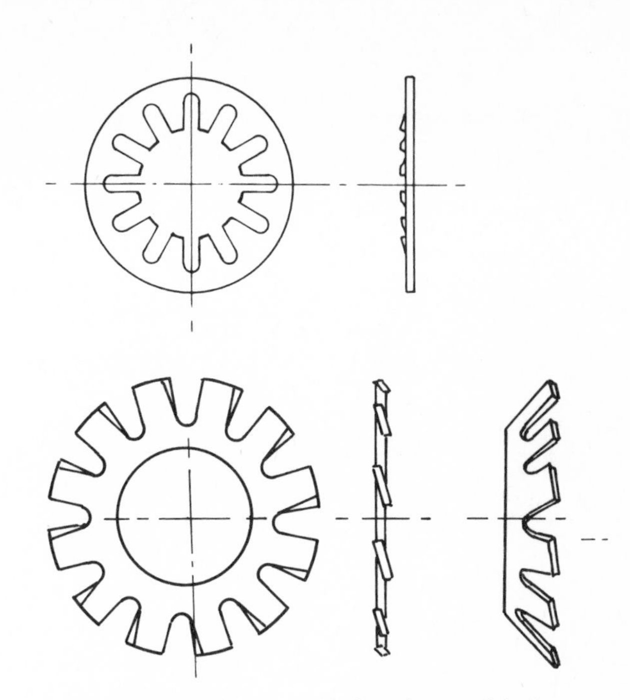

Figure 1.39 *Internally serrated lock washer (tooth lock washer) and externally serrated lock washer, flat and for countersunk hole*

Serrated lock washer (tooth lock washer) These are made of spring steel and consist of annular disks with serrations on either inner or outer diameter. The resulting projections are twisted and have sharp edges. When the nut is tightened the projections are flattened and cut into the faces of the nut and the part in contact.

A conical washer with external serrations is available for use with countersunk head screws.

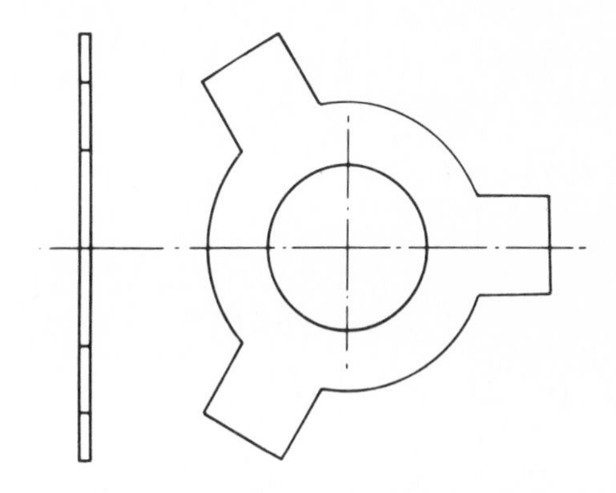

Tab washer The tab washer is made from sheet metal and has a hole for the bolt or stud with tabs on the periphery which are bent at right angles against the faces of the nut and against a face on the adjacent part.

Alternatively, the tab may be punched into a hole previously drilled in the part.

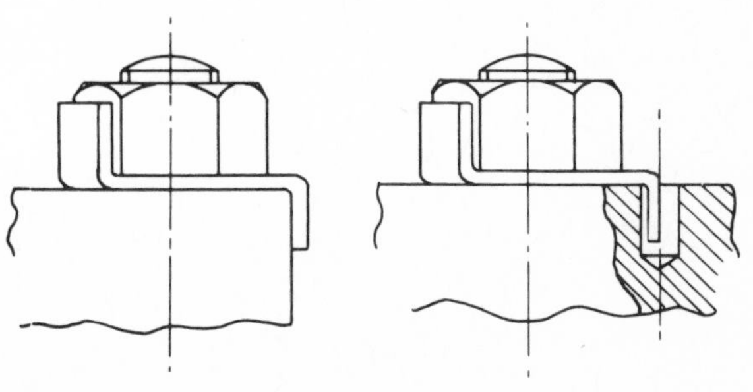

Figure 1.40 *Tab washer and application*

RIVETS

A rivet is a metal pin with a circular shank and a head. It is used to make a permanent joint between two or more pieces of plate. The shank is passed through mating holes in the plates and 'closed' by forming a head on the projecting shank by hammering or pressing.

Steel rivets are often closed when red hot but rivets of softer metals such as copper and aluminium are closed cold. The heads may be round, countersunk, pan-shaped, etc.

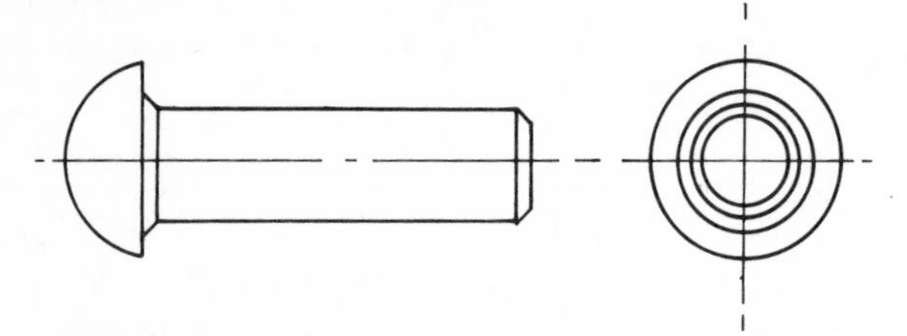

Figure 1.41 *Rivet*

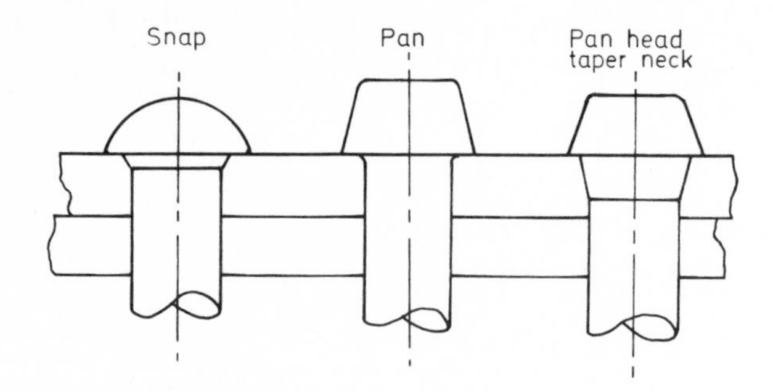

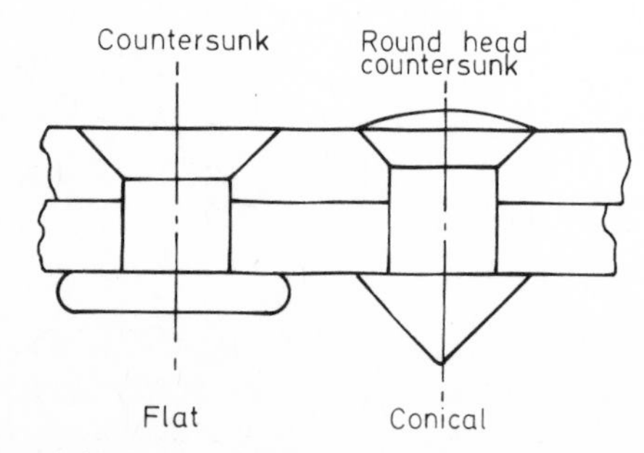

Figure 1.42 *Types of rivet*

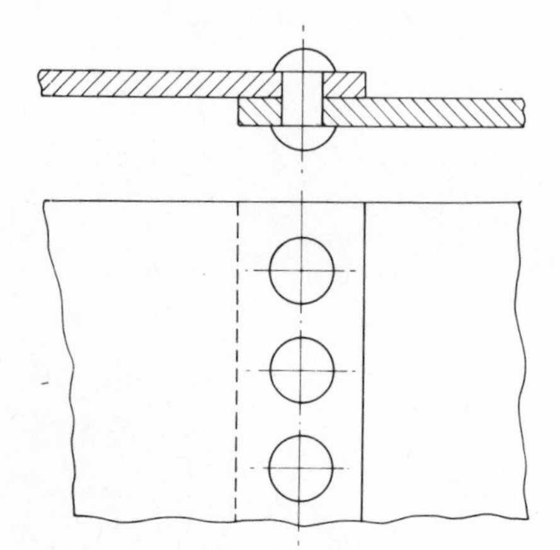

Figure 1.43 *Riveted lap joint*

Riveted joint Metal plates may be joined together by overlapping the edges and riveting using one or several rows of rivets. Alternatively, the plates may be placed edge-to-edge and a butt joint made with butt straps on one or both sides of the joint. One or more rows of rivets are passed through the plates and straps on each side of the joint.

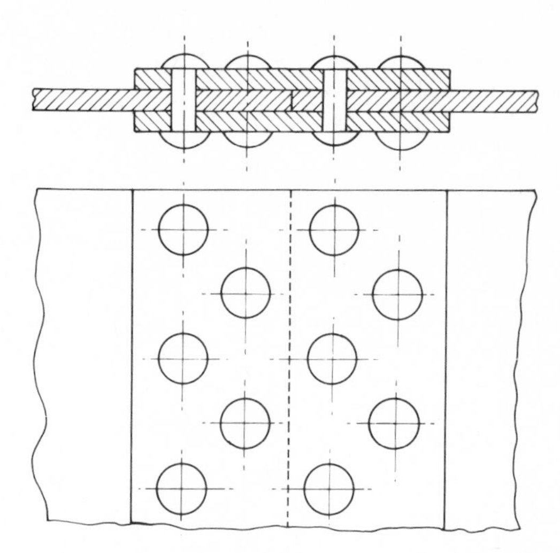

Figure 1.44 *Double riveted butt joint with two straps*

Flush rivet (aircraft type) The head of this rivet is flat and countersunk so that it is flush with the face of one of the plates. This is advantageous in aircraft construction where a smooth surface is required for aerodynamic reasons. The rivets are mostly made of aluminium.

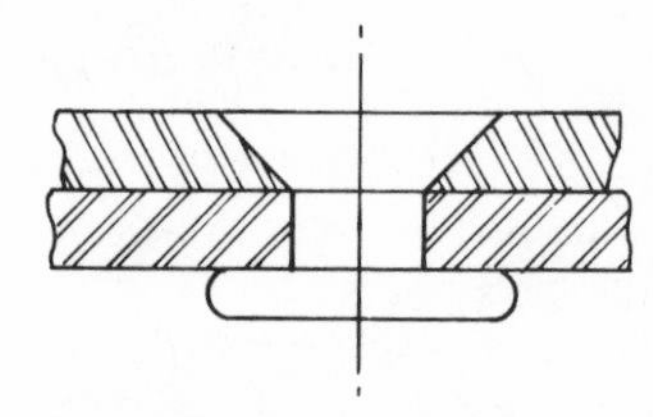

Figure 1.45 *Flush rivet*

Tubular rivet This consists of a piece of soft metal tubing the ends of which are deformed by a special tool. They are used for joining thin metal sheets.

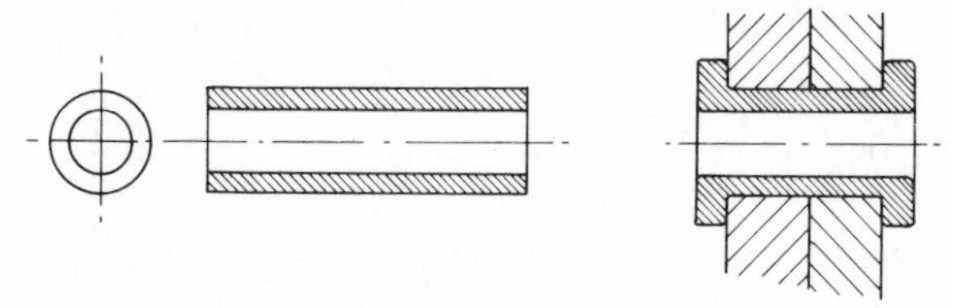

Figure 1.46 *Tubular rivet*

Pop rivet This is a type of tubular rivet which initially has a hard steel pin passing through it. When the rivet is fitted by means of a special tool the head of the pin closes the rivet and snaps off. Riveting is done from one side of the plate.

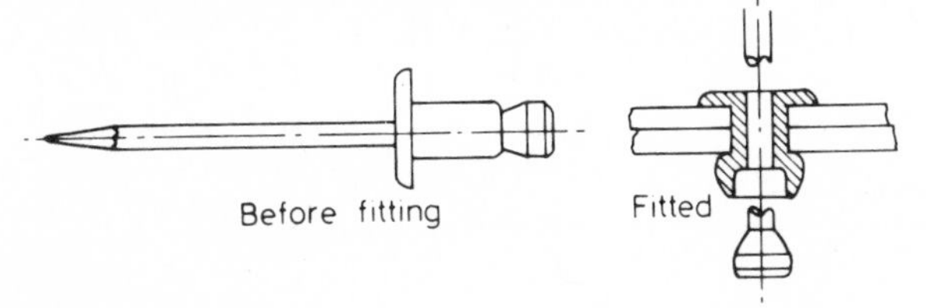

Figure 1.47 *Pop rivet*

Explosive rivet The end of the shank of this rivet is hollowed out to take a small explosive charge. When this is exploded the protruding shank expands to form a joint. This type is used extensively in the aircraft industry.

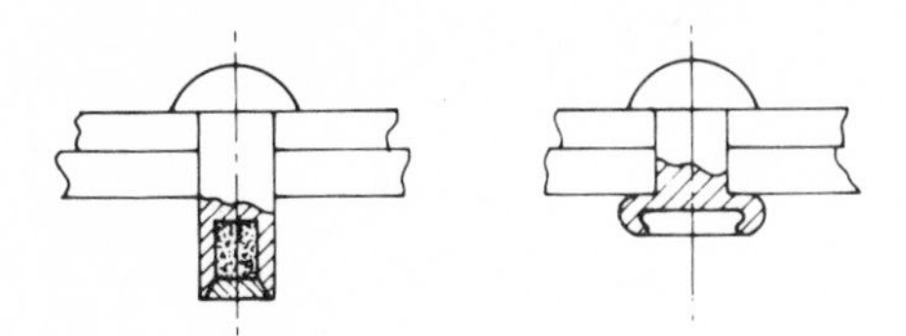

Figure 1.48 *Explosive rivet*

PINS

This term refers to a large range of components consisting basically of a piece of rod or bar, usually of circular section and either solid or hollow. They are used for fixing, locating and load carrying.

Plain pin This is simply a piece of bar which, in most cases, is machined to a good finish and accuracy. It is used for locating parts.

Dowel pin A dowel pin is a straight circular pin, sometimes with a head, which is accurately fitted into holes to locate two or more parts together. This is often used in conjunction with bolts and studs.

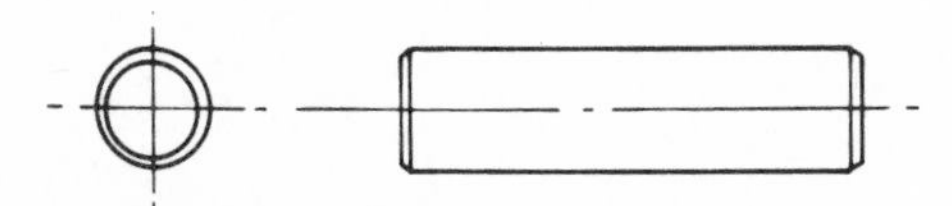

Figure 1.49 *Plain pin*

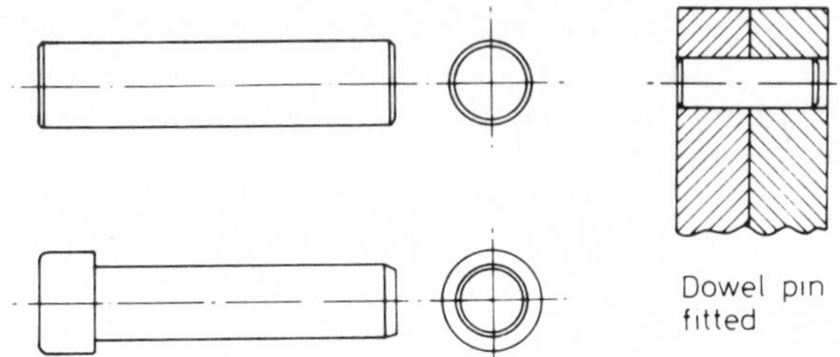

Figure 1.50 *Dowel pins*

Taper pin A type of dowel which has a fine taper so that a tight fit is obtained when it is lightly tapped into a hole which has been drilled and then finished with a taper reamer. Taper pins are often used in conjunction with a sleeve for connecting shafts transmitting low power (*see* Section 2.2 on Shaft couplings).

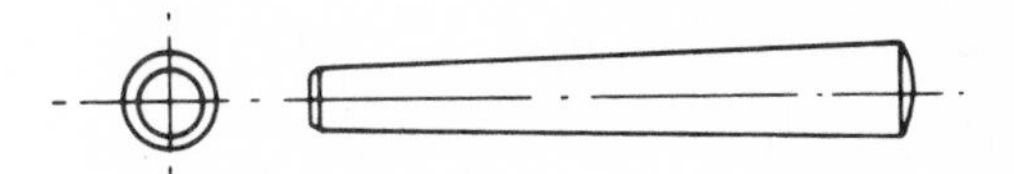

Figure 1.51 *Taper pin*

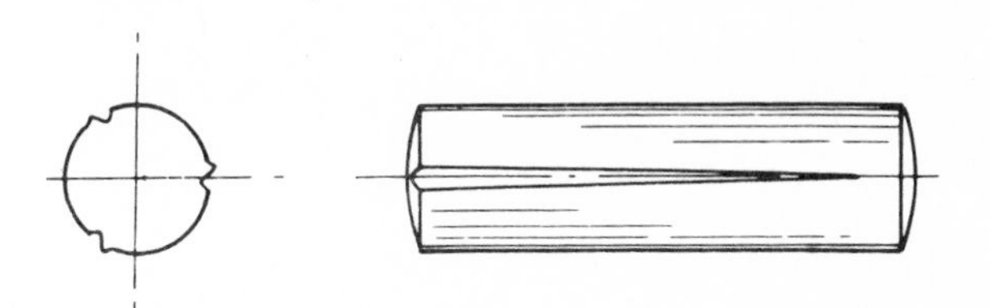

Figure 1.52 *Grooved pin*

Grooved pin This is a straight, circular and solid pin which has longitudinal grooves with raised edges formed by rolling. A tight fit in the hole is achieved when the pin is hammered in. Grooved pins are useful as keys for light power transmission.

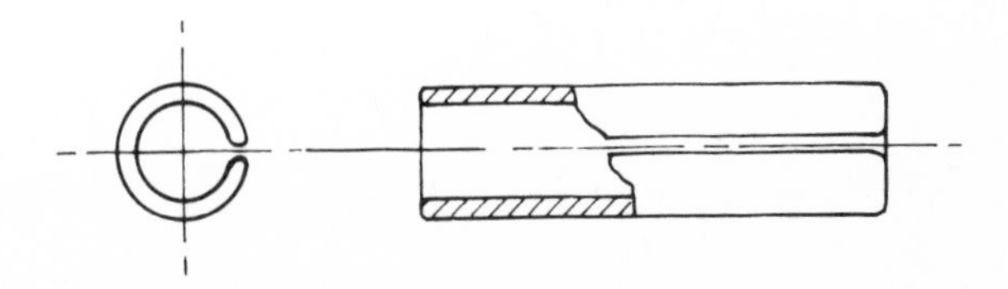

Figure 1.53 *Roll pin*

Roll pin A roll pin is a spring steel tube, with a longitudinal slit, which is driven into a slightly smaller hole so that the slit closes to give a tight fit.

It is easier to fit than solid pins and taper pins, and an example of its use is for attaching hand wheels to valve spindles.

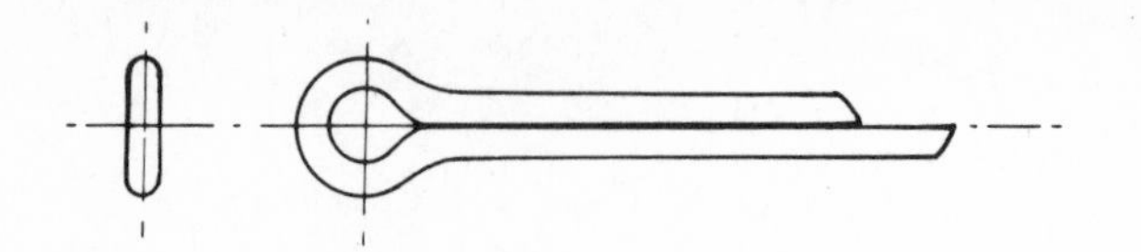

Figure 1.54 *Split pin (cotter pin)*

Split pin (cotter pin) A pin formed from half-round wire folded to give a shank and a head. The pin is passed through mating holes in parts and the protruding ends bent outwards to secure it. It is used mainly for locking slotted nuts.

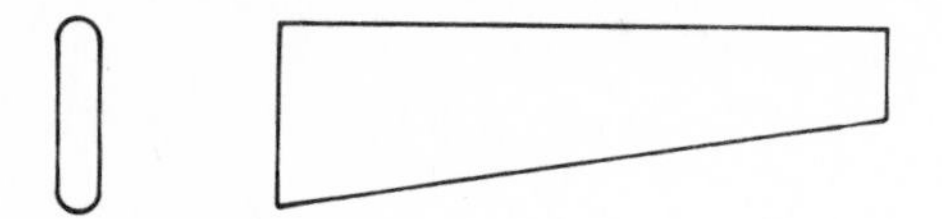

Figure 1.55 *Cotter*

Cotter A tapered pin of rectangular cross-section. It is used to provide a rigid joint between rods under an axial force. The cotter fits into slots in the ends of the rods and may easily be removed if desired (*see* Section 1.7 Cottered joint).

CLIPS

Clips are used for attaching pipes, tubes and cables to other parts to prevent rattling and provide location relative to those parts.

Band hose clip In this type of clip a steel band formed into a circle is tightened onto a hose by means of a screw and nut.

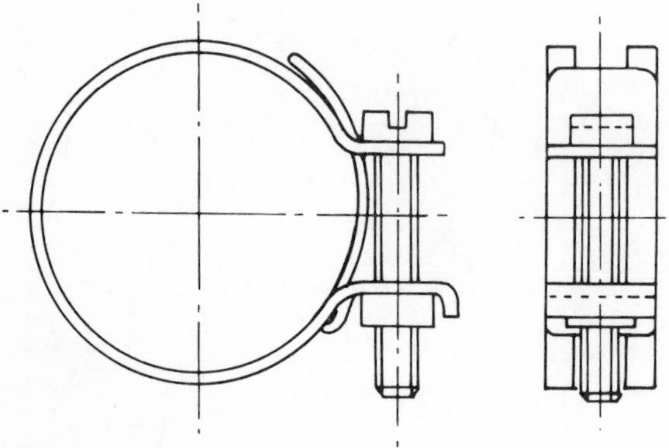

Figure 1.56 *Band hose clip*

Worm-drive hose clip (Jubilee clip) In another type, known as a worm-drive *Jubilee clip*, the screw engages with serrations in the steel band instead of a nut. These clips are used for clamping rubber and plastic hoses to metal pipes.

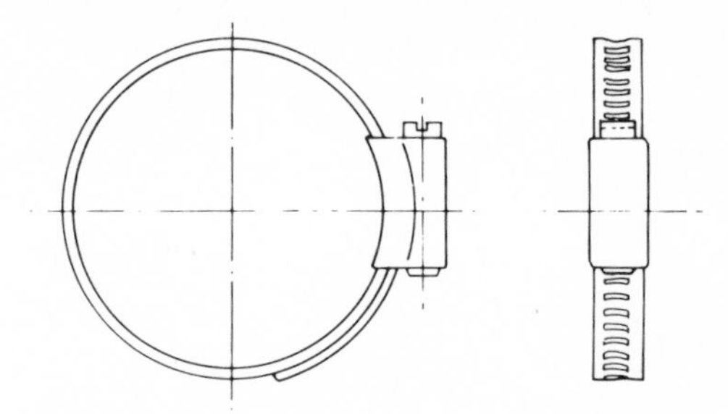

Figure 1.57 *Worm-drive hose clip (Jubilee clip)*

Spring wire hose clip A loop of spring wire with projecting ends is used to clamp a hose onto a pipe. The clip is fitted or removed by opening the loop with pliers.

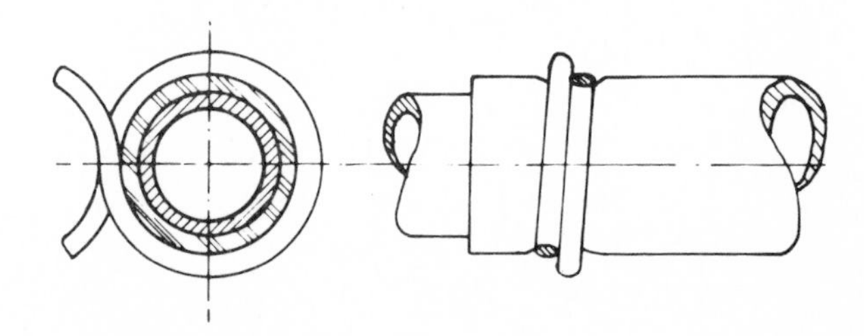

Figure 1.58 *Spring wire hose clip*

Pipe and cable clips These are used for fastening pipes, tubes and cables to machines to provide location and prevent vibration. They are usually made of metal strip, sometimes ribbed for strength, and are fastened by screws or rivets.

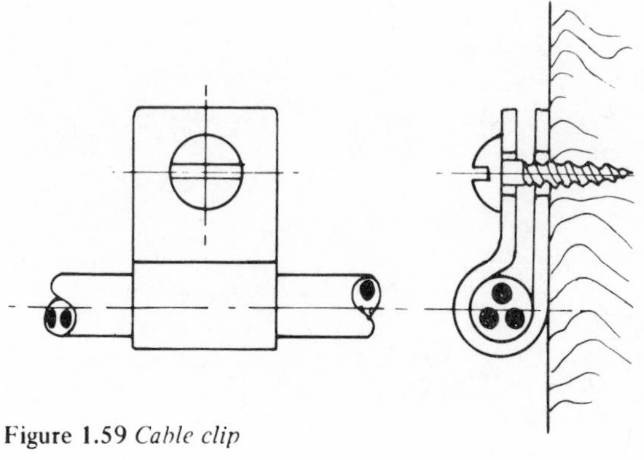

Figure 1.59 *Cable clip*

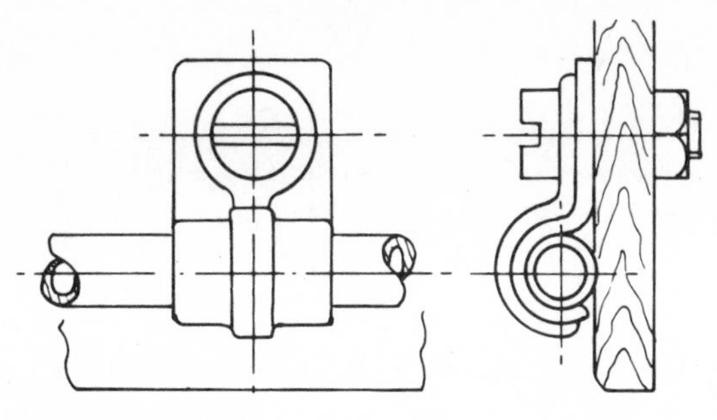

Figure 1.60 *Pipe clip*

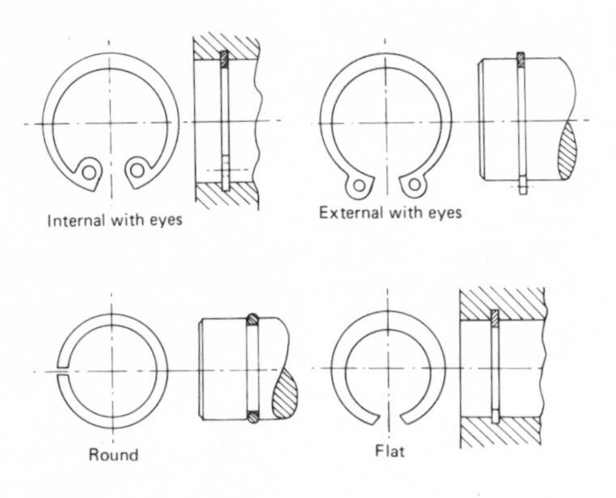

Figure 1.61 *Circlips (retaining rings)*

Circlip (retaining ring) A spring steel clip in the form of an incomplete ring which fits tightly into a circumferential groove on a shaft or in a bore and locates parts axially. Circlips may be of circular or rectangular cross-section. Rectangular section circlips may have internal or external eyes for easier fitting using a special tool.

1.2 SCREW THREADS

A screw thread is formed by cutting or forming a helical groove, or thread, on the surface of a circular bar or in a circular hole. The thread may be right-handed or left-handed, and of various cross-sections such as V, square, trapezoidal, etc. External threads of large diameter are usually produced by machining with a single point tool. Smaller bar is screwed in a lathe using a die box, or by hand using stocks and dies. Threads on bolts, screws and studs are often produced by rolling. The bar is formed by means of a pair of flat or circular dies having the thread form. The method is cheaper for large quantities and gives a better finish as well as a higher strength.

Internal threads of large size are machined with a single point tool. Smaller holes are machine-tapped in quantity or hand-tapped for small numbers off.

V threads are used mainly for fasteners while square and trapezoidal threads are used for power transmission.

V THREAD

A V thread is in the form of an isosceles triangle with the 'crest' and 'root' either flattened or rounded. The main dimensions are: pitch (the distance between adjacent threads); major and minor diameters; V angle; area of cross-section at the bottom of the threads.

V threads are used almost exclusively for fasteners such as nuts and bolts.

The main types of thread form are: Whitworth (BSW) 55°; British Standard Fine (BSF) 55°; British Association (BA) 47.5°; Metric (ISO) 60°; USA Standard 60°; Unified Coarse and Fine (UNC-UNF) 60°.

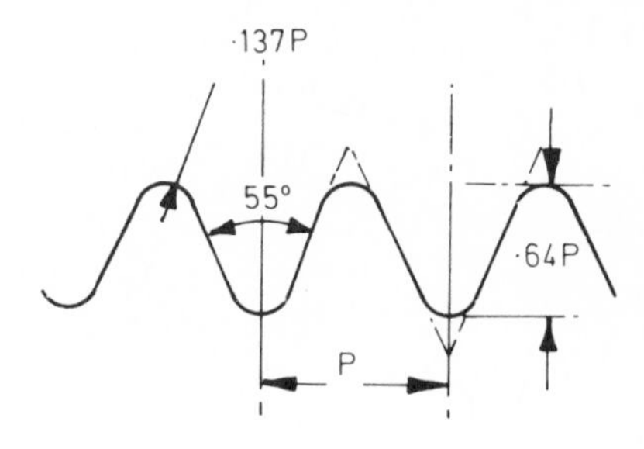

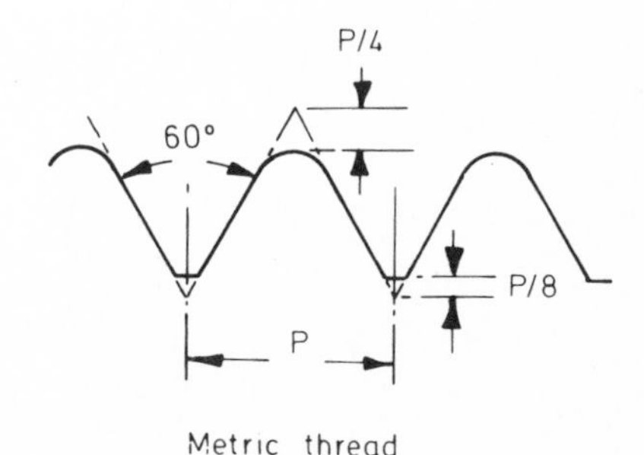

Figure 1.62 *Thread details*

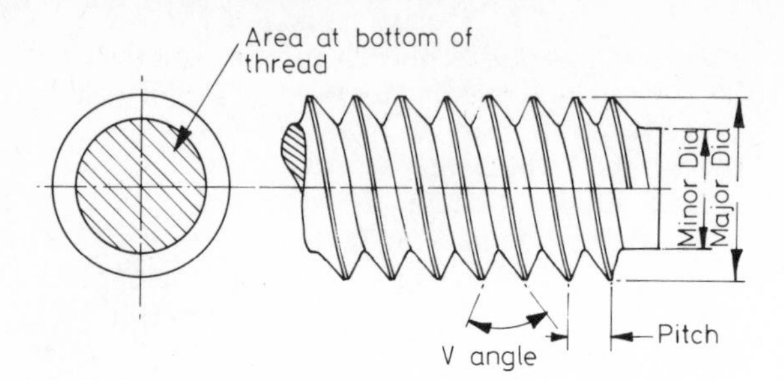

Figure 1.63 *V screw thread*

SQUARE THREAD

The square thread is mechanically strong and is used mainly for power transmission. There is no radial force on the nut and friction is low.

Square threads, and Acme and buttress threads, are formed by machining on a lathe, whereas V threads are often cut by hand with taps and dies.

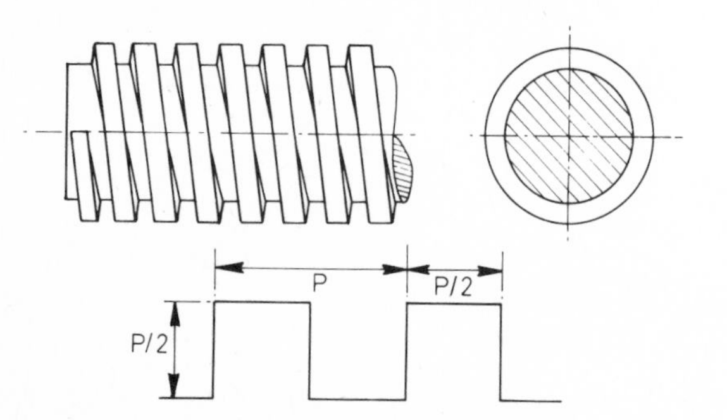

Figure 1.64 *Square thread*

ACME THREAD

Used for power transmission, this is a trapezoidal thread of greater root strength and easier to cut than the square thread. It is sometimes used for the lead screw in lathes.

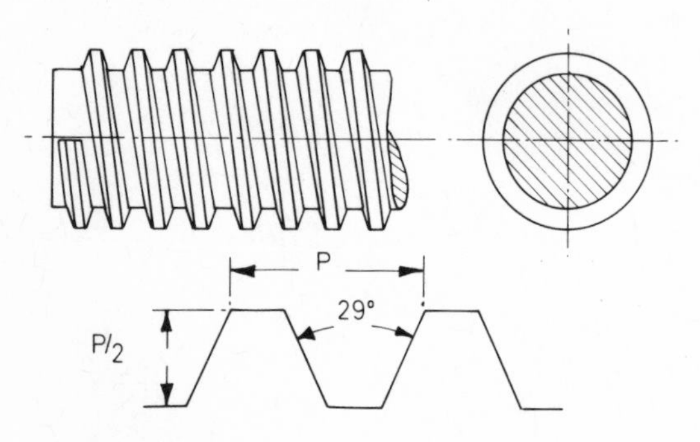

Figure 1.65 *Acme thread*

BUTTRESS THREAD

This is a thread used for power transmission which combines the advantages of both square and Acme threads. The load must be applied in one direction only, and that is on the vertical face.

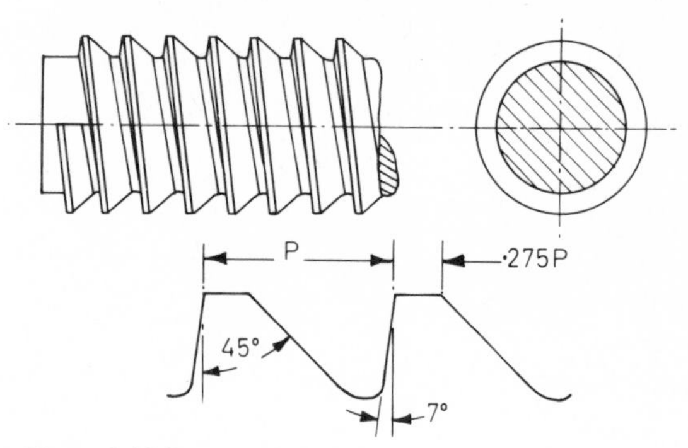

Figure 1.66 *Buttress thread*

MULTI-START THREAD

To obtain a larger pitch without increasing the depth of thread and reducing the strength, two or more threads may be cut on the same screw side by side. The nut advances N times the pitch, where N is the number of thread 'starts' in each revolution. The advance is known as the 'lead'.

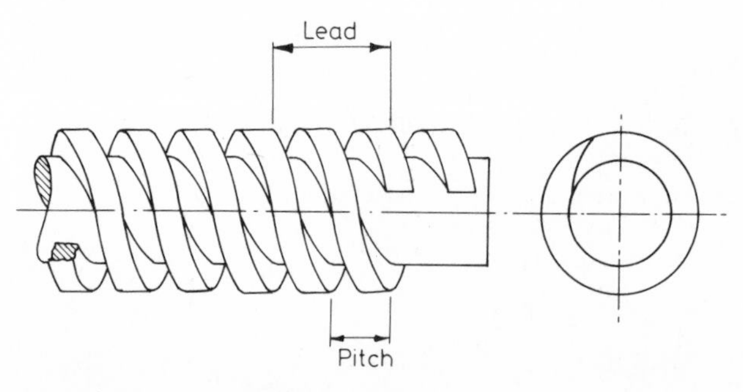

Figure 1.67 *Two-start square thread*

BALL-BEARING POWER SCREW

This is an extremely low friction power screw in which the screw and nut have opposing helical grooves of part-circular cross-section to suit ball bearings situated between them.

Power is transmitted between the screw and nut via the ball bearings which circulate continuously through a tube attached to the outside of the nut.

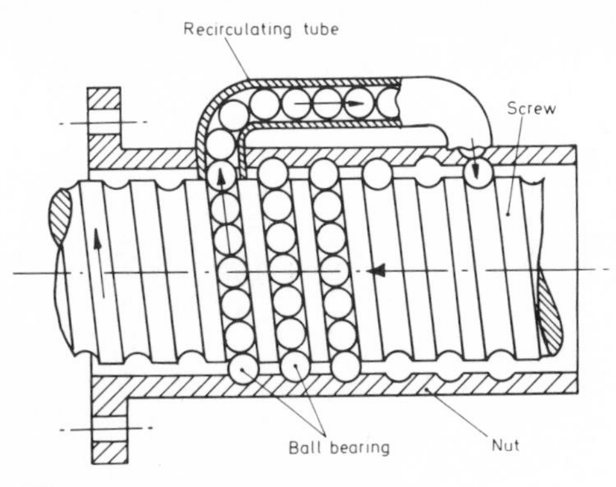

Figure 1.68 *Ball-bearing power screw*

EFFICIENCY OF SCREW THREADS

The efficiency of screw threads is defined as the ratio of the work done by the nut to the work put into the screw.

This may be as low as 20% for a poorly-lubricated V thread but up to 80% for a well-lubricated square or Acme thread. The ball bearing screw has an efficiency approaching 100%.

1.3 SPRINGS

Springs are used extensively in engineering to control movement and to apply forces in machines. They limit impact forces, reduce vibrations by storing energy, and are often used to measure forces.

HELICAL COIL SPRING

This consists of a wire of circular, square, rectangular or other section wrapped around a cylinder to form a helix.

HELICAL COMPRESSION SPRING

In a helical compression spring the coils are sufficiently open to allow shortening of the spring under a compressive load. The ends of the spring are usually flattened and ground to provide a seating and the wire is generally round, but rectangular section wire is also used.

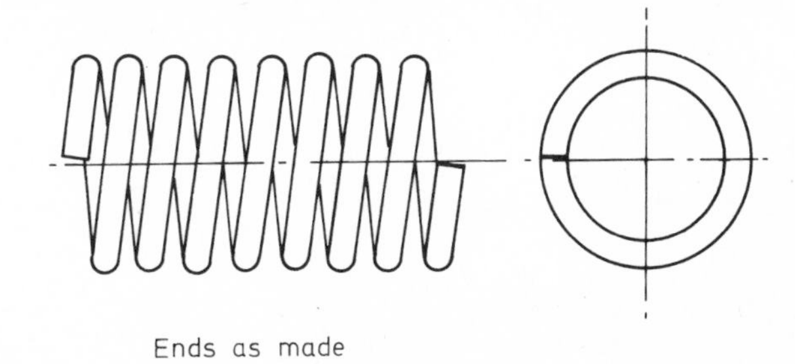

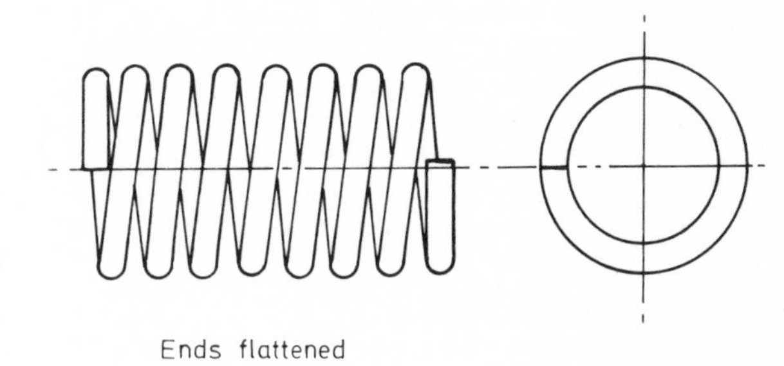

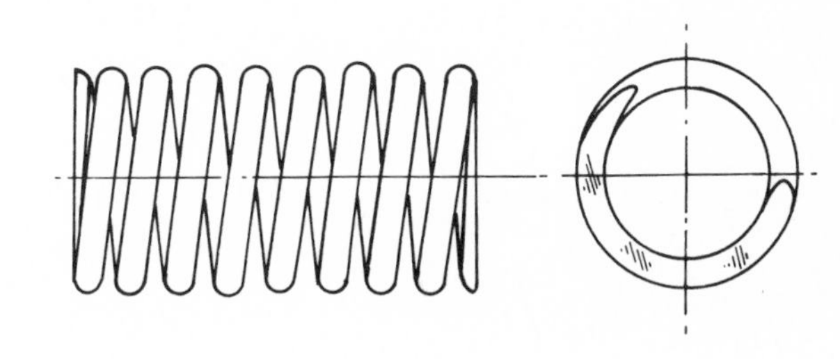

Figure 1.69 *Helical compression springs*

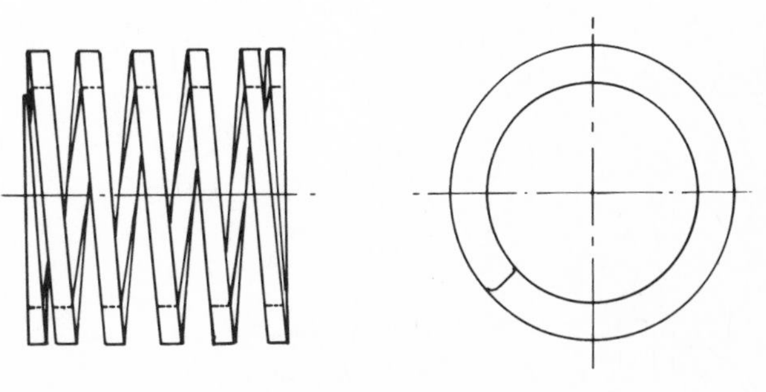

Figure 1.70 *Rectangular-section spring*

HELICAL TENSION SPRING

The ends of helical tension springs are formed into hooks of various types and the springs are usually pre-tensioned so that a small initial load is required to open the coils.

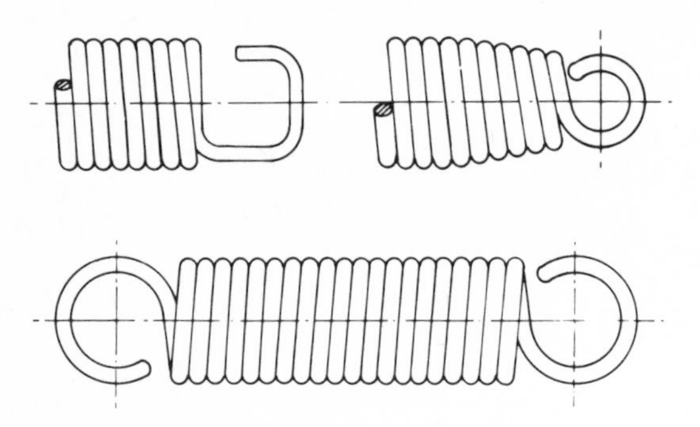

Figure 1.71 *Helical tension springs*

HELICAL TORSION SPRING

This is a helical spring with suitable ends which is subject to a twisting moment or torque.

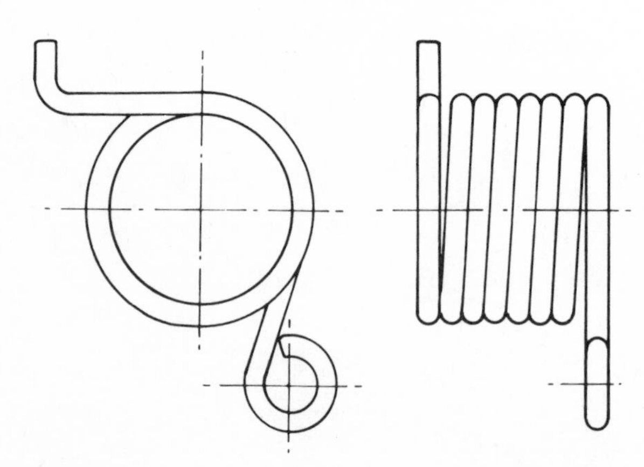

Figure 1.72 *Helical torsion spring*

HELICAL SPRING DATA

The important dimensions are: mean diameter of coils, wire size, free length, loaded length, clearance between coils, number of coils.

It is also necessary to know: design load, material, spring rate or stiffness (the load per unit deflection).

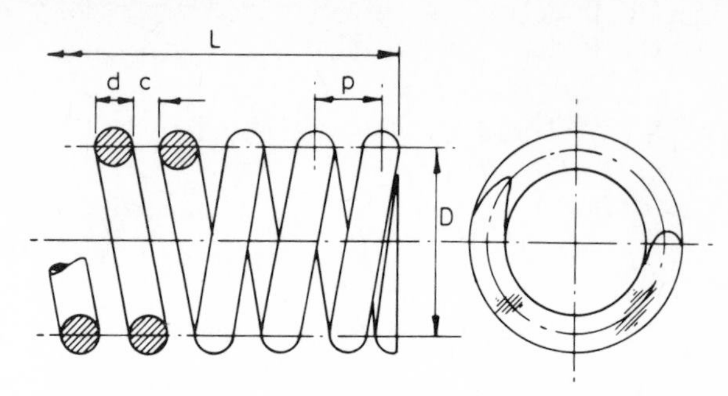

Figure 1.73 *Helical spring dimensions: D = mean diameter of coils; d = wire diameter; c = coil clearance; L = spring length; p = pitch*

HELICAL SPRING MATERIALS

Most springs are made of hard, drawn, spring steel but many other metals are used including chrome vanadium steel, phosphor bronze, beryllium copper and stainless steel. Drawn steel wire is often termed *piano* or *music wire*.

SPIRAL TORSION SPRING

In this spring, the wire of round or rectangular cross-section is wound in a flat spiral and the spring is deformed under the application of a twisting moment, or torque. Small round wire spiral springs are used in locks and catches and as return springs for control rods. The clock spring is a case in which rectangular wire is used.

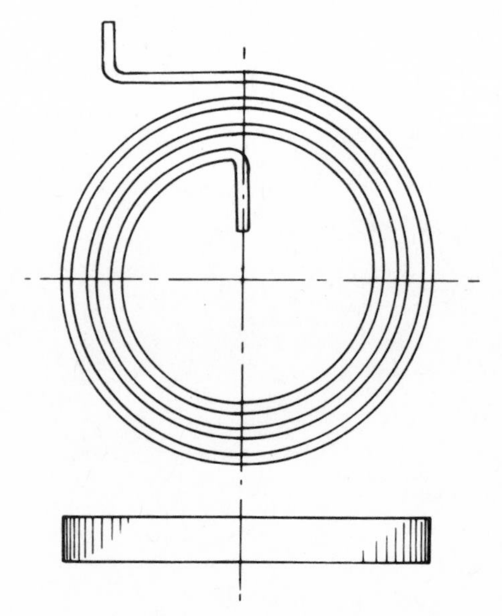

Figure 1.74 *Spiral torsion spring (rectangular section)*

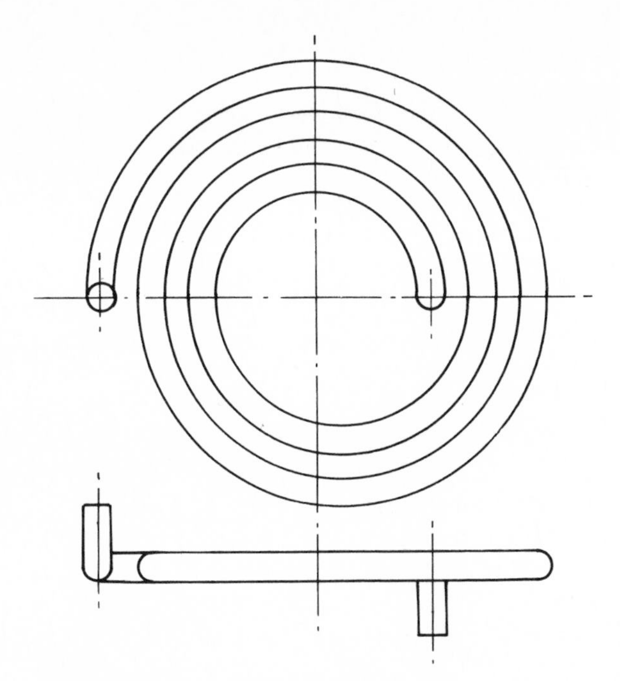

Figure 1.75 *Spiral torsion spring (round wire)*

CONICAL SPRING (UPHOLSTERY SPRING)

This is a helical compression spring in which the coil diameter changes from one end to the other so that a conical form is obtained. The larger diameter coils, which are the least stiff, close first so that the spring becomes stiffer as the load is increased.

An advantage is that the length of the spring when fully compressed is only the diameter of the wire. These springs are used extensively for upholstery.

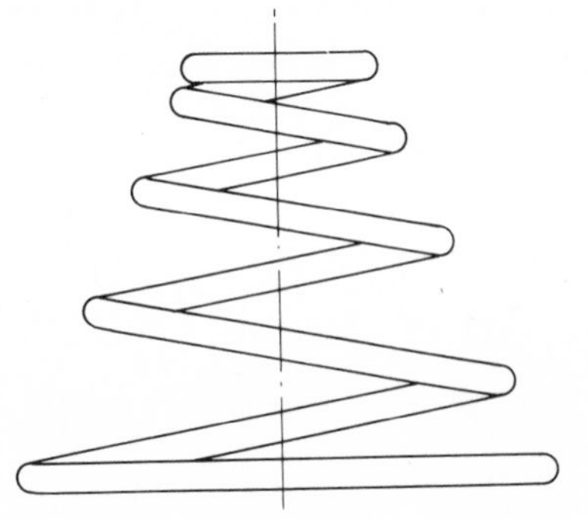

Figure 1.76 *Conical spring (upholstery spring)*

VOLUTE SPRING

A volute spring is made of thin rectangular strip wound into a conical spiral with each successive coil overlapping the previous one, and the cone flattens under sufficient load.

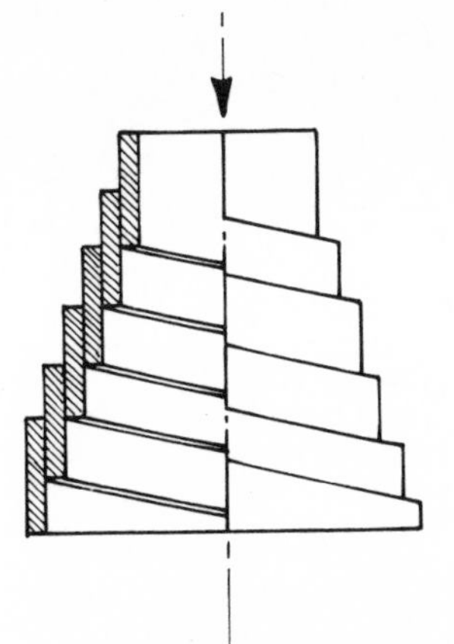

Figure 1.77 *Volute spring*

LEAF SPRINGS

These springs consist of one or several flat or slightly curved bars of steel held at one end and loaded at the other (cantilever) or held at both ends and loaded at the centre (beam).

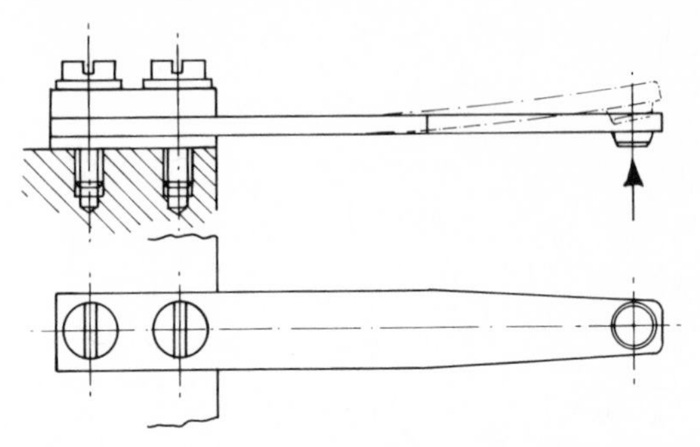

Figure 1.78 *Cantilever leaf spring (electrical contact)*

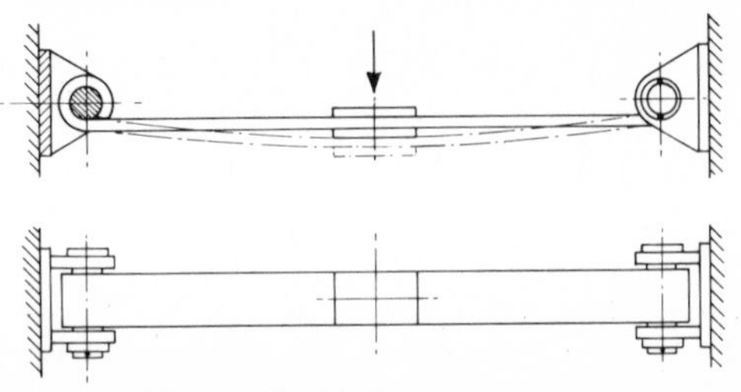

Figure 1.79 *Beam leaf spring*

LAMINATED LEAF SPRING (CARRIAGE SPRING)

A spring used extensively for vehicle suspensions. It consists of several flat strips clamped together and these vary in length to give a higher strength. The ends of the longest strip (usually at the top) are formed into eyes which take the suspension bolts, and the load is applied at the centre. Half of one of these springs may be used as a cantilever spring (Figure 1.80).

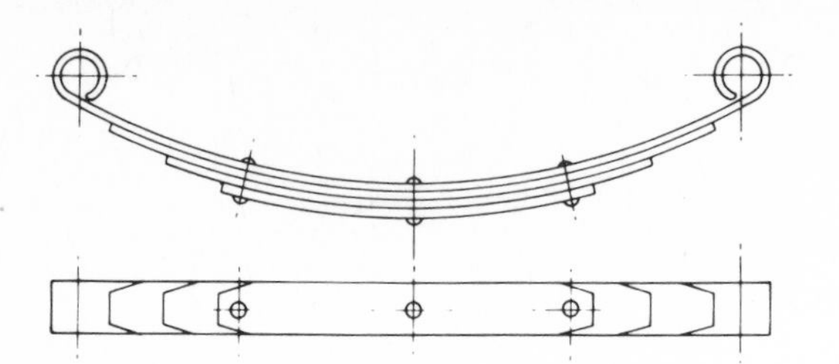

Figure 1.80 *Laminated leaf spring (carriage spring)*

RUBBER SPRING

Rubber, or synthetic rubber, bonded to metal plates is used extensively for springs under all types of loading. The spring may take the form of a block of rubber between two flat plates or a sleeve between two cylinders. Rubber springs have high internal damping and are therefore useful for damping vibrations.

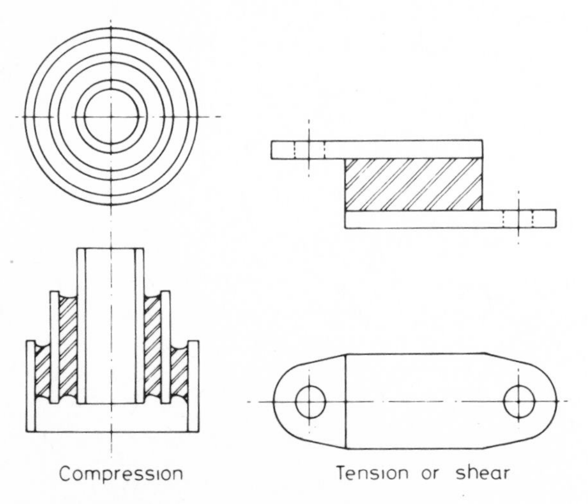

Figure 1.81 *Rubber springs*

AIR SPRING (PNEUMATIC SPRING)

In an air spring the elasticity of the air contained in a cylinder or rubber bellows is used to provide cushioning. The bellows type spring is sometimes used in vehicle suspensions.

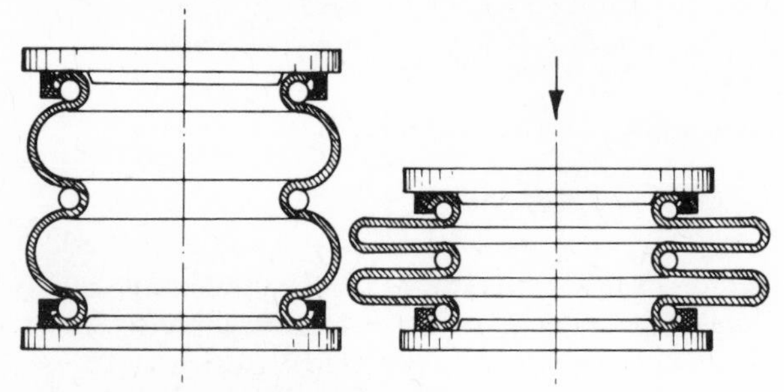

Figure 1.82 *Air bellows spring*

TORSION BAR SPRING

A straight, solid or hollow bar usually of circular but sometimes rectangular cross-section which may be used as a torsion spring. One end is clamped and the other provided with a lever to which the load is applied. They are used a great deal in vehicle suspensions.

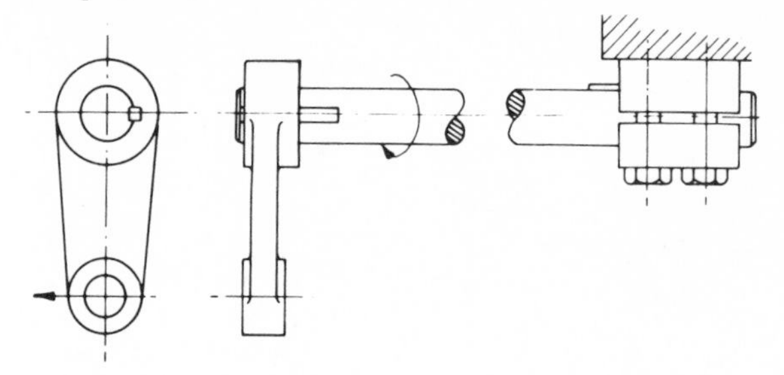

Figure 1.83 *Torsion bar spring*

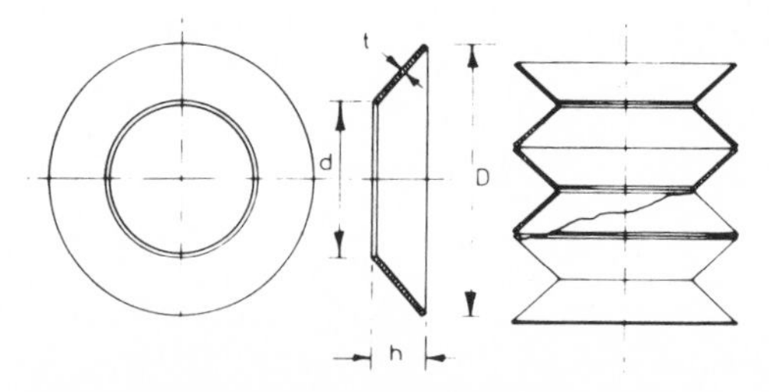

Figure 1.84 *Belleville washer (diaphragm spring)*

BELLEVILLE WASHER (DIAPHRAGM SPRING)

The Belleville washer is an annular steel ring which is slightly dished (or coned) and is loaded axially. To decrease the stiffness, a number of washers may be used in series. This type of spring saves considerable space and provides a wide variation in the shape of the load deflection curve as the ratio h/t is altered.

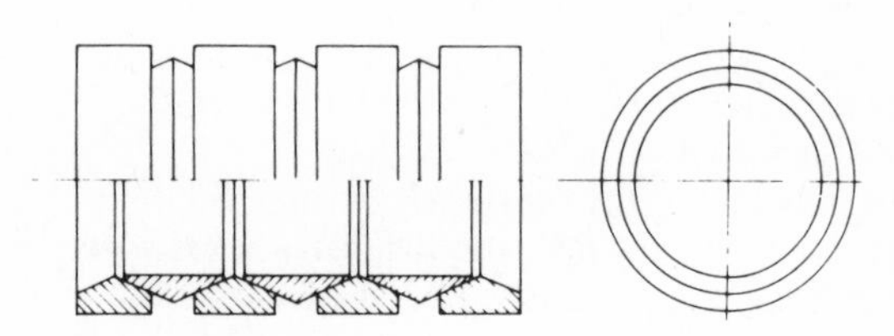

Figure 1.85 *Ring spring*

RING SPRING

This has alternate internally and externally bevelled rings stacked in a cylinder which is axially loaded. Under axial compression the internal rings contract and the external rings expand. These springs have a very high stiffness and high frictional clamping.

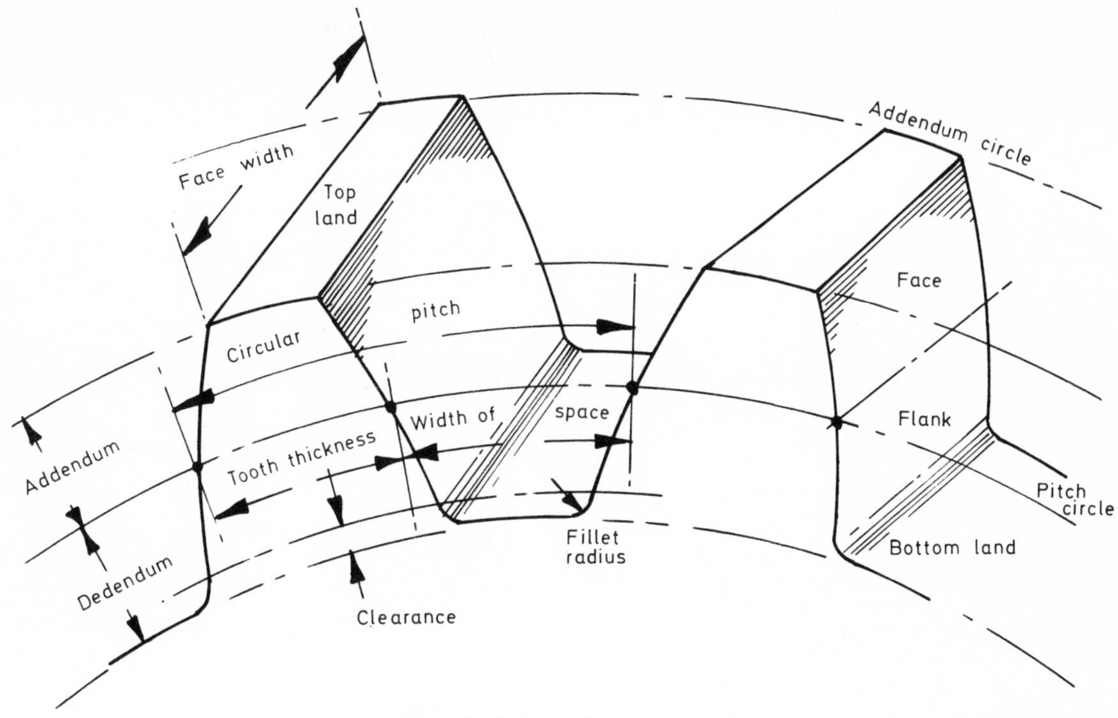

Figure 1.86 *Nomenclature of gear teeth*

1.4 GEARS

Gears are rotating machine elements which transmit motion and power without slip by means of a series of engaging projections known as *teeth*.

SPUR GEARS

Spur gears are disks with straight teeth on their peripheries which run parallel to the axis of rotation. The shafts carrying mating gears are parallel to one another and the ratio of the numbers of teeth on the two gears determines the ratio of the speeds and is inversely proportional to it.

The diameter of the equivalent friction disk is known as the 'pitch circle' and the distance between corresponding points on two adjacent teeth on the pitch circle is called the 'circular pitch'.

The number of teeth per inch of pitch circle diameter (British sizes) is the 'diametral pitch', and the pitch circle diameter in mm divided by the number of teeth (metric sizes) is the 'module'.

The height of that part of a tooth above the pitch circle is known as the 'addendum' and that part below it the 'dedendum'. The corresponding circles are the 'addendum circle' and the 'dedendum circle'.

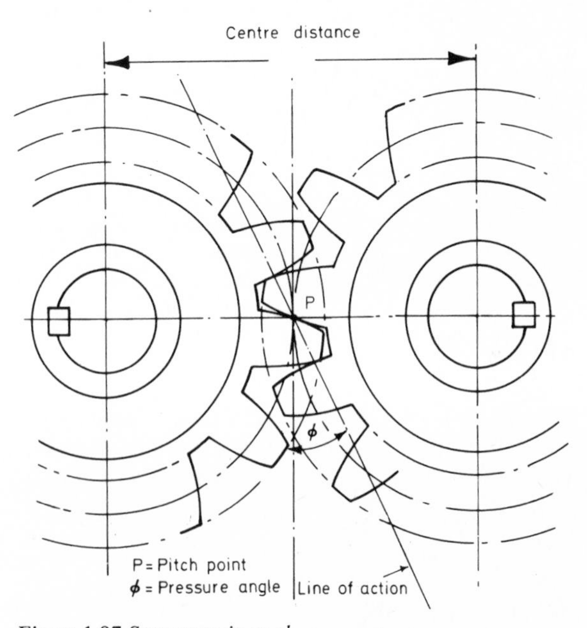

Figure 1.87 *Spur gears in mesh*

INVOLUTE GEAR

Most gears are made with the mating faces in the form of an 'involute' curve. An involute is the locus of (or curve described by) a point on a string as it is unwrapped from around a cylinder. This shape gives the correct rolling action when the teeth mesh. The path along which the teeth make contact is straight and is called the 'line of action'. The angle of this line to the tangent is the 'pressure angle'. The distance between the centres of a pair of meshing gears is called the 'centre distance'.

HELICAL GEAR

The teeth of a helical gear are formed on a helix on the cylindrical surface, that is, in the form of a coarse screw thread. The gradual engagement of the teeth and the resultant smooth transfer of load from tooth to tooth permits the use of higher powers with less noise than for straight teeth.

To eliminate axial thrust *double helical gears* are employed. Two gears with helices of opposite hand are mounted on each shaft. The two gears are often made in one piece, sometimes with a gap between the two sets of teeth. These are often known as *herringbone gears*.

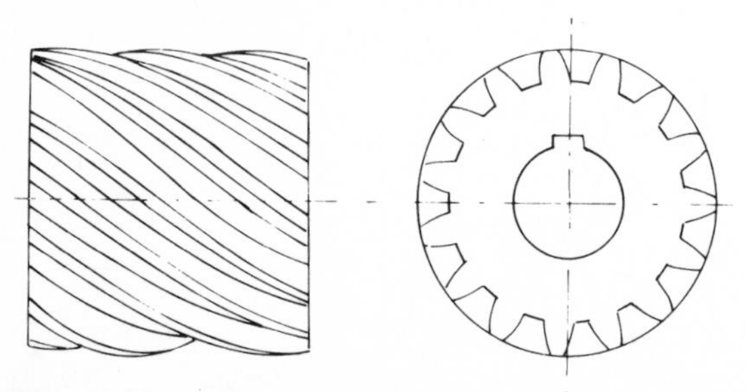

Figure 1.88 *Helical gear*

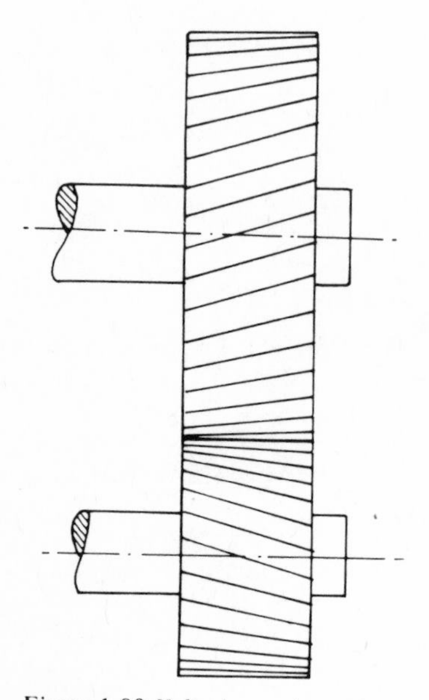

Figure 1.89 *Helical gears in mesh*

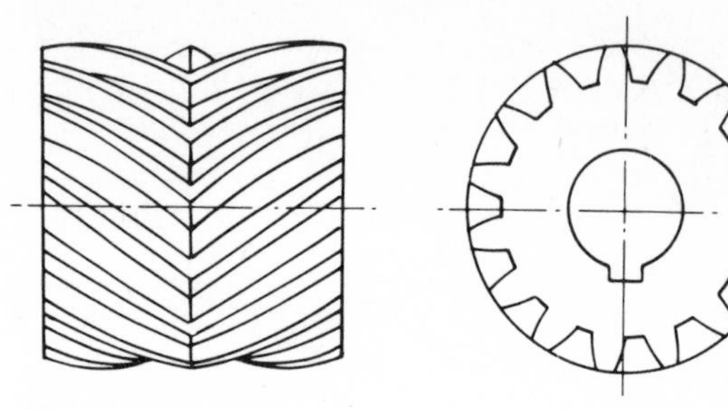

Figure 1.90 *Double helical gear*

BEVEL GEAR

On bevel gears the teeth are cut on a conical surface so that gears with intersecting but non-parallel shafts may be mated.

On *straight bevel gears* the teeth are straight, and on *spiral bevel gears* the teeth are curved in the form of a spiral. In both cases the shafts may be at any angle to one another although in most cases the angle is 90°.

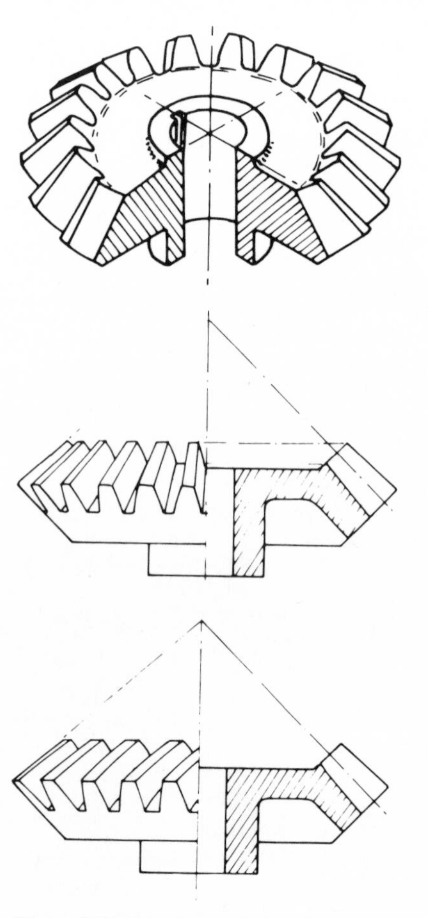

Figure 1.91 *Straight bevel gears (top and centre), and spiral bever gear*

Skew bevel gears have straight teeth but the axes are non-intersecting, and *hypoid gears* have curved teeth the axes of which are non-parallel and non-intersecting.

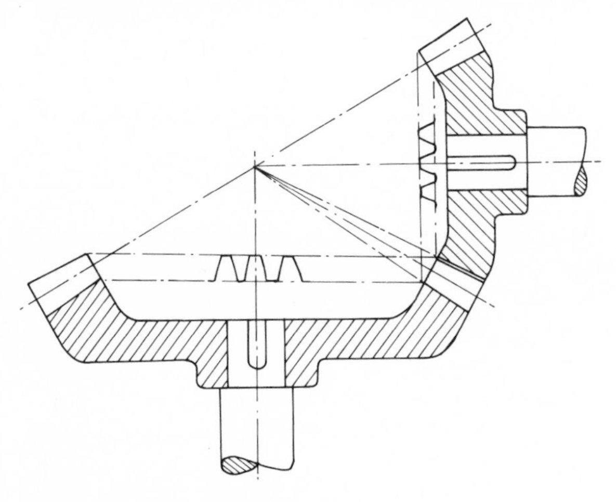

Figure 1.92 *Pair of bevel gears*

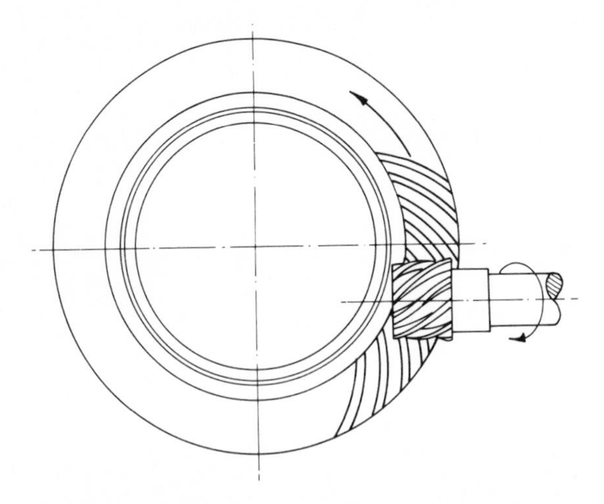

Figure 1.93 *Hypoid gears*

WORM GEAR

On worm gears the shafts are at right angles to each other but do not intersect. In effect the worm is a single or multi-start, trapezoidal-form screw thread which meshes with a much larger diameter worm wheel with teeth curved to suit the worm diameter.

Worm gears are used for speed reduction and have ratios of up to about 300:1.

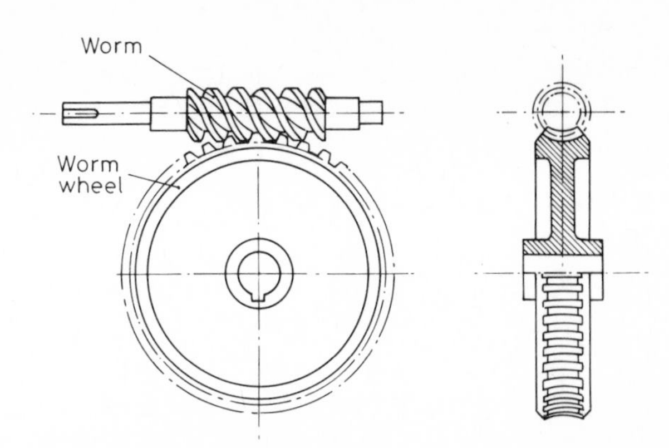

Figure 1.94 *Worm gear*

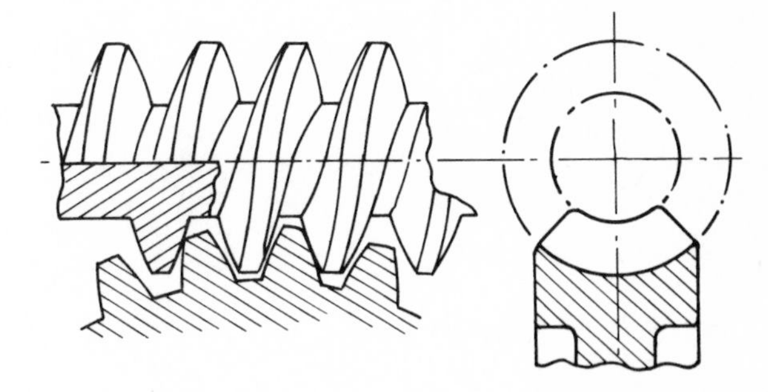

Figure 1.95 *Detail of worm gear*

RACK-AND-PINION GEAR

A rack is a straight bar with teeth which mesh with mating teeth on a gear, or *pinion*. The rack moves in a straight line as the pinion rotates. If the pinion teeth are of involute form the rack teeth will be straight-sided.

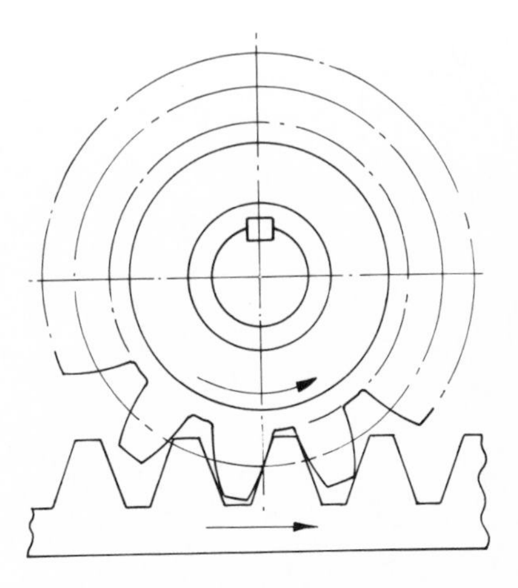

Figure 1.96 *Rack-and-pinion gear*

INTERNAL GEAR

An internal gear has teeth cut on the inside of an annular ring which mesh with teeth on a gear with external teeth which is situated inside the annular ring. Both gears rotate in the same direction.

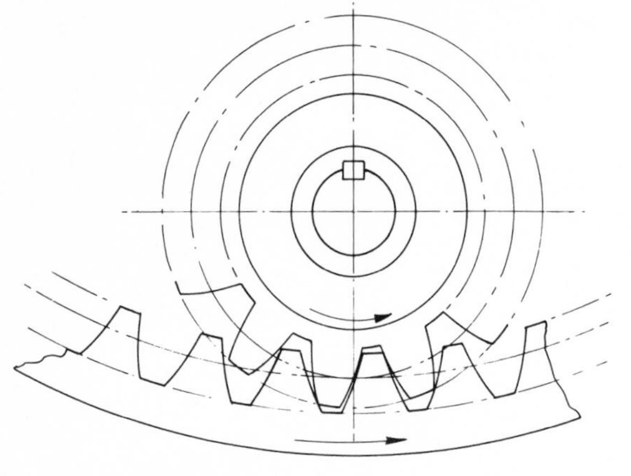

Figure 1.97 *Internal gear*

EPICYCLIC GEAR

An epicyclic gear comprises a *sun gear* keyed to a central shaft, and several *planet gears* which are meshed with and revolve around the sun gear. The planet gears are mounted on spindles held in position by a carrier attached to a sleeve running on the sun gear shaft.

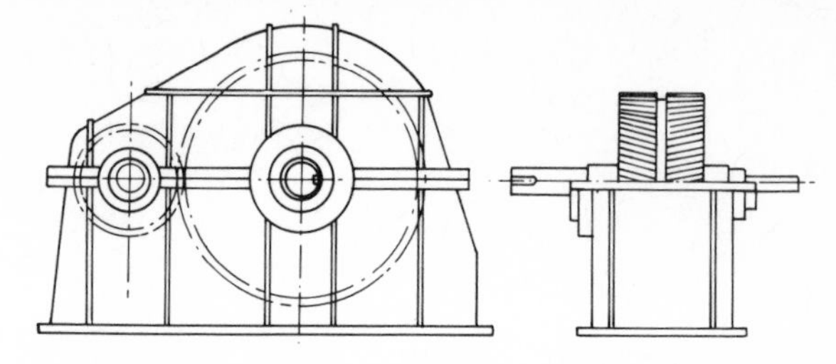

Figure 1.99 *Gearbox*

A second co-axial shaft carries a *ring gear* whose internal teeth mesh with the planet gears.

Various gear ratios can be obtained depending upon which member is held stationary, the inner gear, the outer gear or the planet gear ring. In an epicyclic gearbox the various elements are held by friction brakes as desired.

An advantage of epicyclic gears is that their input and output shafts are concentric.

GEAR TRAIN

When more than two gears are employed the system is known as a *gear train*. When these gears are mounted in a casing with a lubrication system the assembly is called a *gearbox*. An intermediate shaft is called a *layshaft*.

In an automobile gearbox some of the gears are on splined shafts and can be moved by using a hand operated gear selector to give different speed ratios.

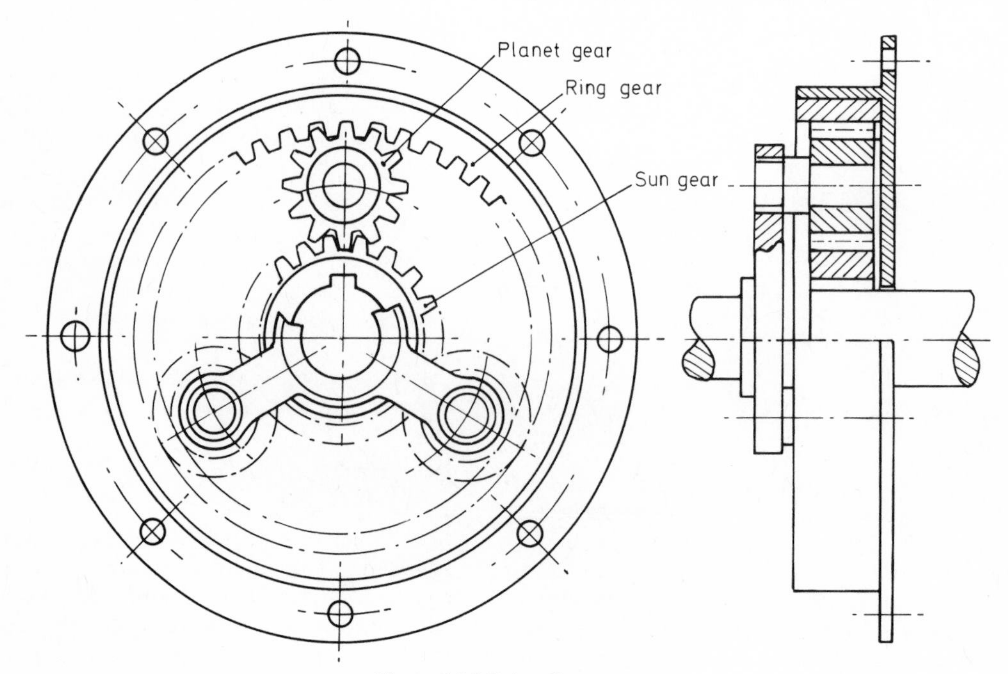

Figure 1.98 *Epicyclic gear*

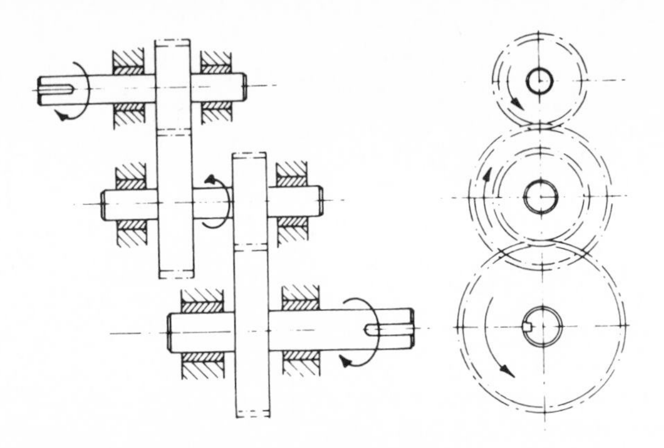

Figure 1.100 *Double reduction gear train*

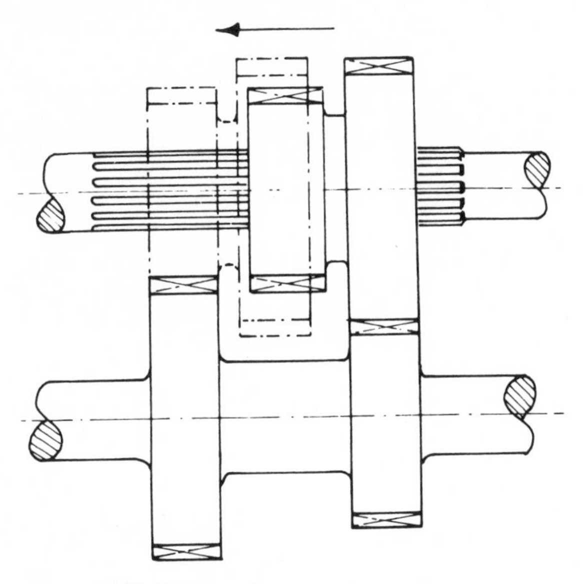

Figure 1.101 *Gear changing*

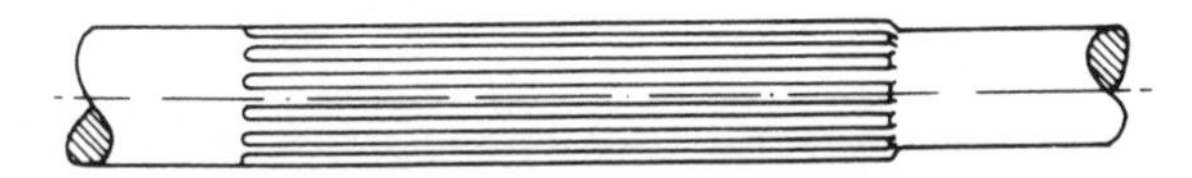

Figure 1.101a *Splined gear shaft*

GEAR MATERIALS

Gears are made from cast iron for light duty, and cast and alloy steels for heavy duty. Bronze is used for worm gears. Plastics, particularly laminates such as Tufnol, are used in special cases.

Small gears are usually cast or forged, and large gears, e.g. marine gears, are welded fabrications. Steel gears often have the teeth case-hardened and ground to a high surface finish.

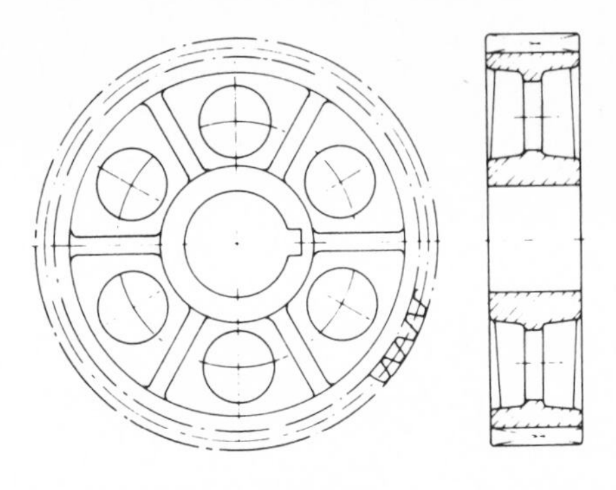

Figure 1.102 *Cast steel gear*

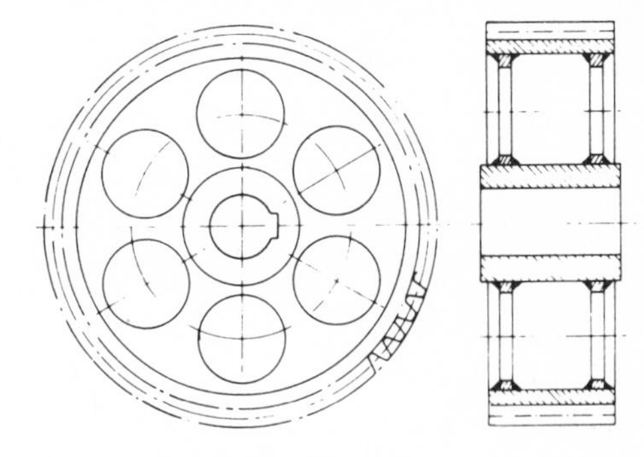

Figure 1.103 *Welded steel gear*

1.5 FLUID SEALS, JOINTS AND GASKETS

FLUID SEALS

Fluid seals are devices for preventing unwanted leakage of liquids and gases in machines. The seal may be between two fixed parts or two parts with relative motion. Seals between fixed parts are generally known as *joints, gaskets* and *sealing washers.* Seals preventing the leakage of lubricants on rotating and sliding shafts and other moving parts are called *oil seals.* The housing for a shaft seal is sometimes referred to as a *gland*.

Various types of jointing cement are used with or without gaskets, e.g. Locktite.

STUFFING BOX (GLAND)

A stuffing box, or gland, is a recess in a casing (surrounding a shaft) containing sealing material, or *gland packing,* which is compressed by means of an adjustable ring to prevent leakage along the shaft. This ring is often termed a *gland-ring* or simply *a gland* (Figure 1.104).

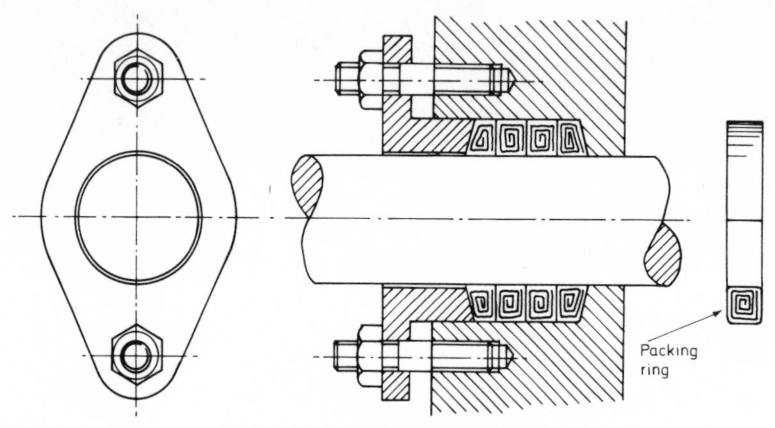

Figure 1.104 *Stuffing box (gland)*

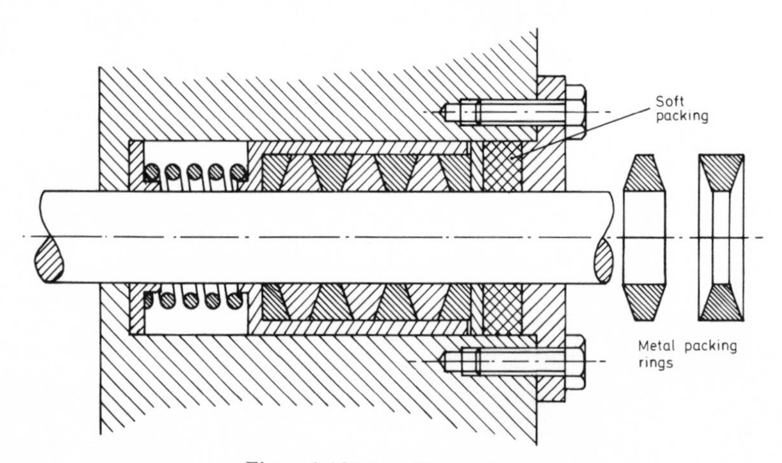

Figure 1.105 *Metallic packing*

GLAND PACKING

The packing in a stuffing box consists of a spiral, or several rings, of woven asbestos, cotton or hemp impregnated with grease and graphite to reduce friction.

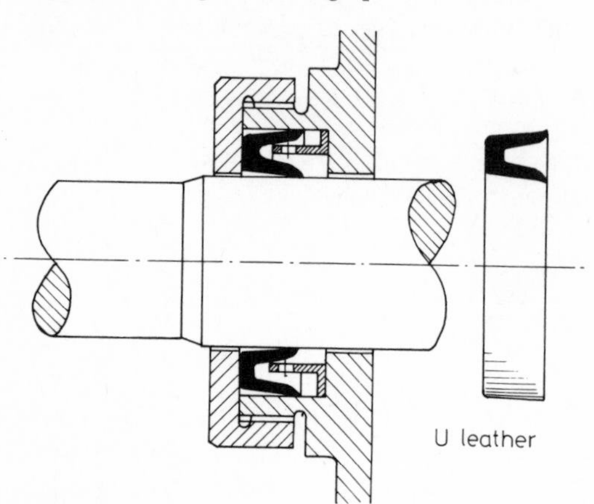

Figure 1.106 *Shaft seal with U leather*

METALLIC PACKING

This consists of alternative triangular-section rings of gunmetal and whitemetal, or sometimes plastic and metal. The rings are compressed, together with a ring of soft packing, either by tightening with bolts or by means of a spring.

U SEAL

A moulded U-section seal of leather or synthetic rubber is held in position by a screwed or bolted ring. The fluid pressure forces the lip of the seal on to the shaft or cylinder, thus improving the sealing action.

This type of seal is used where there is a large pressure difference across it.

LIP SEAL WITH GARTER SPRING

This is a moulded synthetic rubber seal, usually with a metal insert, in which the lip of the seal is held onto the shaft by a circumferential *garter spring*.

It is suitable for low pressures and is used in IC engines, automobile gearboxes, etc.

A double, or duplex, seal is used to prevent the entry of dirt from the atmosphere.

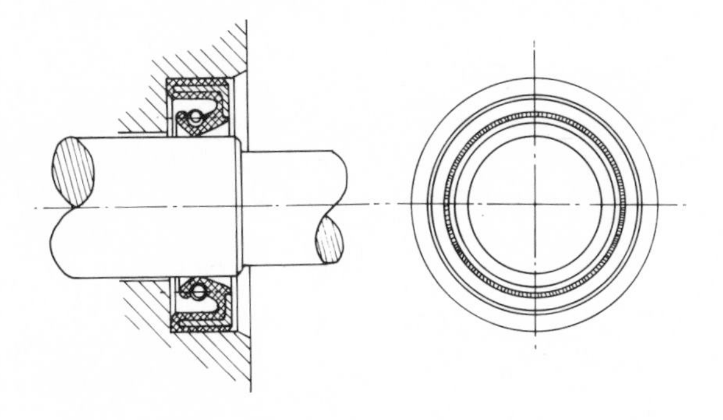

Figure 1.107 *Lip seal with garter spring*

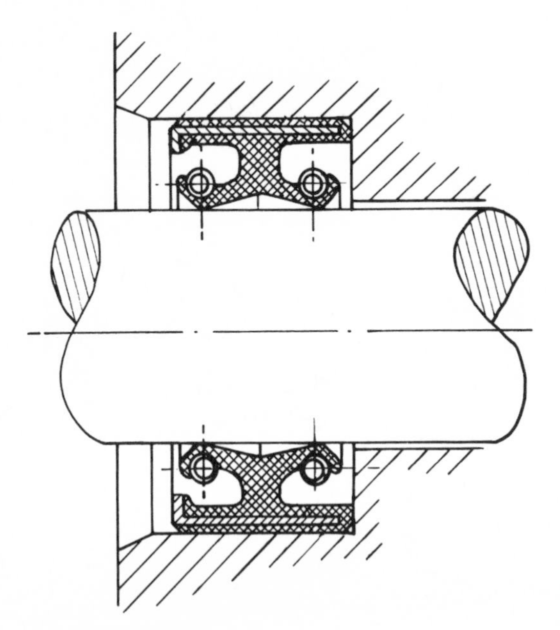

Figure 1.108 *Duplex lip seal*

CUP SEAL

A synthetic rubber or leather seal with a single lip, used for sealing hydraulic and pneumatic pistons. Sealing is aided by compression from the holding flange.

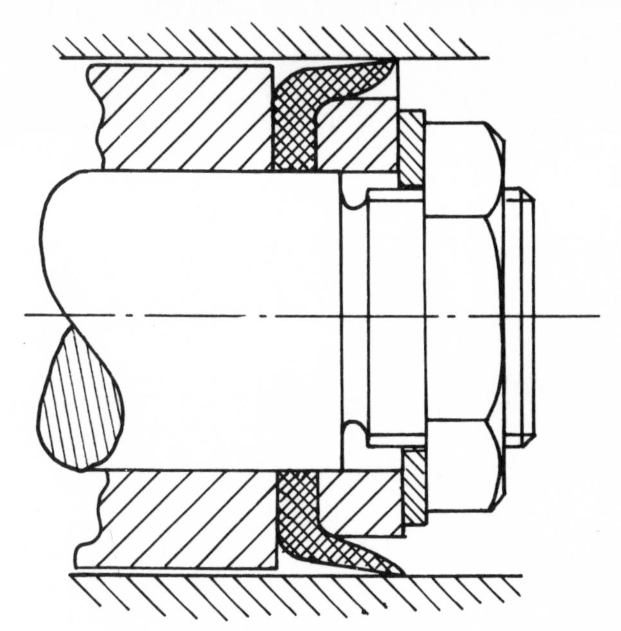

Figure 1.109 *Cup seal*

HAT PACKING

A synthetic rubber packing in the form of a flat washer with a raised sealing lip on the inside edge, used for sealing rods. It relies on controlled compression by a nut to give effective sealing.

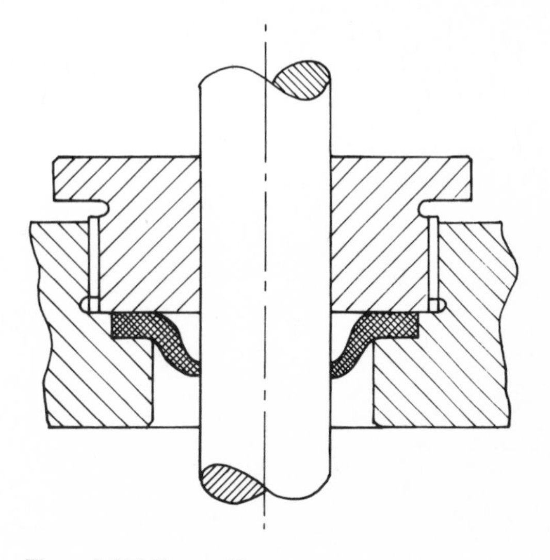

Figure 1.110 *Hat packing*

FELT RING

A felt ring provides a simple and cheap form of seal to retain lubricant and exclude dirt. It is suitable for grease-lubricated, low-speed rolling bearings.

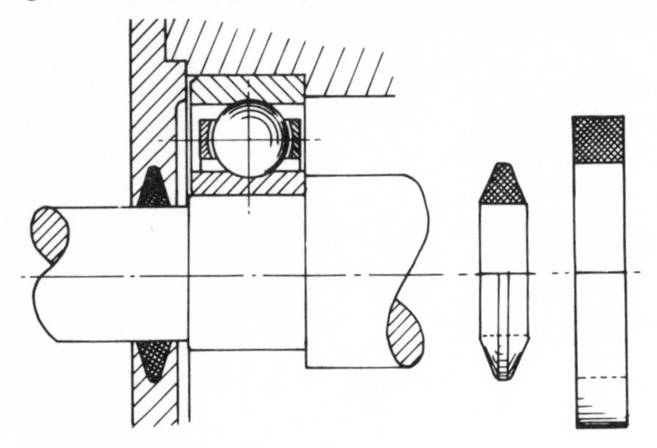

Figure 1.111 *Felt sealing rings*

O RING

An O ring is the simplest form of hydraulic packing. It is a synthetic rubber ring of solid circular cross-section made in a wide variety of ring and cross-section diameters.

O rings are suitable for static sealing, e.g. in pipe joints, cylinder end covers and valve spindles, and also for low speed dynamic sealing of pistons and piston rods in hydraulic and pneumatic cylinders.

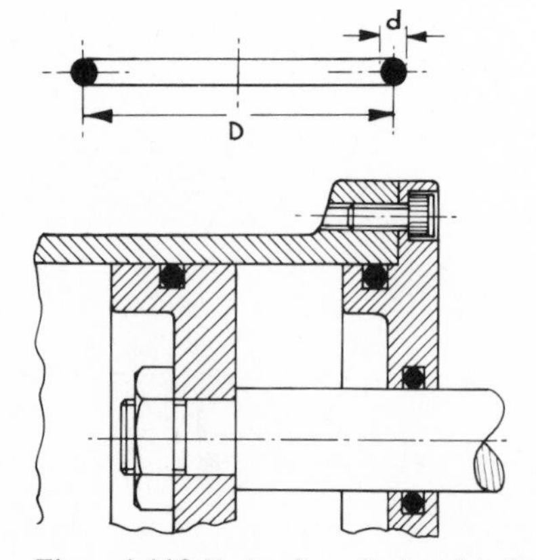

Figure 1.112 *Hydraulic cylinder with O ring seals*

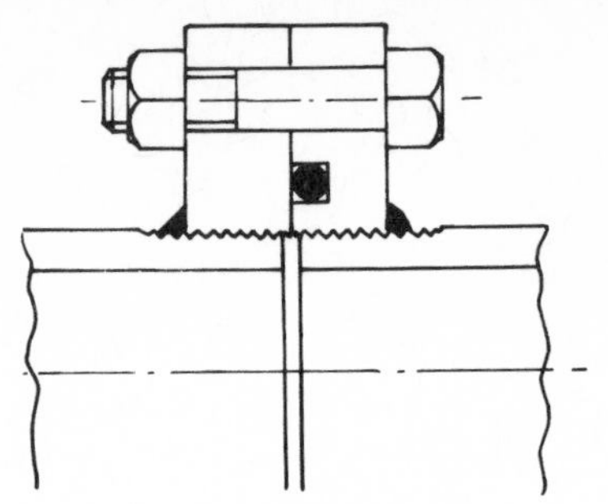

Figure 1.113 *O ring in pipe joint*

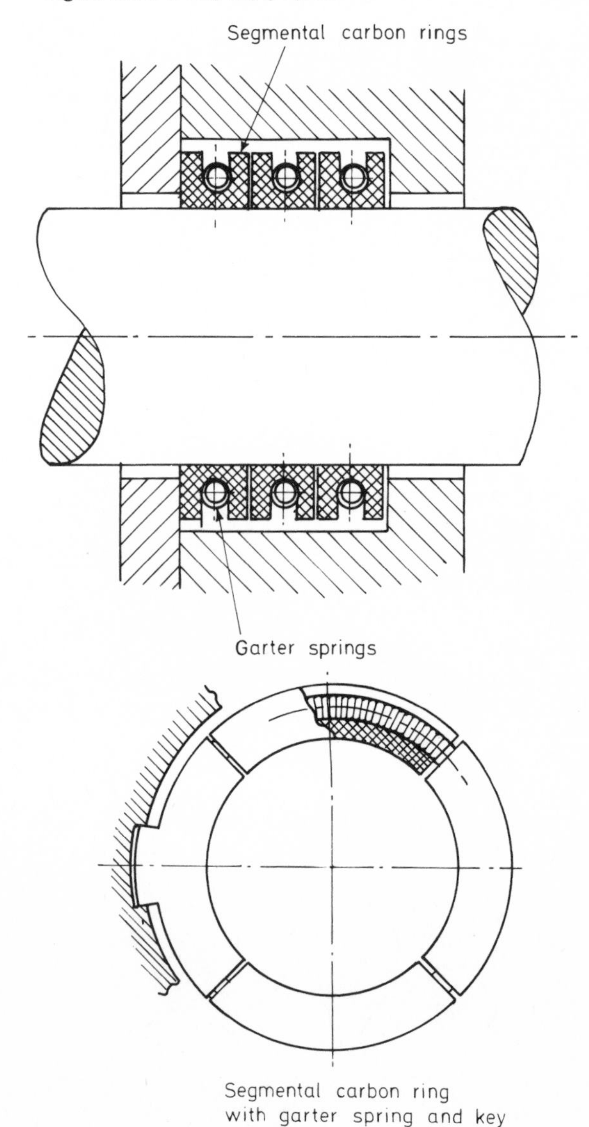

Figure 1.114 *Segmental carbon seal*

CARBON SEALS

In these seals a block or blocks of carbon held in a housing run with zero clearance on the moving surface.

In one type, segmental carbon rings are held on to a rotating shaft by garter springs, and these are used in small steam turbines.

Another type has an annular ring of carbon held on to a thrust collar on the shaft by a spring, and this type is commonly used in automobile engine water pumps.

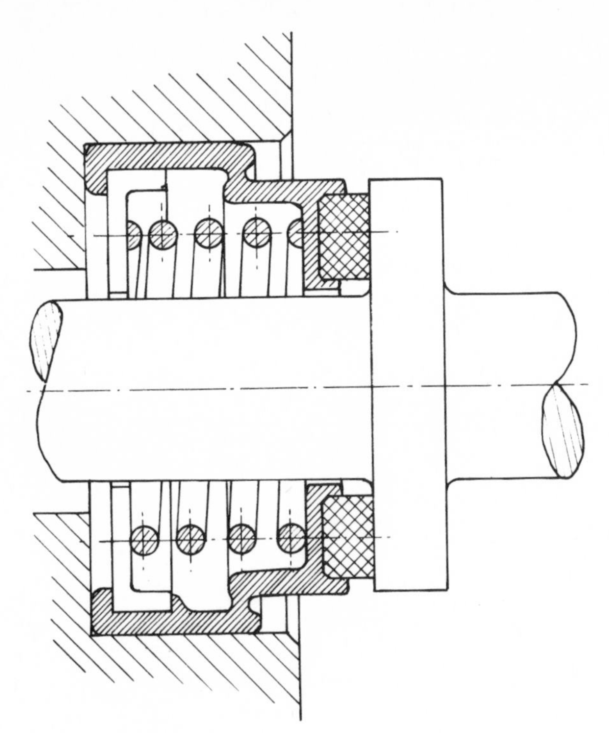

Figure 1.115 *Carbon face seal (spring-loaded)*

BELLOWS SEAL

This seal consists of an annular ring of low friction material running on the face of a thrust collar on a shaft and mounted on a bellows which flexes, thus allowing for any misalignment. The bellows also acts as a spring to give the required pressure between the surfaces.

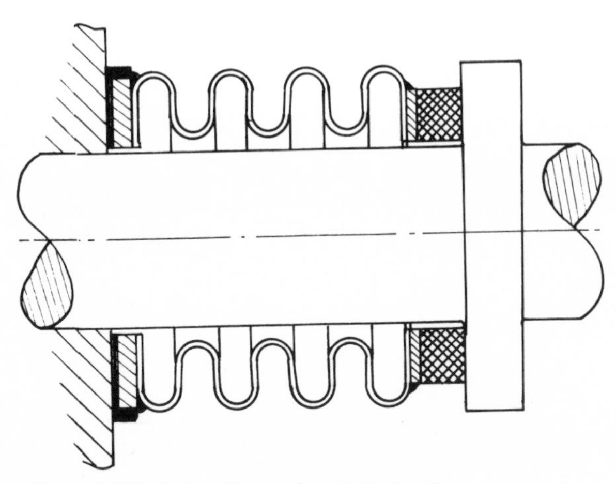

Figure 1.116 *Carbon face seal (with bellows)*

PISTON RING

The pistons of IC engines, reciprocating pumps and compressors are sealed against gas or air pressure by rings on the piston. The rings, which are made of cast iron or steel, are of rectangular cross-section and fit into grooves of the same shape in the piston. The ring is cut across so that it springs out against the cylinder wall to ensure a good seal.

A typical petrol engine piston has two compression rings for gas sealing, and an oil scraper ring which prevents oil from entering the combustion chamber.

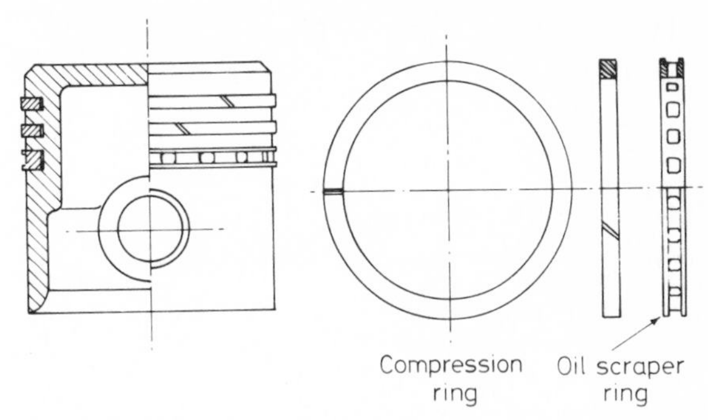

Figure 1.117 *IC engine piston rings*

LABYRINTH GLAND

A labyrinth gland is a type of seal in which there is no contact between seal and moving part. This is important where there may be side movement of a shaft relative to the fixed part. It is inevitable, however, that some leakage must occur.

Labyrinth glands in steam and gas turbines consist of a series of restrictions formed by projections on the shaft and/or casing. The pressure of the steam or gas is broken down by expansion at each restriction.

A type used for rolling bearings has a series of grooves in a fixed sleeve surrounding the shaft.

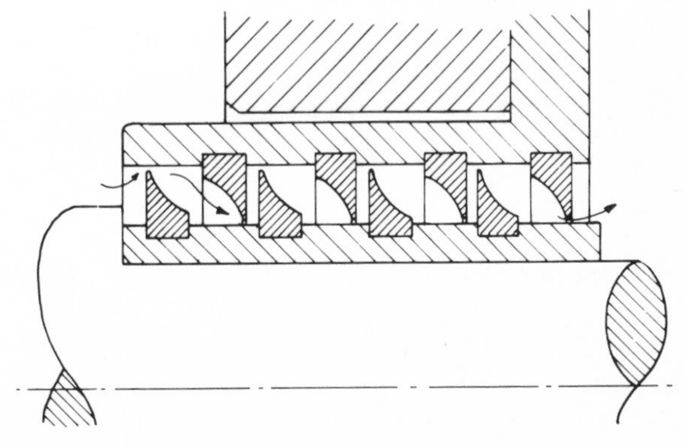

Figure 1.118 *Labyrinth gland for steam turbine*

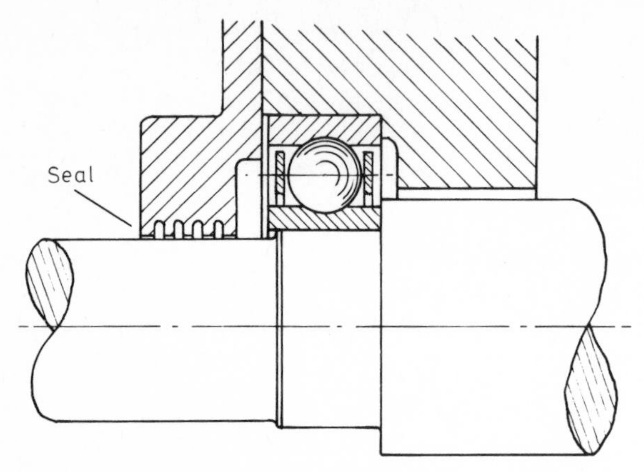

Figure 1.119 *Labyrinth seal for ball bearing*

JOINT AND GASKET

These are static seals consisting of specially-shaped pieces of flat jointing material compressed between mating faces on machine parts.

Soft materials such as cork, rubber, paper and asbestos are used for low pressure, low temperature applications and will accommodate a high degree of roughness of the faces.

For high pressures and temperatures metallic gaskets are used. These are made of soft metals, such as copper or aluminium, and are often used in the form of a sandwich with a soft non-metallic material.

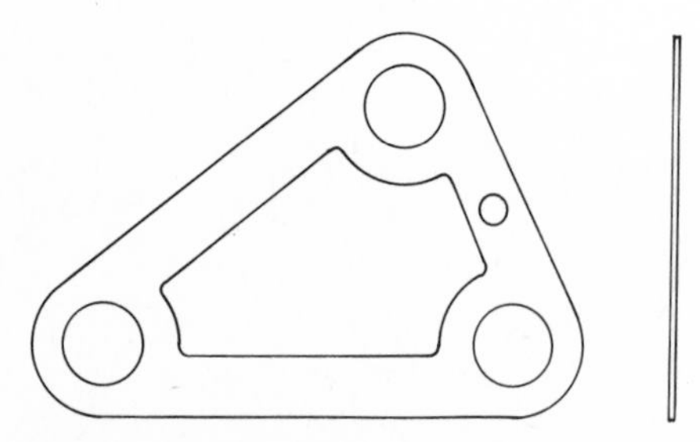

Figure 1.120 *Paper gasket*

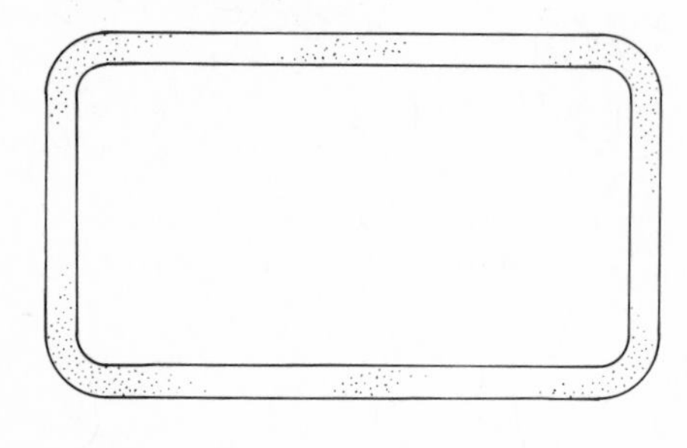

Figure 1.121 *Cork gasket*

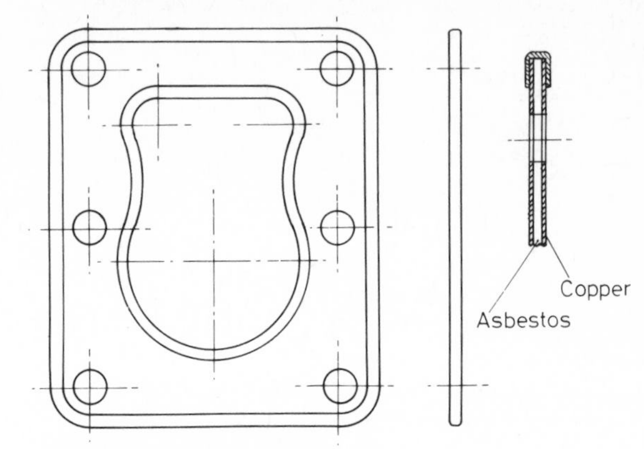

Figure 1.122 *Copper-asbestos gasket*

SEALING WASHER

Sealing washers are used to prevent leakage of fluids past the threads of bolts and screwed plugs. Metal washers are made of annealed copper or aluminium and compress on tightening.

Leather, fibre and plastic sealing washers are also used and there are several designs of metal sealing washers with synthetic rubber inserts.

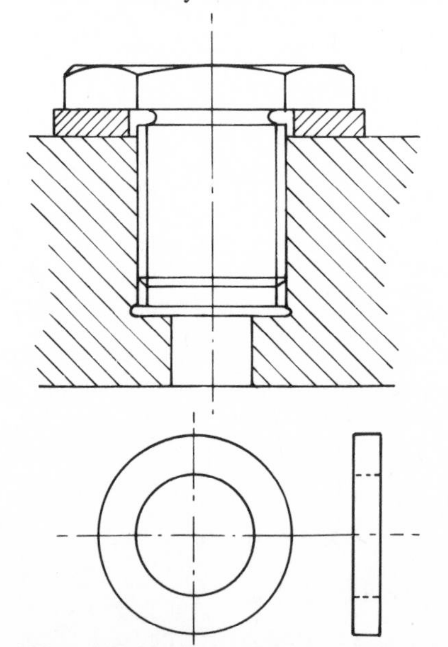

Figure 1.123 *Copper or aluminium sealing washer*

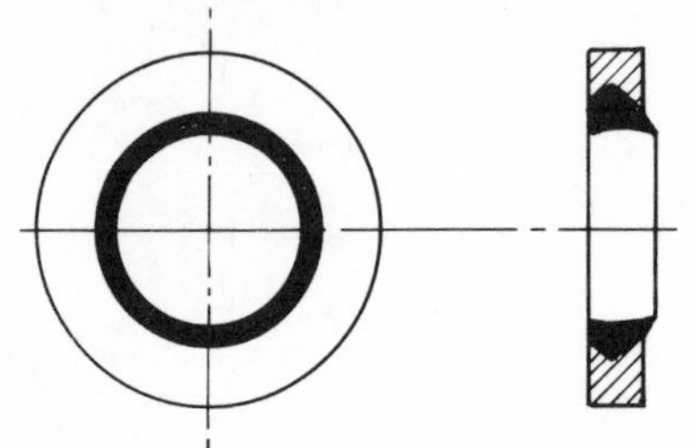

Figure 1.124 *Steel sealing washer with rubber insert*

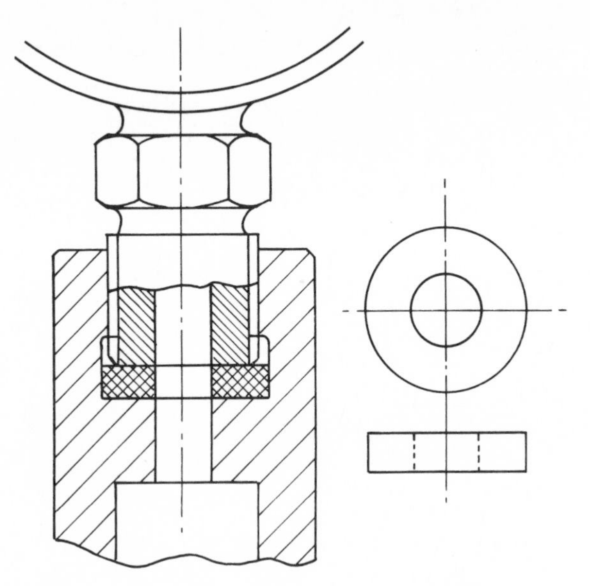

Figure 1.125 *Leather sealing washer for pressure gauge*

1.6 PIPES, PIPE FITTINGS, DUCTS AND VALVES

Pipes are tubes of metal, plastics, rubber, glass, etc., usually circular in section, used for conveying fluids or mixtures of solids and fluids.

The term *duct* is generally applied to pipes of large size made of sheet metal which are used for gases such as air.

A wide range of standard pipe and duct fittings, such as bends, couplings and valves is available.

SCREWED IRON PIPE JOINTS AND FITTINGS

These are made of wrought iron or malleable cast iron and they have ends to suit screwed fittings. They are used for water, air and gas mains.

The pipe ends are threaded and their fittings are provided with internal matching threads. To ensure perfect sealing the threads are treated with various jointing materials and cements before assembly.

The main types of fitting are:

Socket A threaded sleeve for joining straight pipes.

Elbow For joining pipes at right angles.

Slow Bend For right-angled bends but with a larger radius of curvature than the elbow.

T joint For joining three pipes, two of them in line and the other at right angles to them.

Reducer A straight fitting for joining pipes of different diameter.

Cap For closing the end of a pipe. A cap has an internal thread and it is fitted round the end of a pipe.

Plug This has an external thread and is used for closing the end of a fitting.

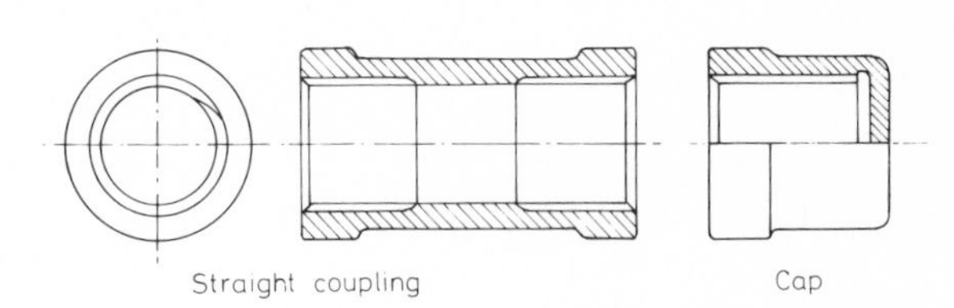

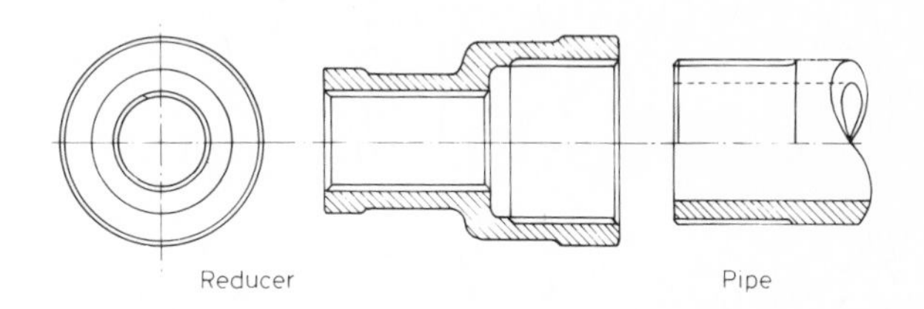

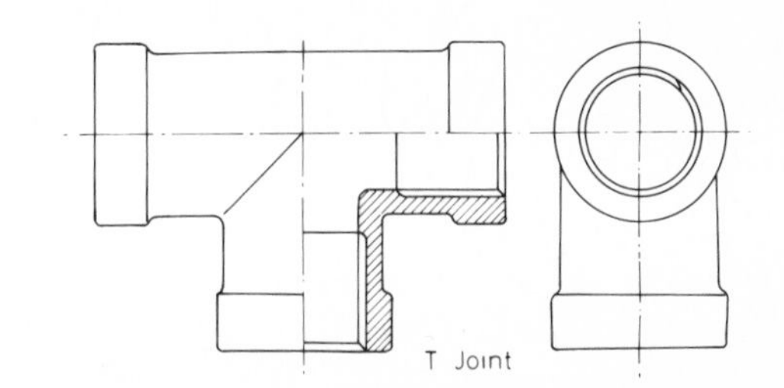

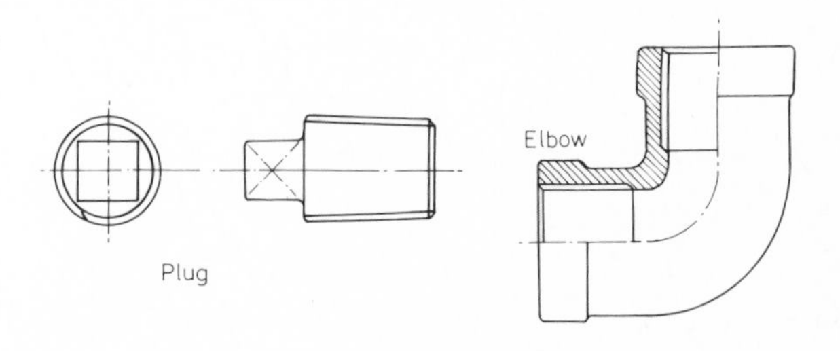

Figure 1.126 *Screwed iron pipe fittings*

FLANGED PIPE JOINTS

Medium and large bore pipes are often joined by bolted flanges either screwed or welded, or both screwed and welded, to the ends of the pipes. The joint may be 'face-to-face' or sealed with a washer or gasket.

Heavy-duty pipe joints have screwed and welded flanges with flanges and bolts which are larger than those used in low or medium pressure joints. A common type of *hydraulic pipe joint* has two-bolt flanges of heavy construction and a soft copper sealing ring which fits into a recess in one of the flanges. *Flanged pipe bends* are available with various ratios of bend radius to pipe bore.

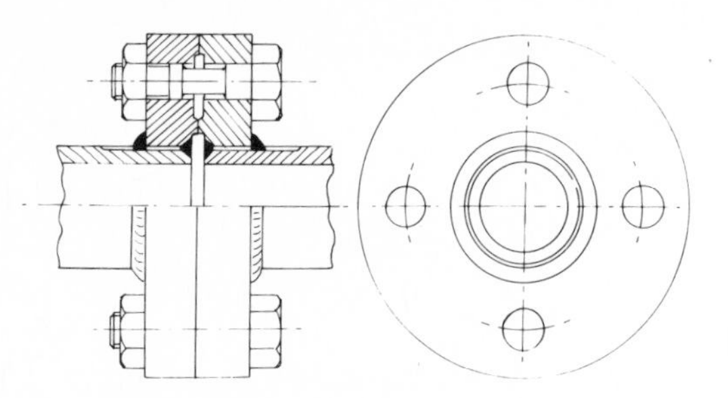

Figure 1.127 *Flanged pipe joint*

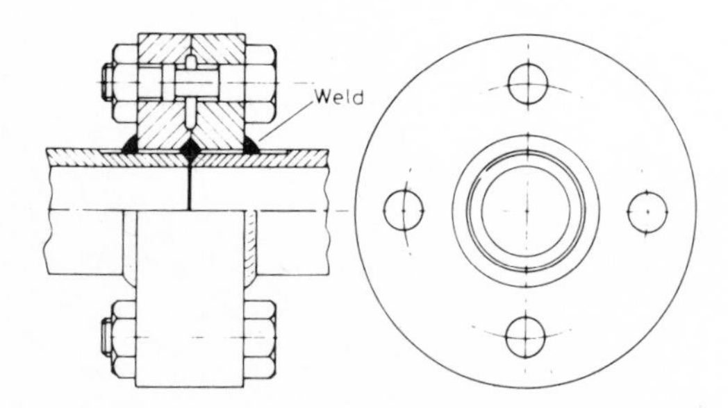

Figure 1.128 *Heavy-duty pipe joint*

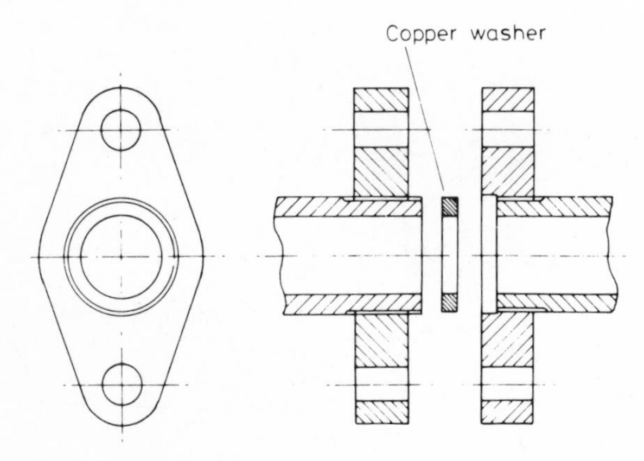

Figure 1.129 *Hydraulic pipe joint*

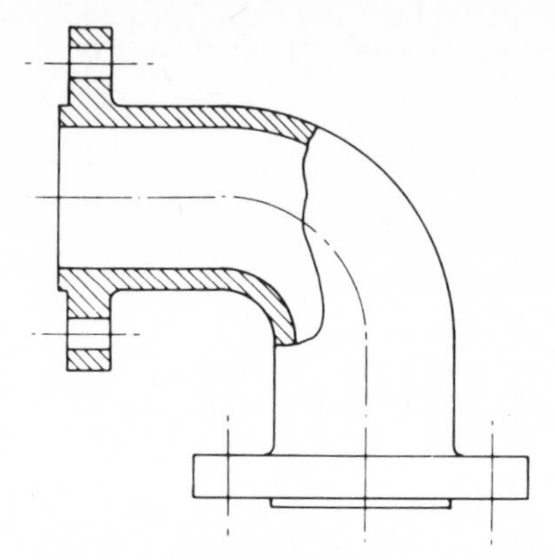

Figure 1.130 *Flanged pipe bend*

SOLDERED COPPER PIPE FITTINGS (CAPILLARY PIPE FITTINGS)

These fittings, designed for use with copper pipes, contain solder and only require to be heated by a blowlamp to make the joint.

The pipe, which must first be cleaned, is inserted into the fitting containing an internal ring of soft solder which, when melted, flows by capillary action and bonds the pipe to the fitting.

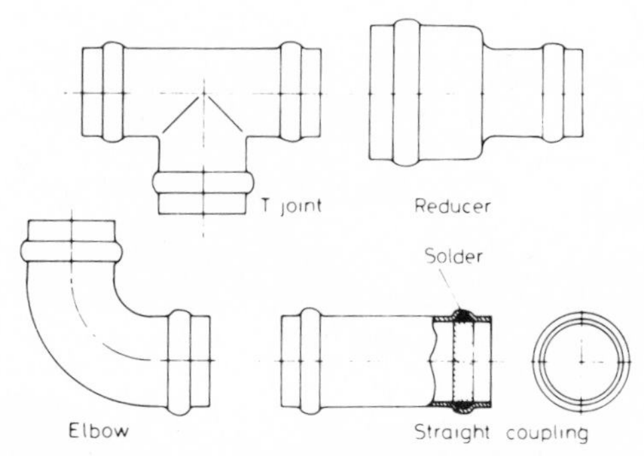

Figure 1.131 *Soldered copper pipe fittings*

PIPE AND DUCT MATERIALS

Pipes for all kinds of fluids are made from metals, plastics, rubber and canvas, etc.

Copper pipe This is made in bore sizes from a few mm up to 15cm and is used for water, oil, gas, and low pressure steam.

Heavy gauge steel Used for hydraulic pipes.

Lap-welded wrought iron Pipes of large and medium bore for conveying water are made from this material.

Solid drawn steel Used in the making of large and medium bore pipes for steam.

Brass For small size pipes as used in lubricating systems.

Galvanised steel/aluminium alloy sheet Metals used in the manufacture of ducting.

Plastics Polythene, PVC, nylon, etc. are examples of plastics utilised for the making of flexible pipes.

SCREWED BRASS PIPE COUPLINGS AND FITTINGS

A number of types of screwed pipe couplings are available and these may be used with copper pipes of up to about 40mm bore. They usually have a ring, known variously as a nipple, ferrule, olive or sleeve, fitted over the end of the pipe and secured to it by soldering, brazing or compression. The joint is made by means of a nut which holds the ring tightly onto the part to which the pipe is to be attached.

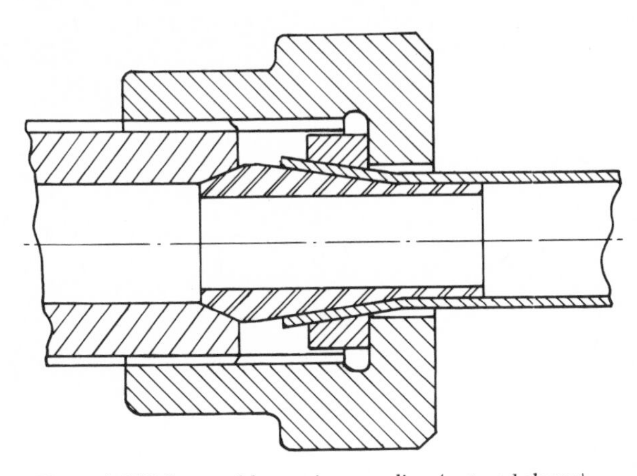

Figure 1.132 *Screwed brass pipe coupling (nut-and-sleeve)*

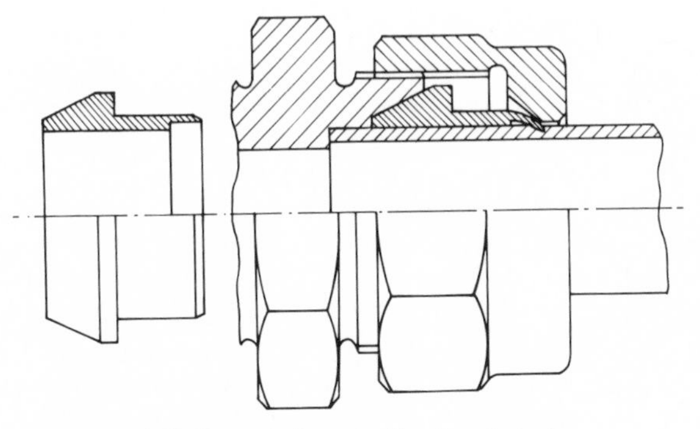

Figure 1.133 *Ermeto pipe coupling (steel pipe)*

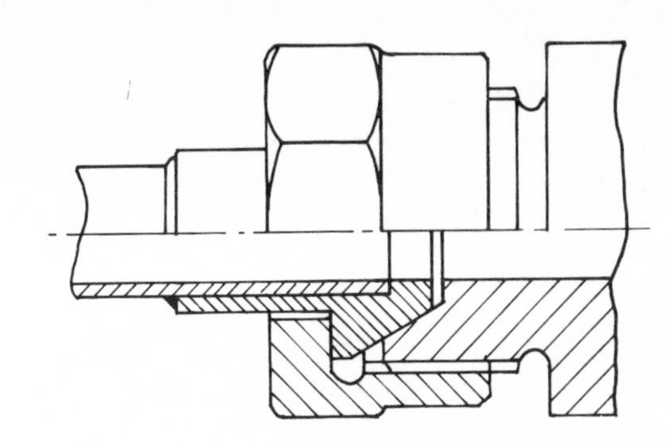

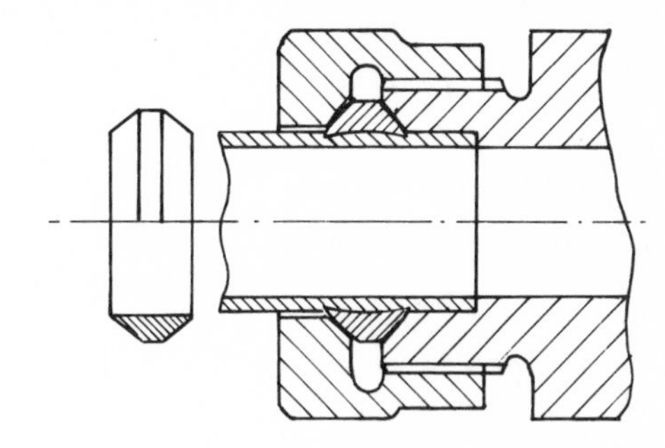

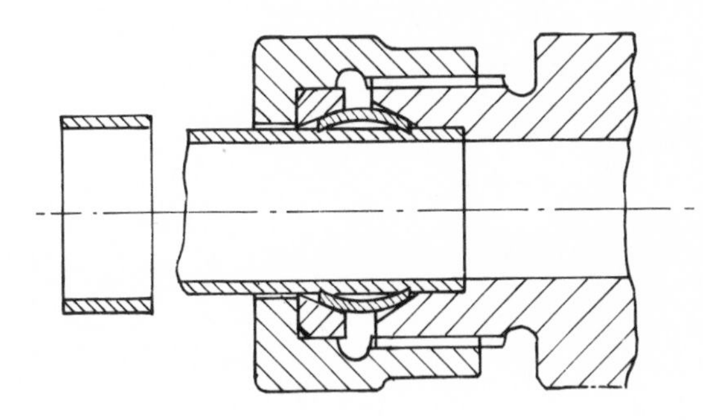

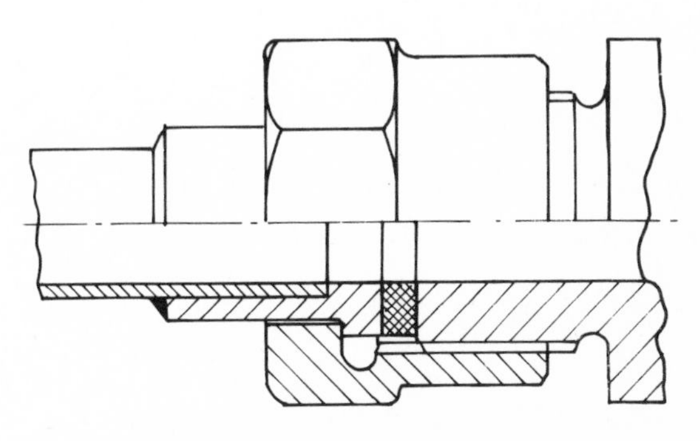

Figure 1.134 *Screwed brass pipe couplings*

The *nut-and-sleeve coupling* has a tapered sleeve which fits into and opens out the bore of the pipe, and a coned ring on the outside of the pipe. When the nut is tightened the pipe is nipped between the sleeve and the ring.

Sleeves attached by soldering or brazing may be single coned or double coned. Straight sleeves are compressed into the pipe by tightening the nut so that they deform and become curved.

One type of compression coupling, the *Ermeto coupling,* has a coned steel sleeve used with steel pipe, and this system is suitable for high pressure hydraulic pipes.

SCREWED BRASS PIPE FITTINGS

The *straight coupling* is used to connect two pipes in line: the *stud coupling* connects a pipe to some other parts; the *elbow* connects pipes at right angles; the *T* coupling connects two pipes in line and a third at right angles.

For each of these fittings the ends may be of different sizes (reducer), and one or more ends may have a female (internal) thread.

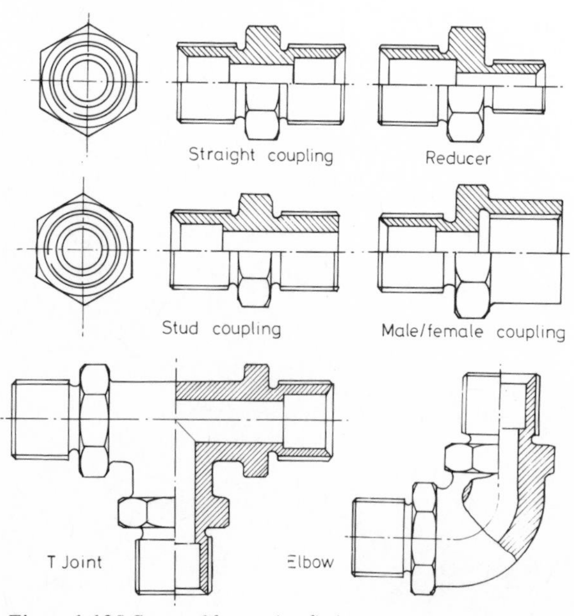

Figure 1.135 *Screwed brass pipe fittings*

EXPANSION JOINTS AND BENDS

When there may be relative movement of the ends of a pipeline it is necessary to introduce flexibility, and this can be done by using flexible pipes or flexible joints.

The *sliding expansion joint* consists of two tubes, one sliding inside the other with a gland to prevent leakage, and rods limiting the movement.

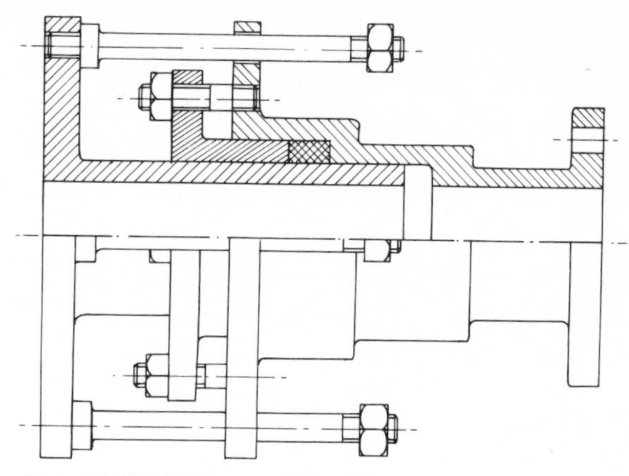

Figure 1.136 *Sliding expansion joint*

An alternative, the *bellows joint,* has a section of pipe replaced by a metal bellows which expands or contracts with relative movement of the pipes. If only an angular movement is desired a hinge is fitted.

Flexibility can be obtained from either U or lyre-shaped bends in which the elasticity of the pipe material itself is used.

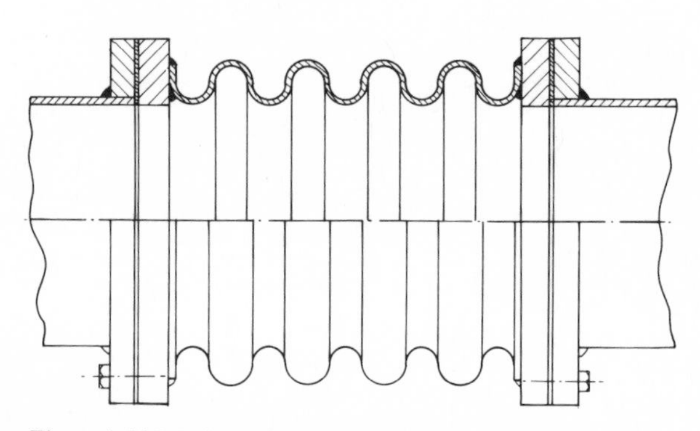

Figure 1.137 *Bellows flexible pipe joint*

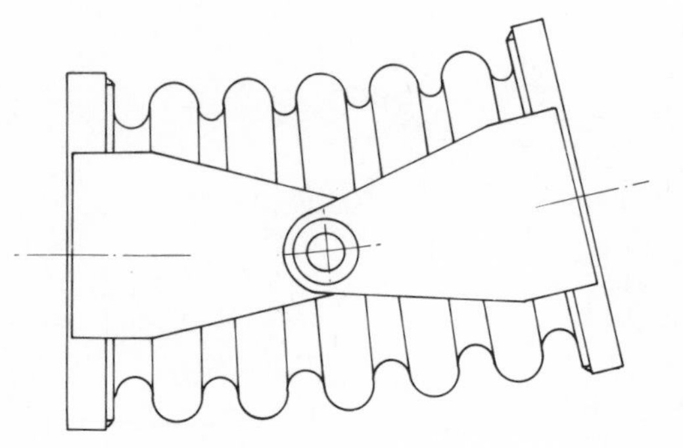

Figure 1.138 *Hinged bellows joint*

FLEXIBLE PIPES

Flexible pipes are used extensively in engineering.

Hydraulic hose, made of synthetic rubber reinforced with steel braiding and canvas, is able to withstand high pressures. Screwed couplings are attached to the ends.

Braided plastic petrol pipe is used for IC engines.

Canvas-reinforced rubber pipes (or hoses) are used for water cooling systems in automobiles.

Flexible metal pipes include the types shown in *Figure 1.143* and also the bellows type similar to that shown in *Figure 1.147*.

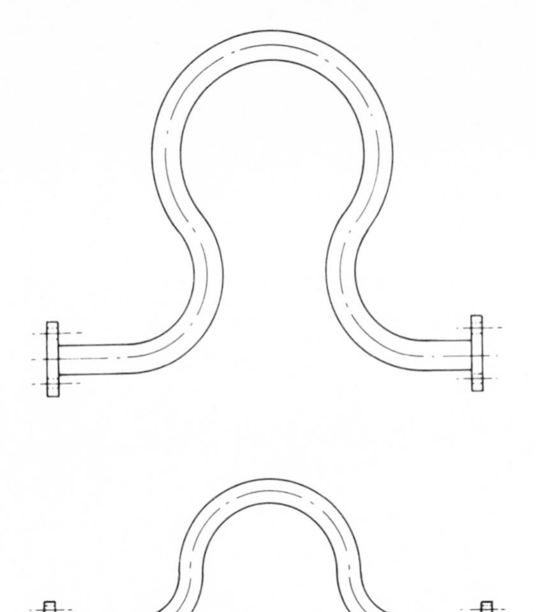

Figure 1.139 *Flexible expansion pipe bends*

Figure 1.142 *Flexible petrol pipe*

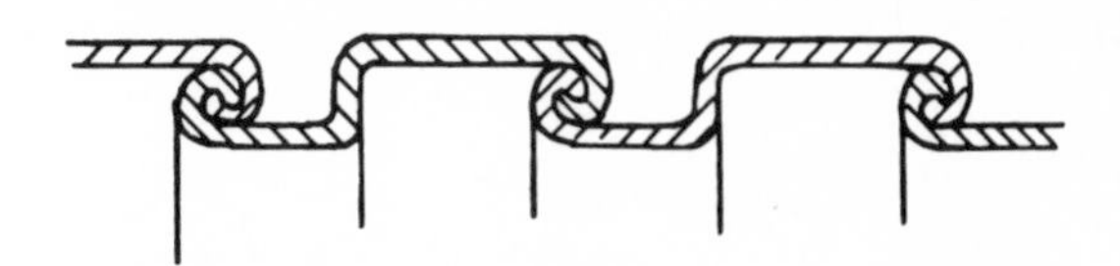

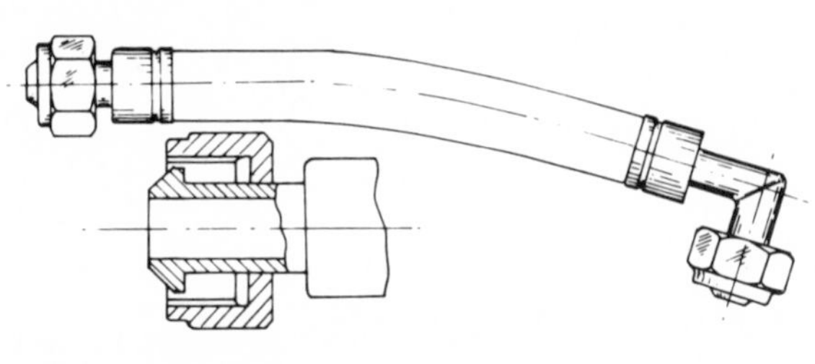

Figure 1.140 *Hydraulic hose and fittings*

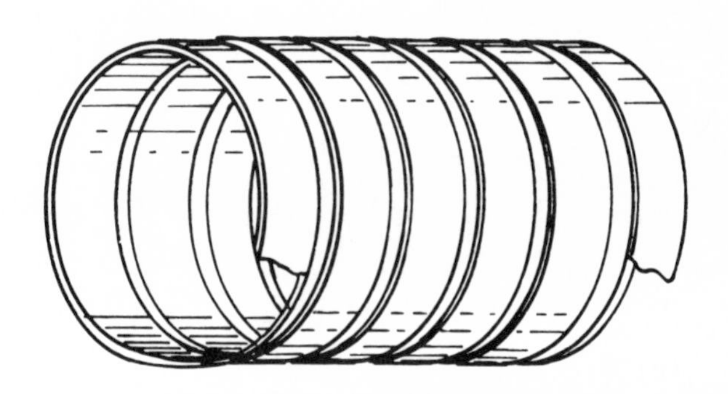

Figure 1.143 *Flexible metal pipe*

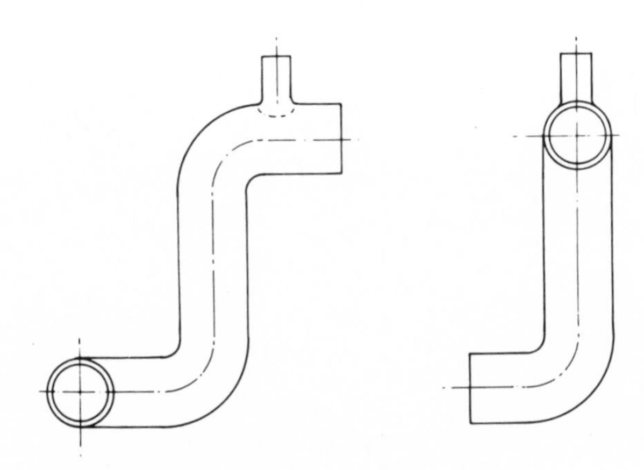

Figure 1.141 *Rubber hose for automobiles*

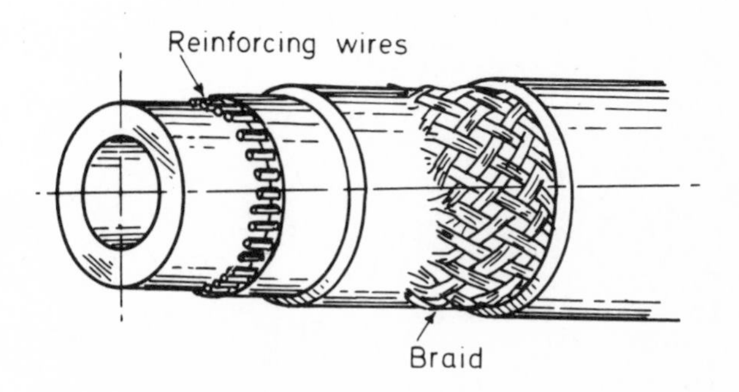

Figure 1.144 *Construction of high pressure hydraulic hose*

FITTINGS FOR DUCTING

Ducts made of sheet metal are usually joined by bolted flanged joints with gaskets of rubber, cork and proprietary jointing.

Fittings used include bends, transition pieces for joining ducts of different cross-section, and branched pipes.

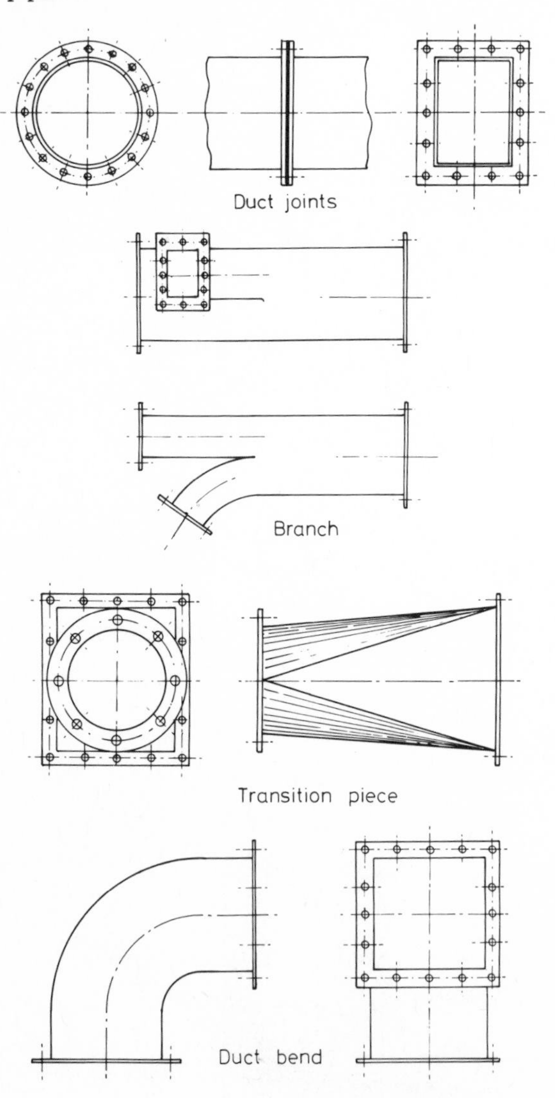

Figure 1.145 *Ducting and fittings*

VALVES

Valves are devices for controlling the flow of a fluid and they may be manually or automatically operated.

Stop valve Stop valves are used for shutting off the flow of steam, gas or liquids. One type is known as a *screw shut-down valve* or, because of its shape, a *globe valve*. This has a vertical spindle passing through a nut and carrying a chamfered valve disc which rests on a conical valve seat when the valve is closed. The spindle is provided with a gland.

For small bore systems the *needle screw-down valve* is used. In this type the spindle is tapered to a conical point which closes onto a seat. The inlet and outlet pipes are connected by coned screwed unions.

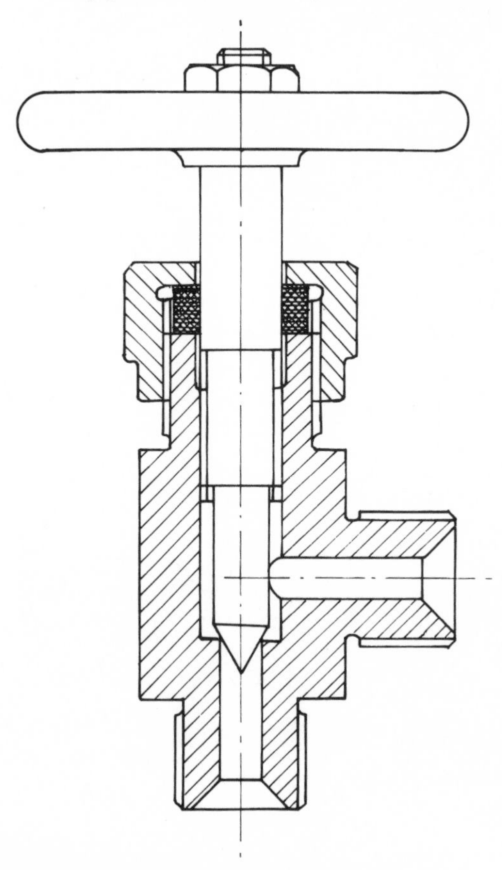

Figure 1.146 *Needle screw-down valve*

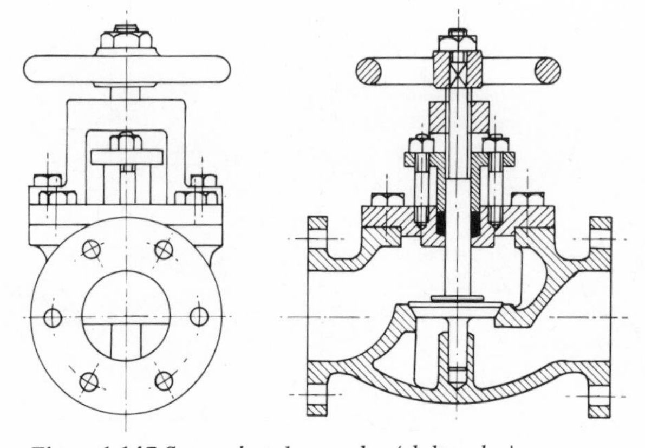

Figure 1.147 *Screw shut-down valve (globe valve)*

Steam safety valve The valve is normally kept closed by a dead weight, a weighted lever, or a spring which is initially compressed. At the required pressure the valve opens and allows steam to flow until the pressure has fallen sufficiently. The operating pressure is adjusted by moving the weight on the lever or altering the spring compression.

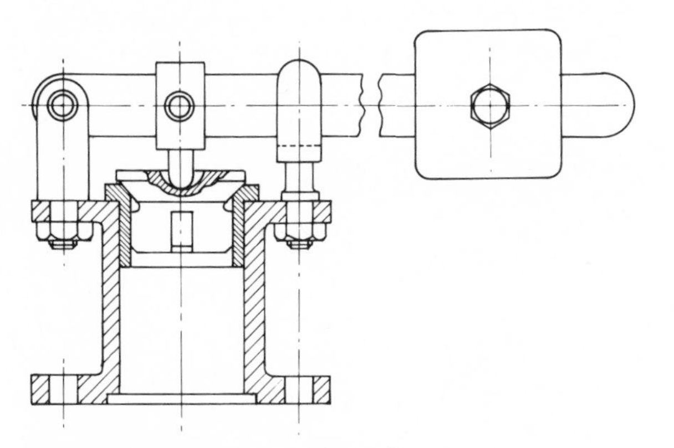

Figure 1.148 *Dead-weight safety valve*

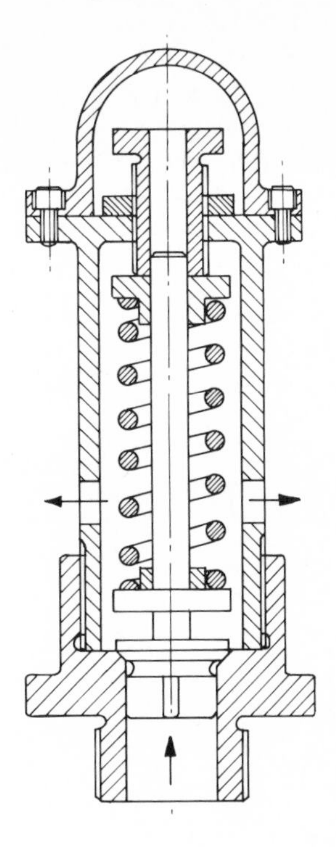

Figure 1.149 *Spring-loaded safety valve*

Hydraulic relief valve A valve used in hydraulic systems to prevent excessive pressure and subsequent damage.

A typical design has a spring-loaded pilot valve which opens at the desired pressure and causes a flow through a small hole in a large piston which normally holds the main valve shut. The flow results in a pressure difference across the piston and the main valve opens to allow the oil to flow to a tank.

Non-return valve, check valve These are valves which permit flow in one direction only.

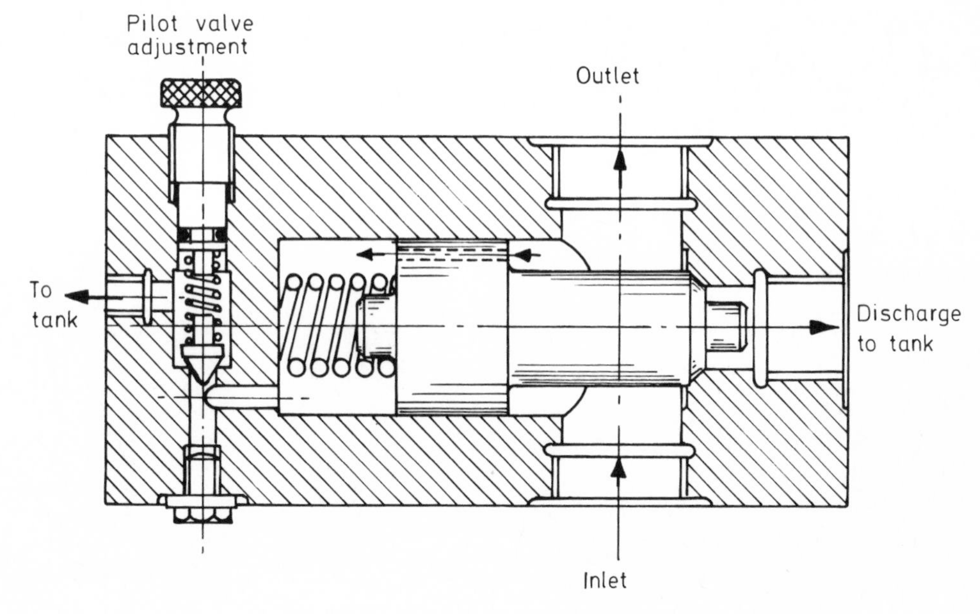

Figure 1.150 *Hydraulic relief valve*

In one type a ball, needle or disk, etc. is held onto a seat by means of a loaded spring and it opens with the fluid flow. In another valve a spring-loaded piston covers a port, and a third has a hinged flap held closed by gravity and opened by the flow of fluid. This last type is used to prevent blow-back when an explosion takes place in gas pipes.

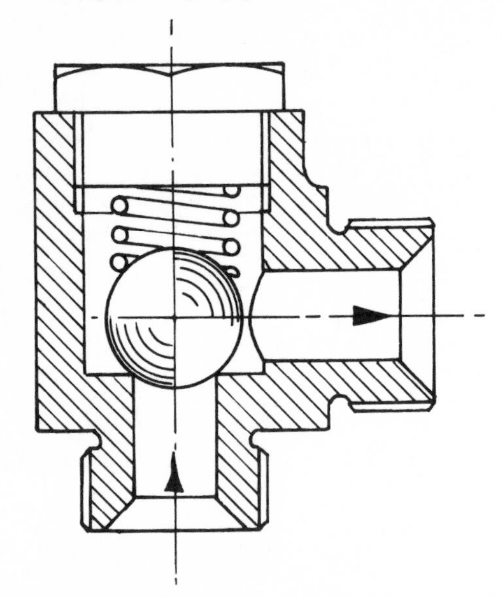

Figure 1.151 *Ball-type non-return valve*

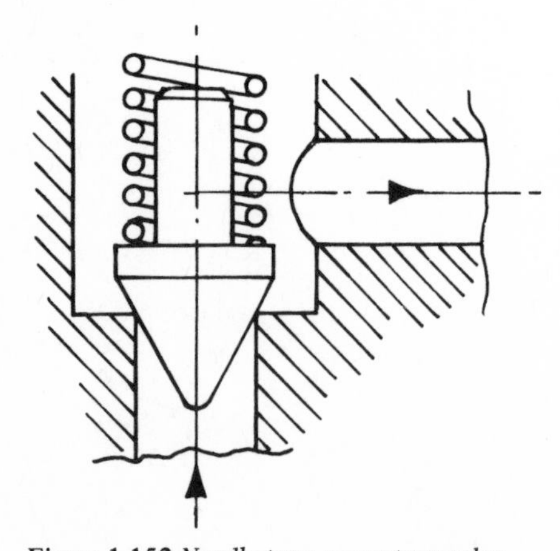

Figure 1.152 *Needle-type non-return valve*

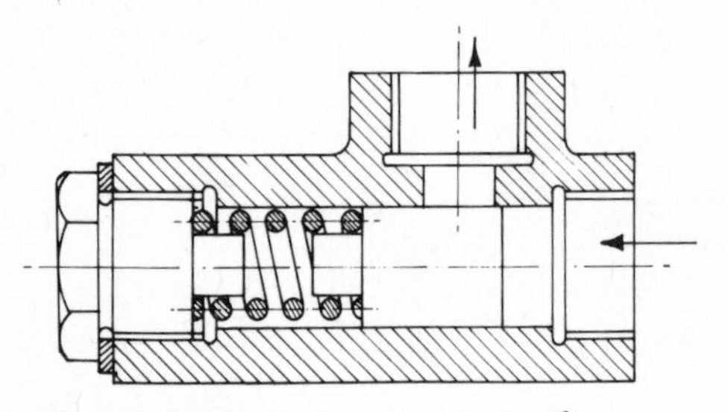

Figure 1.153 *Piston-type non-return valve*

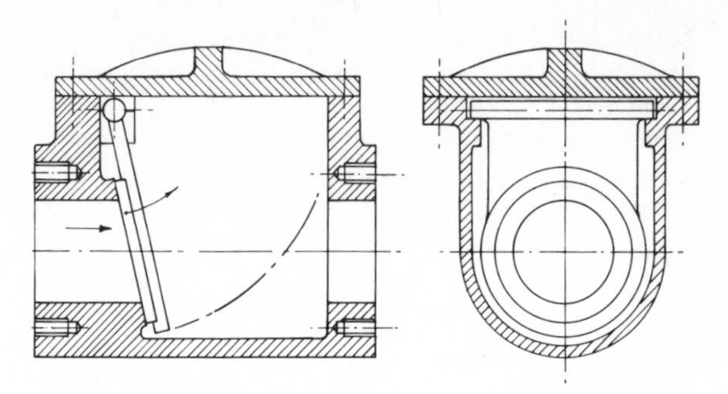

Figure 1.154 *Hinged flap valve*

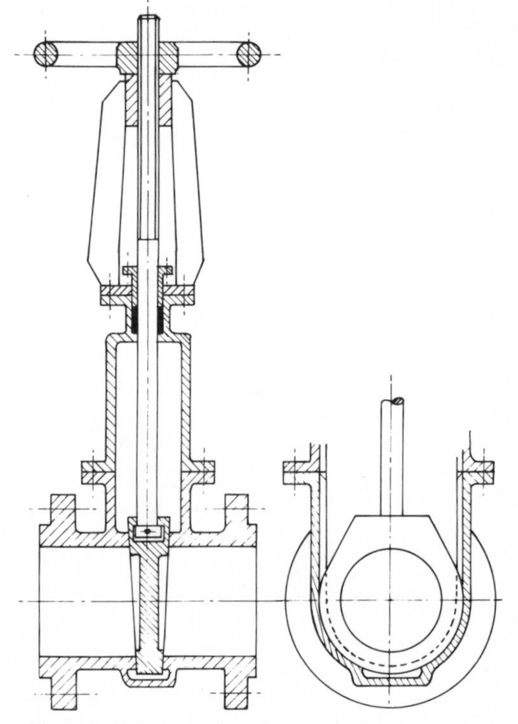

Figure 1.155 *Gate valve (sluice valve)*

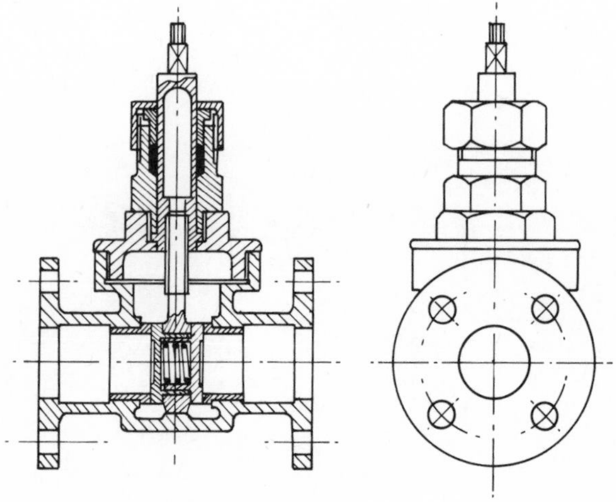

Figure 1.156 *Parallel face gate valve*

Gate valve The gate valve is intended as a shut-off valve but may be used to control the flow.

A *gate,* or shutter, which may be wedge-shaped or have spring-loaded parallel faces, is moved by a screw on the handle across the bore thus shutting off the flow. The gate slides in machined faces.

The wedge type of gate valve is also known as a *sluice valve*.

Butterfly valve The butterfly valve has a disk, pivoted about its diameter, which fits exactly into the bore of a pipe. The disk is rotated on the pivot to close or partially close the bore. This valve is used extensively in automobile engine carburettors for the throttle valve but is also made as a separate unit in large sizes.

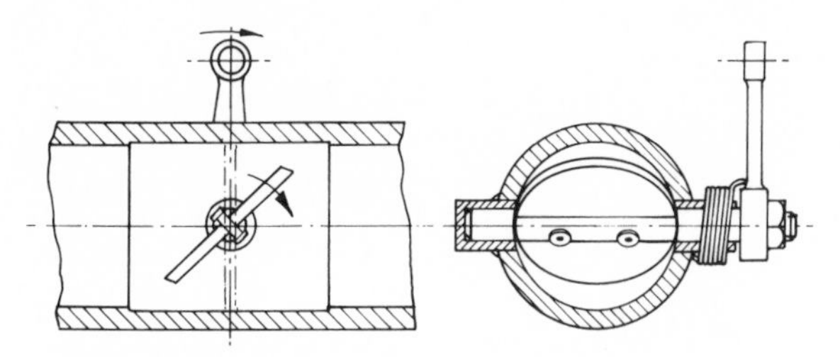

Figure 1.157 *Butterfly valve*

Saunders valve This is a proprietary shut-off and control valve in which a rubber diaphragm is moved down by a screw onto a metal bridge. The resistance to flow when fully open is small. The inside of the valve may be lined with materials resistant to heat, corrosion, etc.

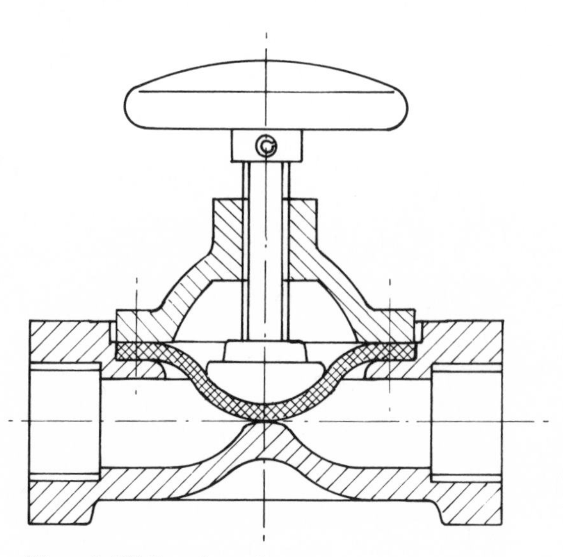

Figure 1.158 *Saunders valve*

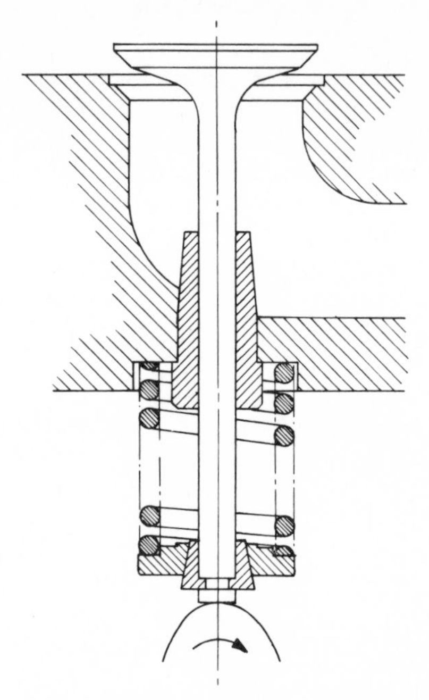

Figure 1.159 *Automobile-type poppet (mushroom) valve*

Poppet valve (mushroom valve) Most internal combustion engines use this type as inlet and outlet valves. The head rests on a conical seat and the valve is lifted by a cam against a compressed spring.

Sleeve valve A sleeve valve consists of a sleeve, pierced with *ports,* or openings, sliding or rotating in a cylinder also having ports which are made to open and shut. This valve is used in some IC engines.

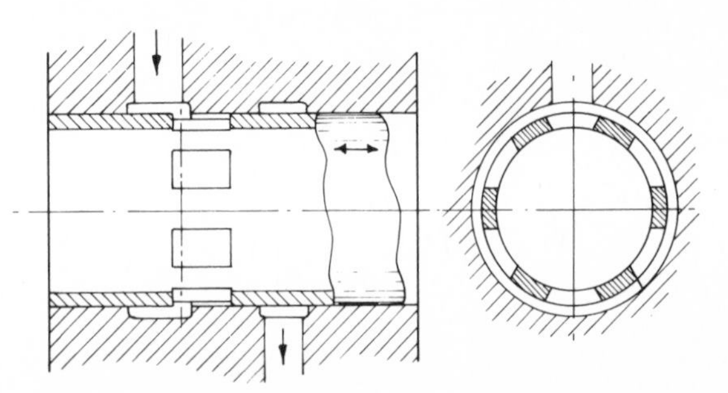

Figure 1.160 *Sleeve valve*

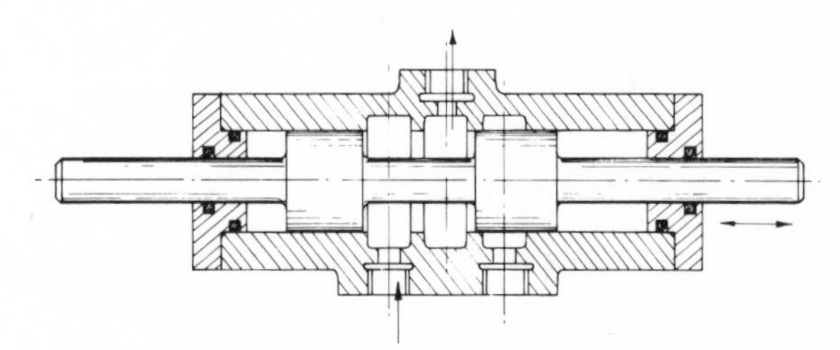

Figure 1.161 *Spool valve*

Spool valve Spool valves are used in hydraulic power circuits to control the flow of fluids. Pistons on a sliding rod open and close ports in a cylinder.

Plug cock The plug cock is used mainly for controlling gases. A taper plug fits into a tapered hole (in the body) at right angles to the flow direction. A hole drilled through the plug coincides with the bore of the body, and to close the cock the plug is turned through a right angle. For this purpose the plug may be fitted with a handle or have a square head to suit a key or spanner.

A similar valve of larger size has a spherical plug.

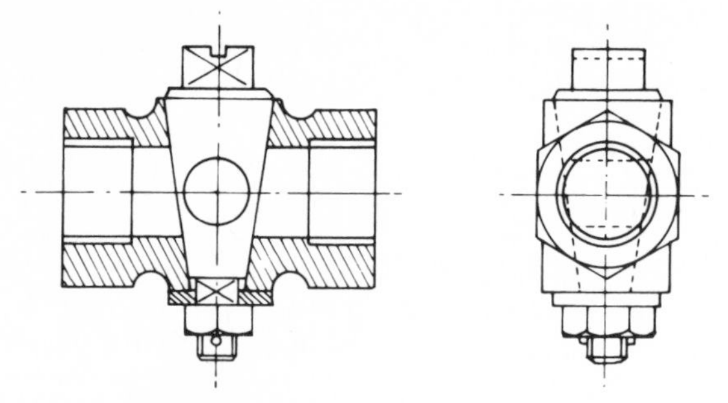

Figure 1.162 *Plug cock*

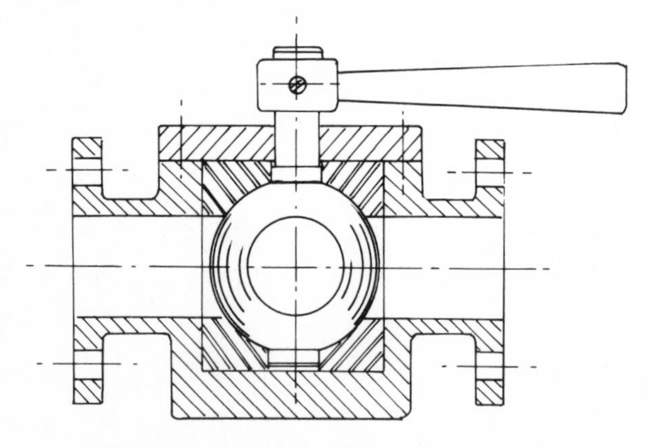

Figure 1.163 *Spherical plug cock*

1.7 SHAFTS AND RODS

SHAFTS

A shaft is a machine element used for transmitting motion and power by means of rotation. It is invariably of circular cross-section, may be solid or hollow, rotates in bearings, and carries gears, rotors, wheels, etc. It is subject to torsion and to transverse and longitudinal loads which are often fluctuating. Small diameter shafts are also called *spindles*.

Materials Most shafts are made of low or medium carbon steel, the later often heat treated. The surface may be heat treated to harden it to limit wear, as for bearings and seals. Shafts are also made of high-strength steel and aluminium alloys and are sometimes protected by plating or by nonferrous sleeves, e.g. in pumps.

Applications Shafts are used extensively in machines of all kinds, e.g. machine tools, gearboxes, automobile and marine engines, aero-engines, domestic appliances, etc.

Surface finish The surface finish is generally that produced by turning but some sections are ground to a high finish for bearing journals and where there are contact oil seals.

Solid shaft Most shafts have a solid circular cross-section with steps or shoulders for the location of parts mounted on them. The ends of the shaft and the ends of sections are often chamfered to prevent burring, and internal corners are often given a radiused fillet to prevent stress-concentration. The shaft may have non-circular sections, e.g. square, hexagonal, etc.

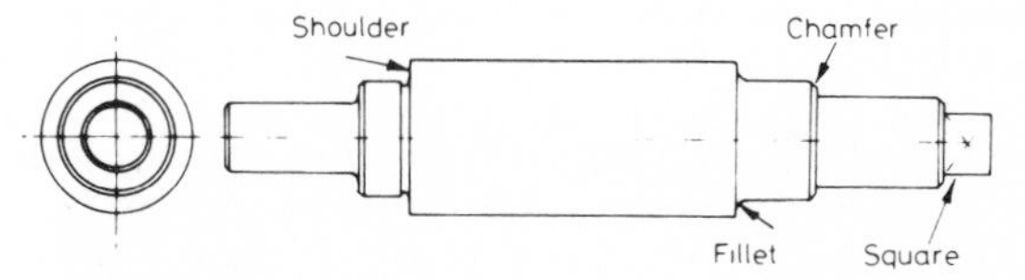

Figure 1.164 *Solid shaft*

Hollow shaft A hollow shaft is much stronger both in torsion and in bending than a solid shaft of the same weight. Often used where lightness is essential, as for example in aero-engines.

Another application is that of concentric shafts where a solid shaft may run inside a hollow one.

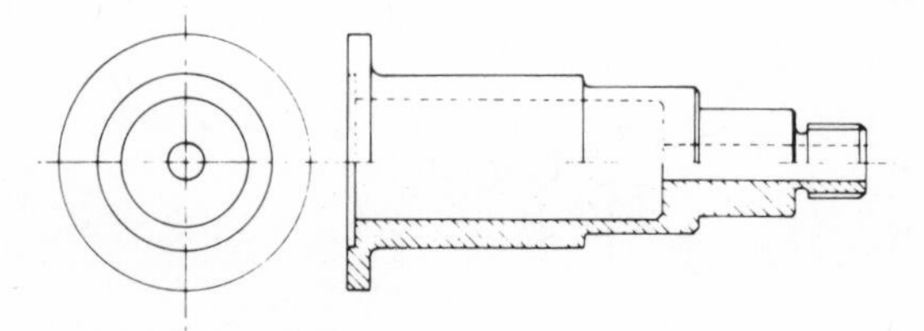

Figure 1.165 *Hollow shaft*

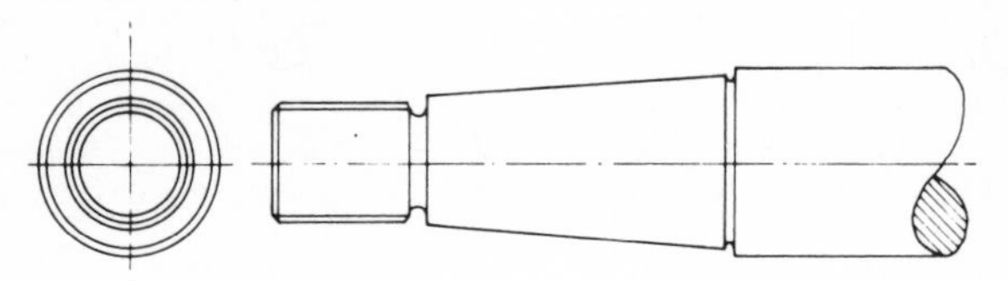

Figure 1.166 *Taper shaft*

Taper shaft Parts of shafts are sometimes tapered to suit components with a matching taper bore. A nut is used to give an extremely tight fit and a key provided to prevent relative rotation.

Screwed shaft Parts of a shaft may be screwed to take nuts which are used to attach components rigidly to the shaft. Hollow sections of shaft may also have internal screw threads.

The screw may be used for power transmission, as for example on the lead screw of a lathe, with a thread of square or buttress section.

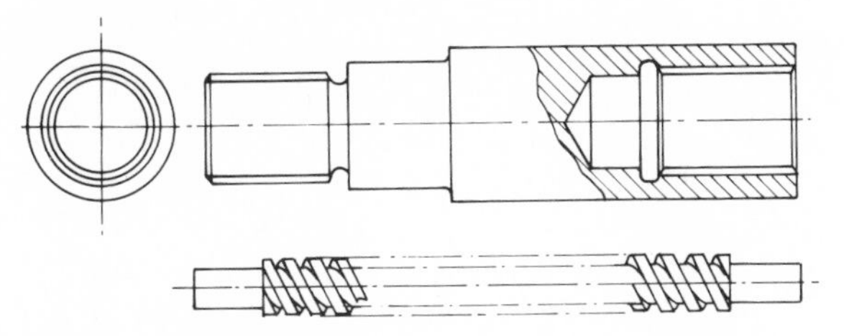

Figure 1.167 *Screwed shafts*

Crankshaft A crankshaft is a shaft having one or more levers, called *cranks* keyed to it or integral with it. The cranks have pins, known as *crankpins*, which are parallel to the shaft. The crank is sometimes fitted with a balance weight to offset the weight of the crank, crankpin and any part mounted on the crankpin.

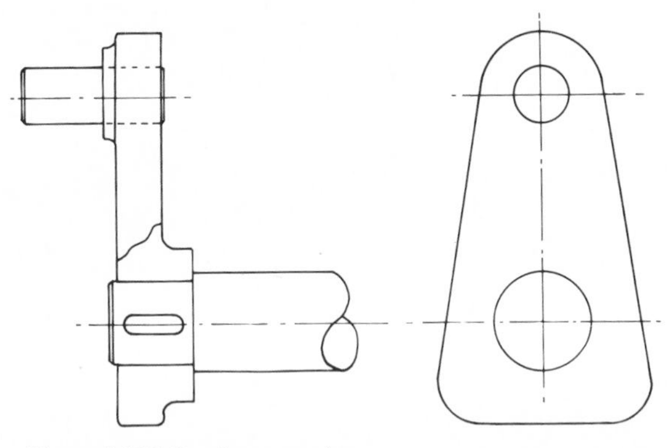

Figure 1.168 *Overhung crank*

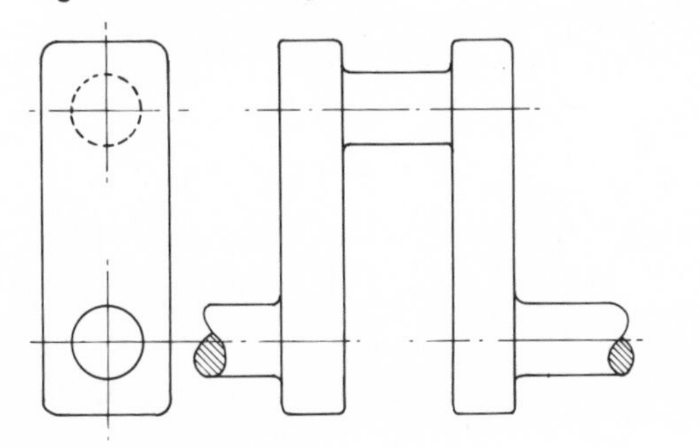

Figure 1.169 *Crank*

Camshaft A shaft on which a cam (or cams) is fitted. A typical example is the camshaft of an automobile engine.

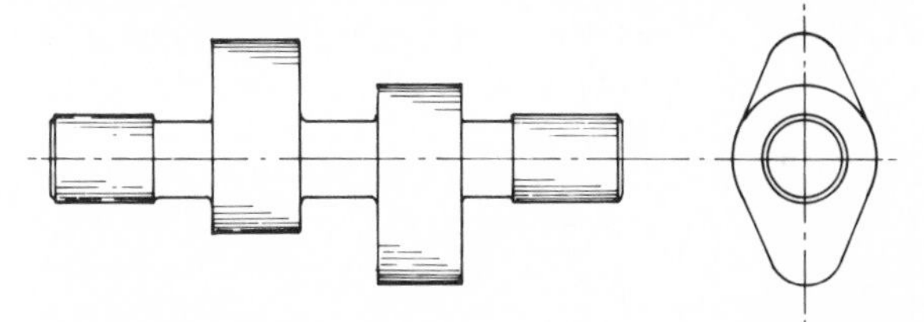

Figure 1.170 *Camshaft*

Grooves in shafts Grooves are often machined circumferentially in shafts for the location of *circlips* and for supplying oil to bearings. They may be of semi-circular or rectangular section.

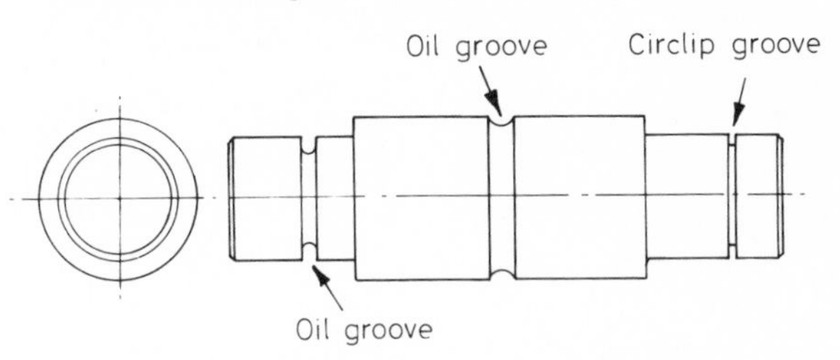

Figure 1.171 *Grooves in shaft*

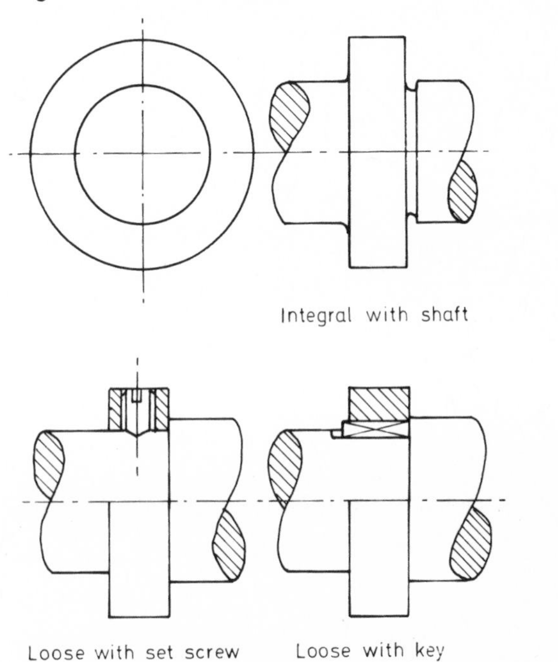

Figure 1.172 *Shaft collars*

Shaft collars A collar is a short section of increased diameter (on a shaft) used to locate parts mounted on the shaft, or to take an axial load from a thrust bearing.

Oilways Holes are drilled in a shaft to supply oil to bearings supporting it. A typical example is an automobile crankshaft in which oil is fed through a system of oilways to the main and connecting-rod bearings.

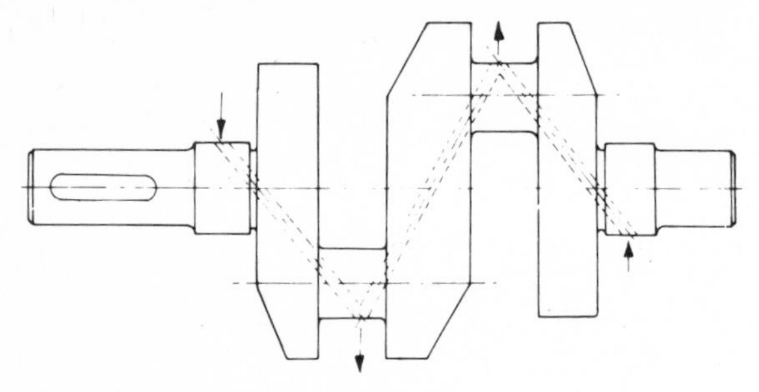

Figure 1.173 *Oilways in crankshaft*

SPLINES

Splines consist of a number of longitudinal ribs equally spaced around the circumference of a shaft which engage in corresponding grooves in the hub of a part to be mounted on the shaft. The form of the splines may be rectangular or triangular (usually referred to as serritions), or involute as in the case of gear teeth. The hub is often made a sliding fit on the shaft where axial movement is required.

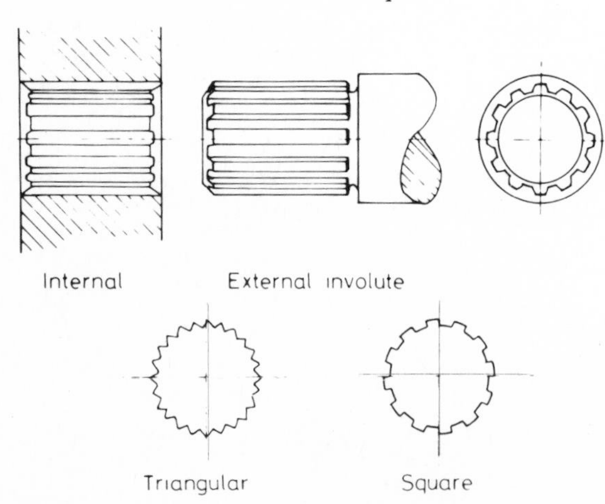

Figure 1.174 *Splines*

KEYS AND KEYWAYS IN SHAFTS

A key is used to prevent a machine part from moving relative to another part in a given direction. On shafts they prevent the rotation of a part relative to the shaft but may allow sliding along it. The key must be strong enough to transmit the shaft torque.

Materials Because they are subject to severe stresses keys are made of high tensile steel or steel alloys.

Applications Keys are used for couplings, pulleys, gears, clutchplates, flywheels, etc. There are three classes of fit: 'free', where the hub slides easily; 'close', where an accurate fit is required; 'normal', where a minimum of fitting is necessary, as in cases of mass-production.

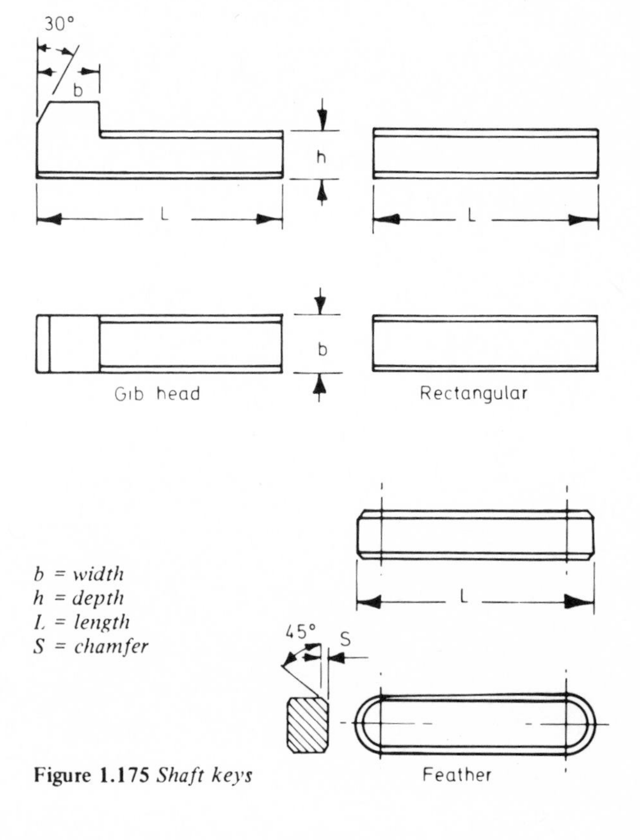

Figure 1.175 *Shaft keys*

KEYWAY

A keyway is a slot in a shaft into which a key is fitted, and it is usually produced by milling.

TYPES OF KEY

Rectangular key This consists of a piece of rectangular-section bar with chamfered edges having a slight taper to assist fitting. It is located in a longitudinal rectangular slot, or keyway, which has been milled in the shaft to a depth of half that of the key. A corresponding keyway is machined in the bore of the part to be keyed to the shaft.

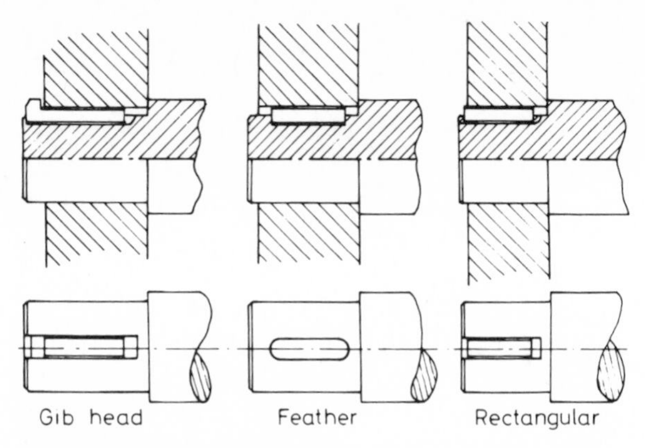

Figure 1.176 *Key applications*

Feather key A rectangular key with radiused ends fitting into a keyway of the same shape in the shaft which is end milled and closed at each end. The keyway in the hub is open at one or both ends.

Gib head key The gib head key is used at the end of a shaft and is tapered to give a rigid fixing when hammered into place. A head is provided to assist removal of the key.

Woodruff key This is in the form of a circular segment which fits into a slot of the same shape. It is often used on taper shafts and can be tilted for easy assembly.

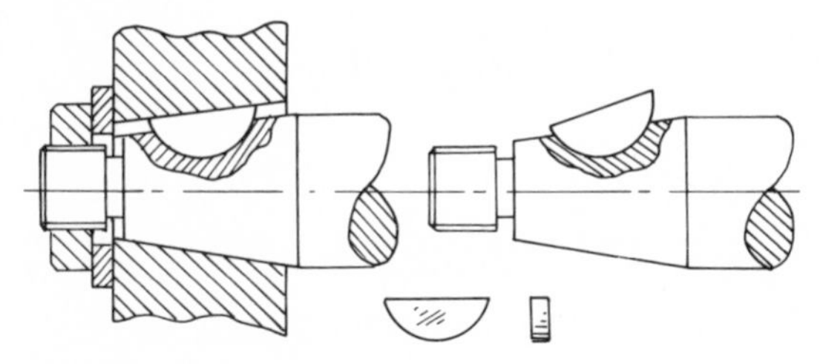

Figure 1.177 *Woodruff key*

Saddle key For a saddle key a rectangular slot is required in the hub but only a 'flat' is necessary on the shaft. It is intended for light duty only.

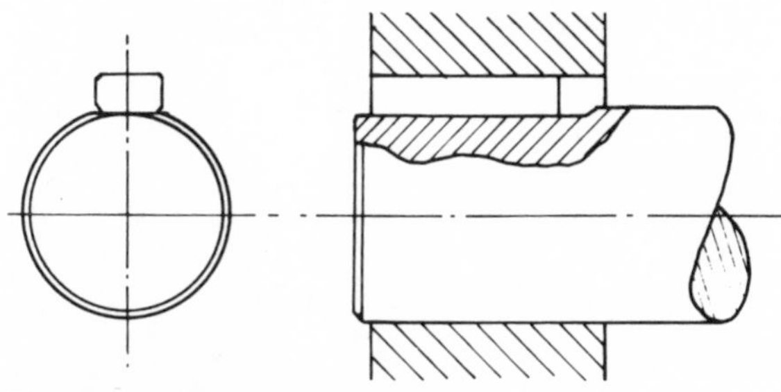

Figure 1.178 *Saddle key*

Round key This type provides a cheap method of keying requiring only a hole to be drilled (parallel to the axis of the shaft) which is half in the hub and half in the shaft. The key is a piece of stock bright bar or a taper pin.

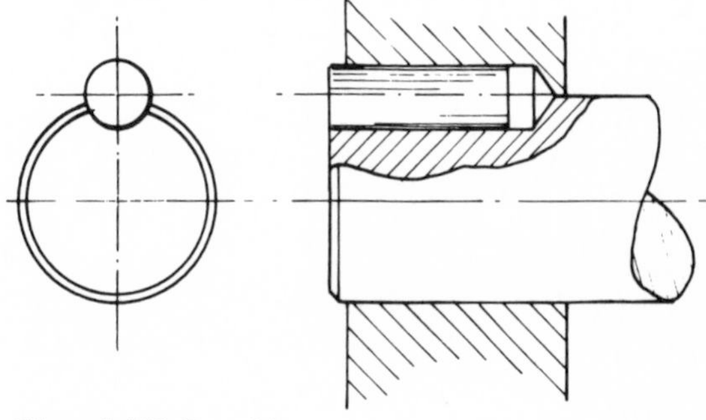

Figure 1.179 *Round key*

RODS

Rods are bars, usually circular in cross-section, which transmit tensile or compressive forces, or limited rotary movement. Rods in tension are known as *tie bars* or *tie rods*.

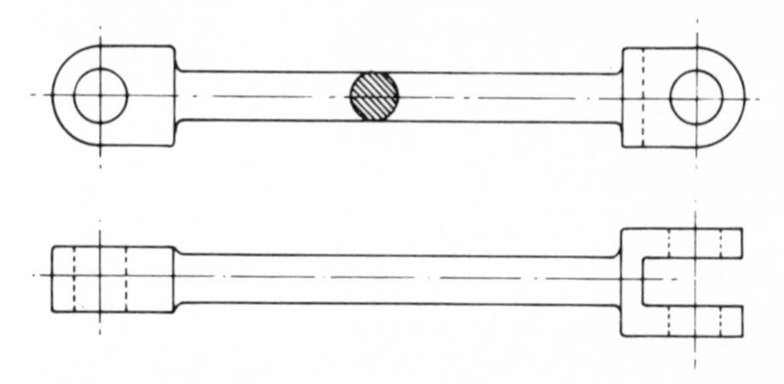

Figure 1.180 *Tie rod*

PIN JOINT, KNUCKLE JOINT

This is a hinged joint, connecting two or more rods, used as a tie for roof trusses.

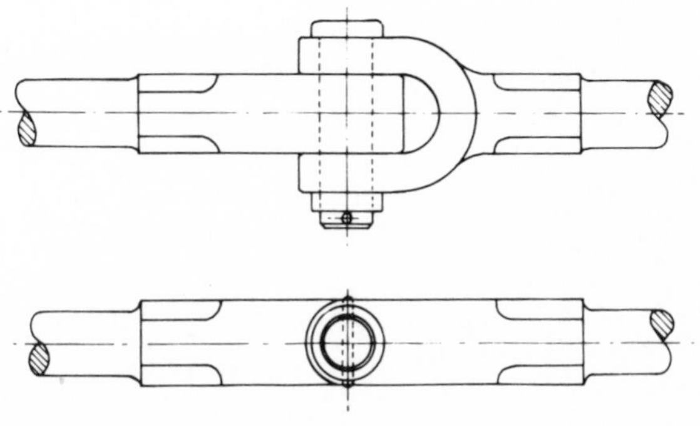

Figure 1.181 *Pin joint for rods*

COTTERED JOINT

A rigid joint connecting two rods in which a cotter pin is used.

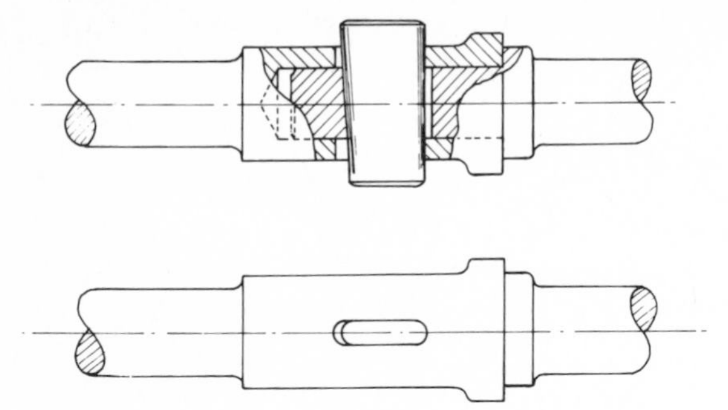

Figure 1.182 *Cottered joint for rods*

1.8 BEARINGS

Bearings are used in engineering to restrain or guide the movement of one machine part relative to another with the minimum of friction and wear. In most cases they are used between rotating parts, such as shafts, and machine frames, but they may also be used for linear motion.

Shaft bearings may be *journal bearings* (the term 'journal' refers to the shaft) which take radial forces, or *thrust bearings* which take axial forces.

A lubricant is required between the sliding surfaces, and this may be solid, liquid or gaseous.

There are two main classifications of journal and thrust bearings: *sliding contact*, e.g. a shaft running in a plain sleeve; *rolling contact*, e.g. ball and roller bearings.

PLAIN JOURNAL BEARING, SLEEVE BEARING

This comprises a *bush* or sleeve, made of brass, bronze, etc., held in a stationary member in which a shaft rotates. It is supplied with a suitable lubricant through holes and/or grooves. The gap between the shaft and the bush is known as the 'clearance'.

PEDESTAL BEARING

The bearing may be mounted in a support bolted to a flat surface. This is known as a pedestal and it may be a casting, forging or weldment. The pedestal is sometimes split at the centreline of the shaft and the bush made in two pieces called *brasses* or *shells*.

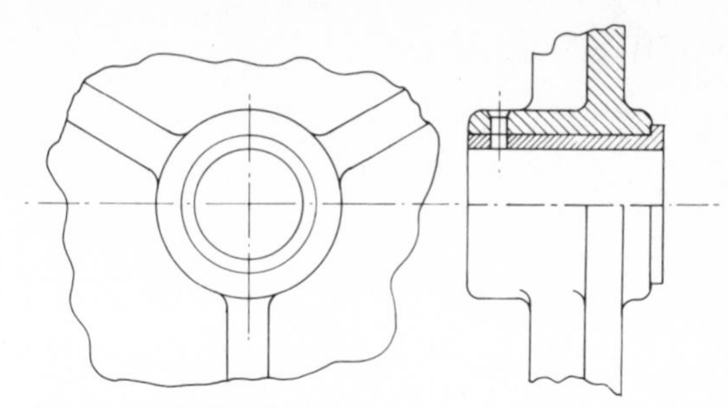

Figure 1.183 *Plain bearing*

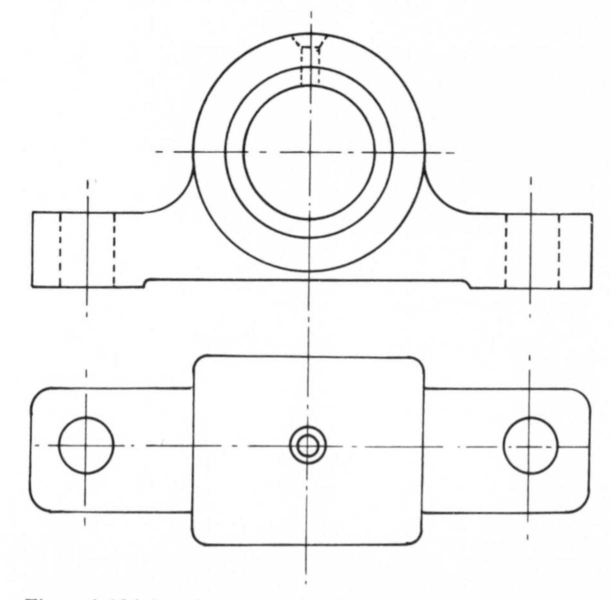

Figure 1.184 *Simple pedestal bearing*

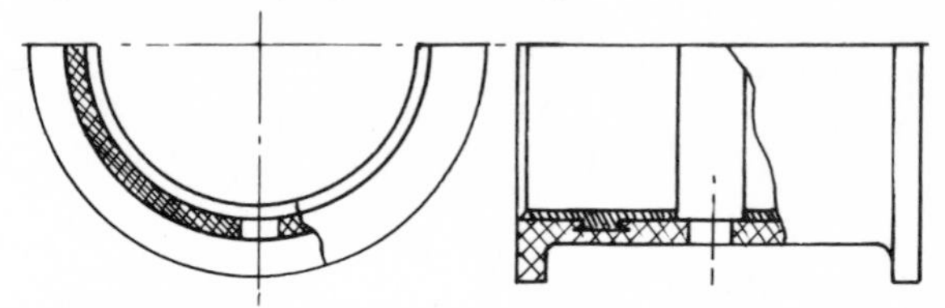

Figure 1.185 *Journal bearing shell*

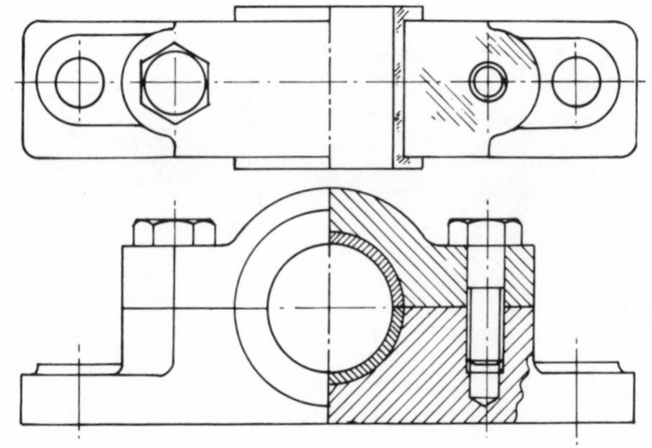

Figure 1.186 *Split or halved pedestal bearing*

RING OILER BEARING

A loose ring rolls on the shaft by friction and picks up oil from a bath. The oil flows from the shaft into the bearing.

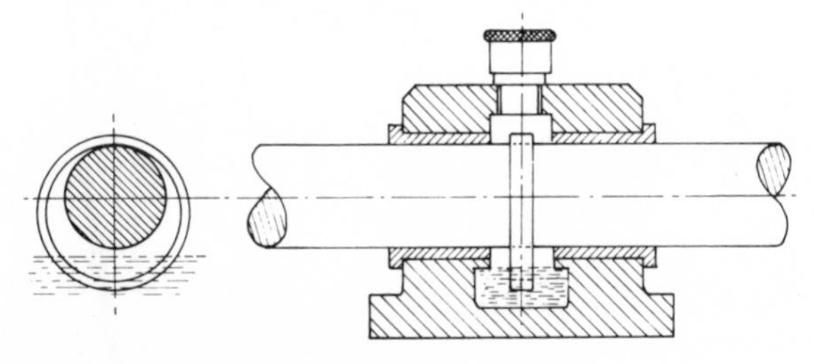

Figure 1.187 *Ring oiler bearing*

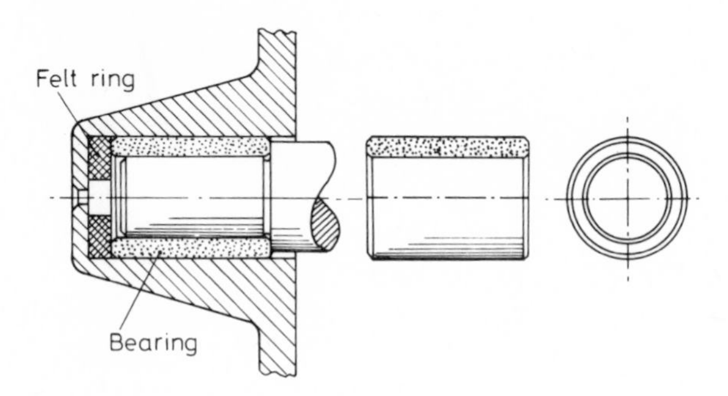

Figure 1.188 *Automobile dynamo porous bearing*

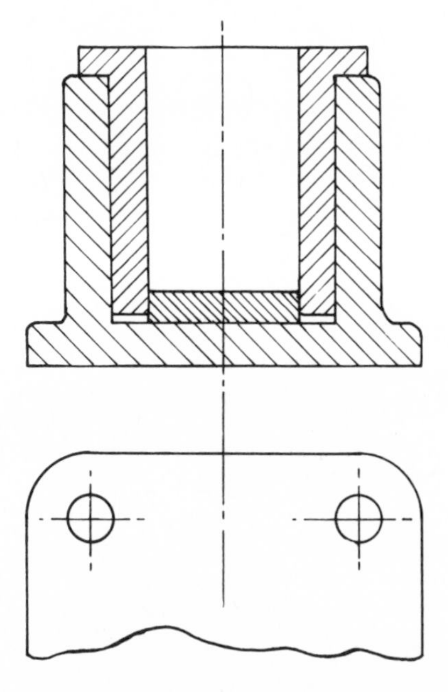

Figure 1.189 *Footstep thrust bearing*

POROUS BEARING, SELF-OILING BEARING

This is a bush made of porous metal containing oil or grease, often requiring no further lubrication during its life.

FOOTSTEP THRUST BEARING

A bearing used for the lower end of a vertical shaft. A bush takes the horizontal load and a hardened steel pad takes the weight of the shaft or any thrust.

PLAIN THRUST BEARING

A flat ring of brass, bronze, etc. taking the thrust on a shaft via a collar.

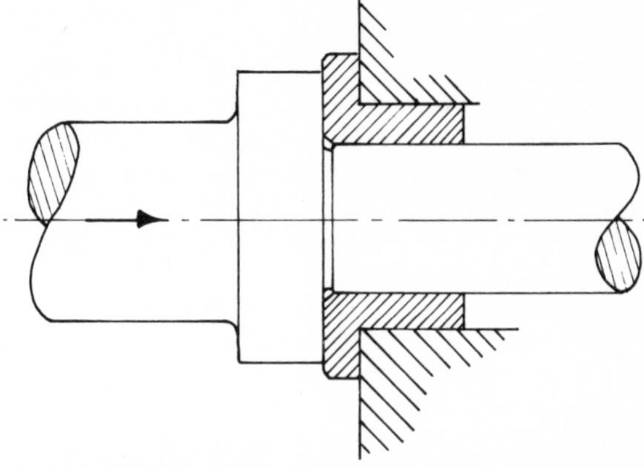

Figure 1.190 *Plain thrust bearing*

MICHELL THRUST BEARING (PIVOTED SEGMENT BEARING)

A thrust bearing in which a thrust collar on a shaft bears on segmental 'pads' faced with bearing metal. These tilt to provide a high-pressure oil 'wedge'. This bearing is used for marine propeller shafts and other large, high-duty applications (Figure 1.192).

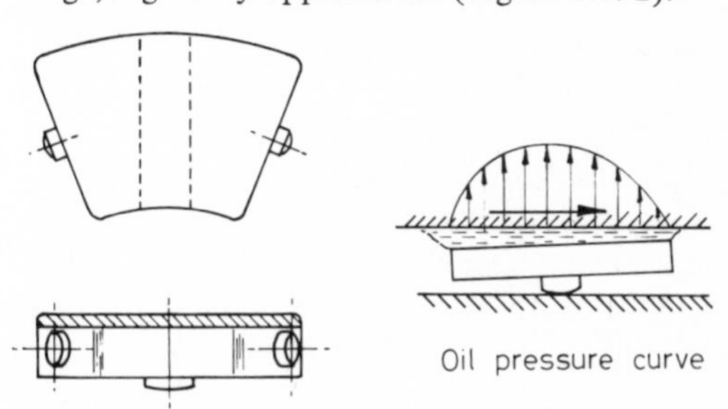

Figure 1.191 *Thrust pad*

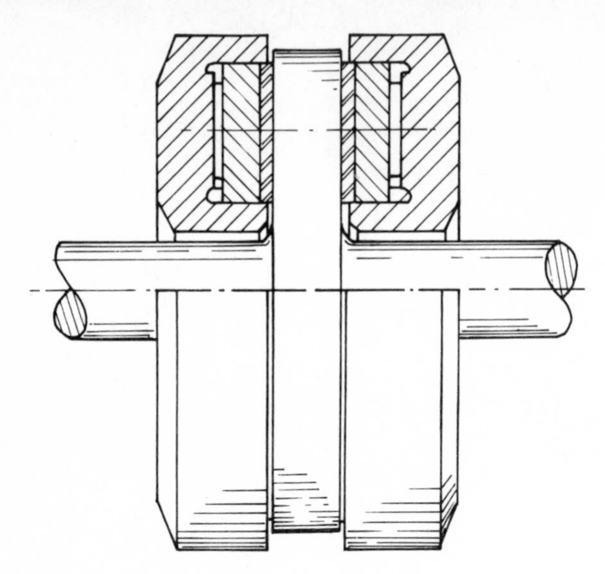

Figure 1.192 *Double Michell thrust bearing*

GAS BEARINGS

Gases, such as air, nitrogen, etc., may be used as lubricants in both journal and thrust bearings. The gas is introduced through radial holes in a sleeve surrounding the shaft.

Gas bearings are used for low friction and high speed applications and where contamination by oils is undesirable. A typical example is the air bearings in a dentist's drill driven by an air turbine.

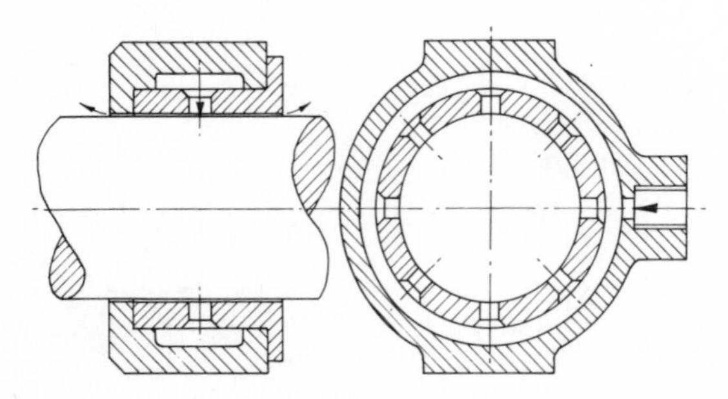

Figure 1.193 *Air bearing*

BEARING MATERIALS

Plain bearings use brass, bronze and gunmental bushes. Linings for shell bearings and thrust pads use white metal (an alloy of tin, antimony and copper) and lead alloys which also include tin, antimony, copper, etc. Also used are various plastic materials such as nylon, Tufnol and PTFE.

ROLLING CONTACT BEARINGS

This is a general name given to a wide range of bearings in which hardened steel balls or rollers run between housings (or *'races'*) on the shaft and the fixed member.

They are often termed *anti-friction bearings* because of their extremely low frictional resistance, especially at low speeds. The small clearances involved permit accurate alignment of shafts.

Ball and roller bearings, although more complicated than plain bearings, may compare favourably in price when made in large quantities.

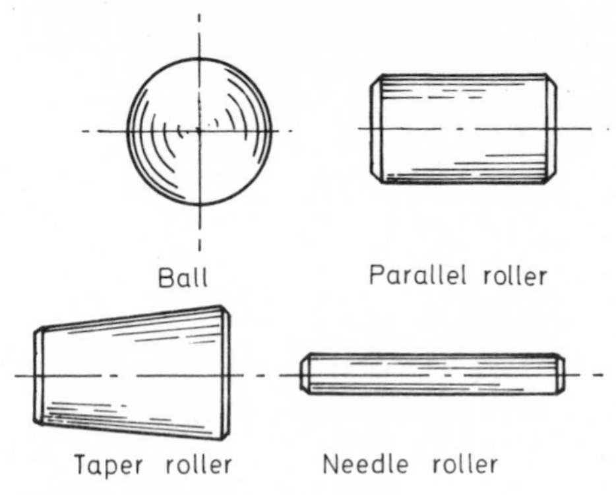

Figure 1.194 *Types of bearings*

SINGLE ROW BALL BEARINGS

The bearing consists of inner and outer grooved rings of hardened steel between which run hardened steel balls held and spaced in a retainer or cage. This bearing will take a certain amount of axial thrust but for higher thrusts *angular contact bearings* are more suitable.

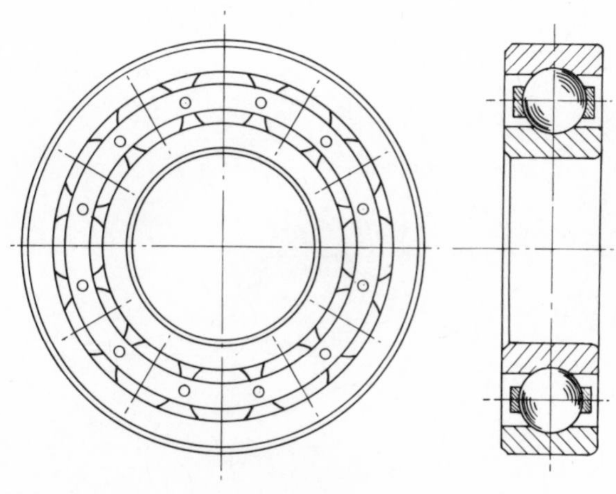

Figure 1.195 *Standard ball bearing*

Self-aligning bearings are used when there is doubt about the alignment of the housing.

Sealed bearings packed with grease require no further lubrication during the life of the bearing.

Deep groove bearings are designed for higher thrusts.

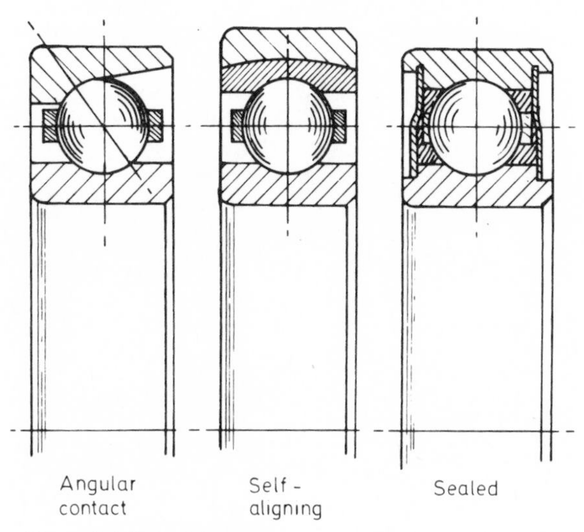

Figure 1.196 *Ball bearings*

DOUBLE ROW BALL BEARINGS

Double row ball bearings designed to take radial and/ or thrust loads will withstand higher loads without increasing the outer diameter.

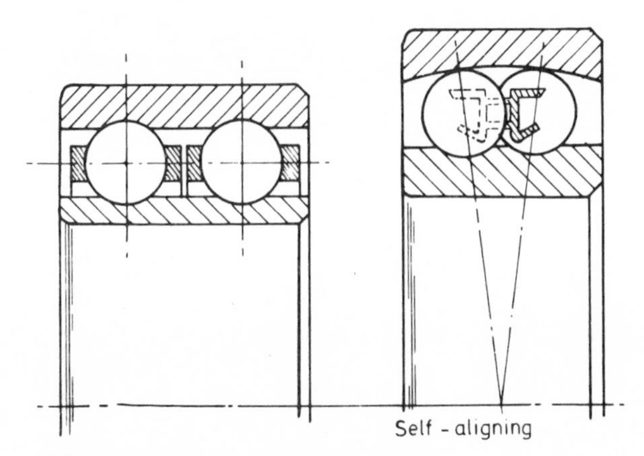

Figure 1.197 *Double row ball bearings*

ROLLER BEARINGS

Roller bearings will withstand much greater radial loads than ball bearings but parallel rollers will not take thrust loads. These bearings may be designed so that either the inner or outer ring may be detached.

If the rollers are tapered and arranged in the form of a cone, a *taper roller bearing* capable of carrying very high radial and thrust loads is obtained. These are often used in opposing pairs.

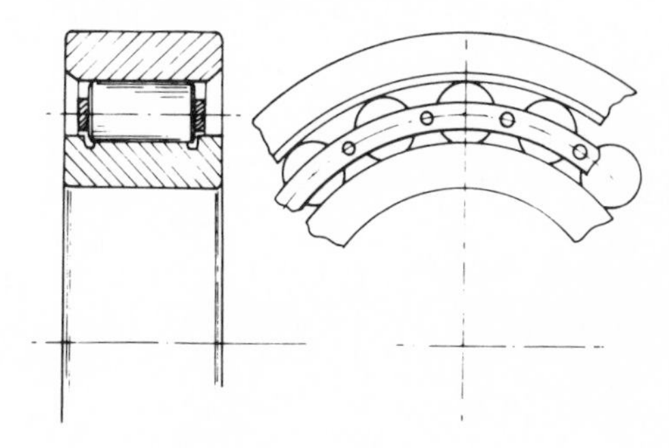

Figure 1.198 *Roller bearing*

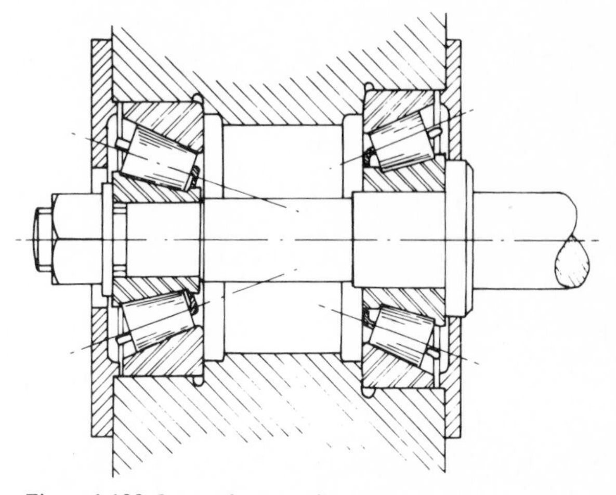

Figure 1.199 *Opposed taper roller bearing*

NEEDLE ROLLER BEARINGS

Where space is restricted very small diameter needle rollers are used. The rollers run on the surface of the shaft which must be hardened and ground. Needle rollers are used in automobile gearboxes and backaxles.

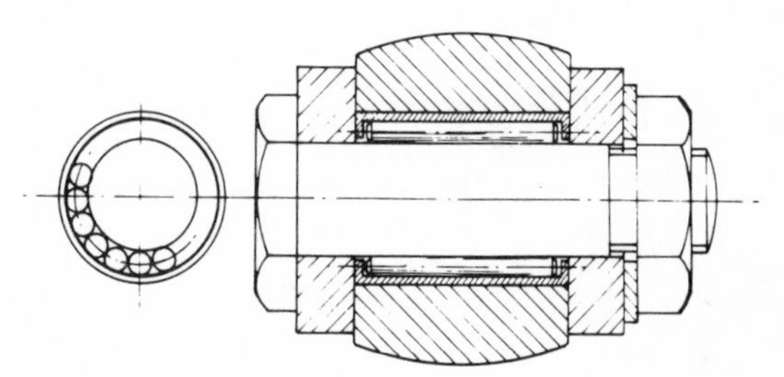

Figure 1.200 *Needle roller bearing*

BALL THRUST BEARINGS

The balls are mounted in a cage and run between the faces of two annular rings, and these may be used to take the weight of a vertical shaft in a footstep bearing.

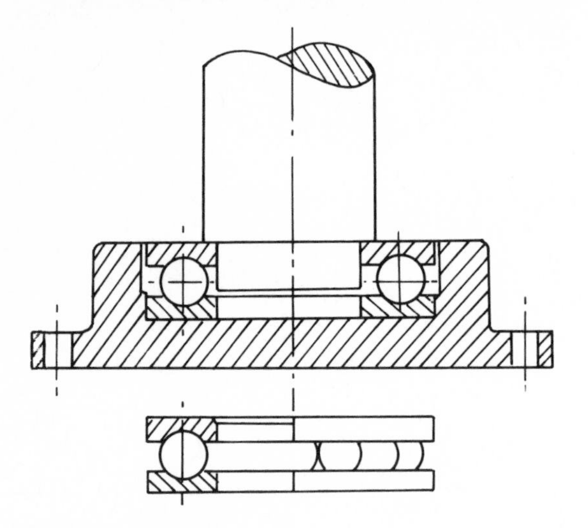

Figure 1.201 *Ball thrust bearing*

ROLLER THRUST BEARINGS

These are similar to ball thrust bearings except that tapered rollers are used.

BEARING HOUSINGS

The fixed part into which a bearing fits is known as a 'housing', and the outer ring of the bearing must be a good fit in this housing to ensure correct operation. As some form of closure is necessary to prevent loss of lubricant and keep dirt out, oil seals are often included.

BEARING LUBRICATORS

Plain bearings are usually lubricated by oil, and this is pressure fed for high duty cases. Ball and roller bearings may be lubricated by grease or oil. Grease may be fed to the bearing by means of a grease nipple and gun or by a screw-down greaser, or the bearing may be packed with grease and sealed for life. Oil may be fed from a sight feed drop oiler or by splash feed, oil bath, oil jet or oil mist.

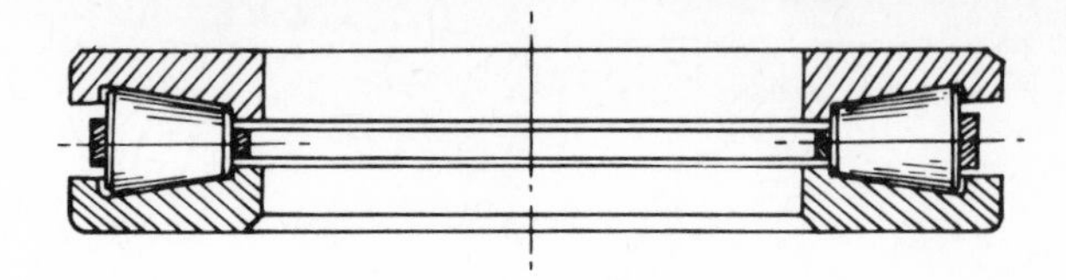

Figure 1.202 *Taper roller thrust bearing*

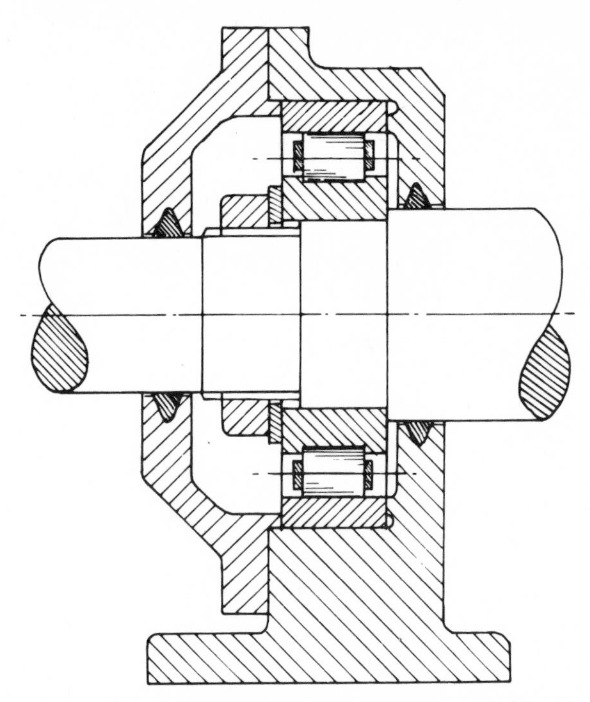

Figure 1.203 *Roller bearing in sealed housing*

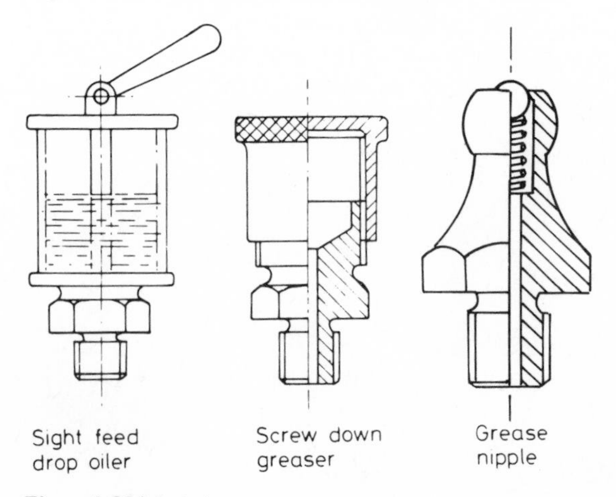

Figure 1.204 *Lubricators*

LUBRICANTS

Most bearings are lubricated with petroleum oils and grease made from those oils, but vegetable oils are used in special cases. Air and other gases may be used.

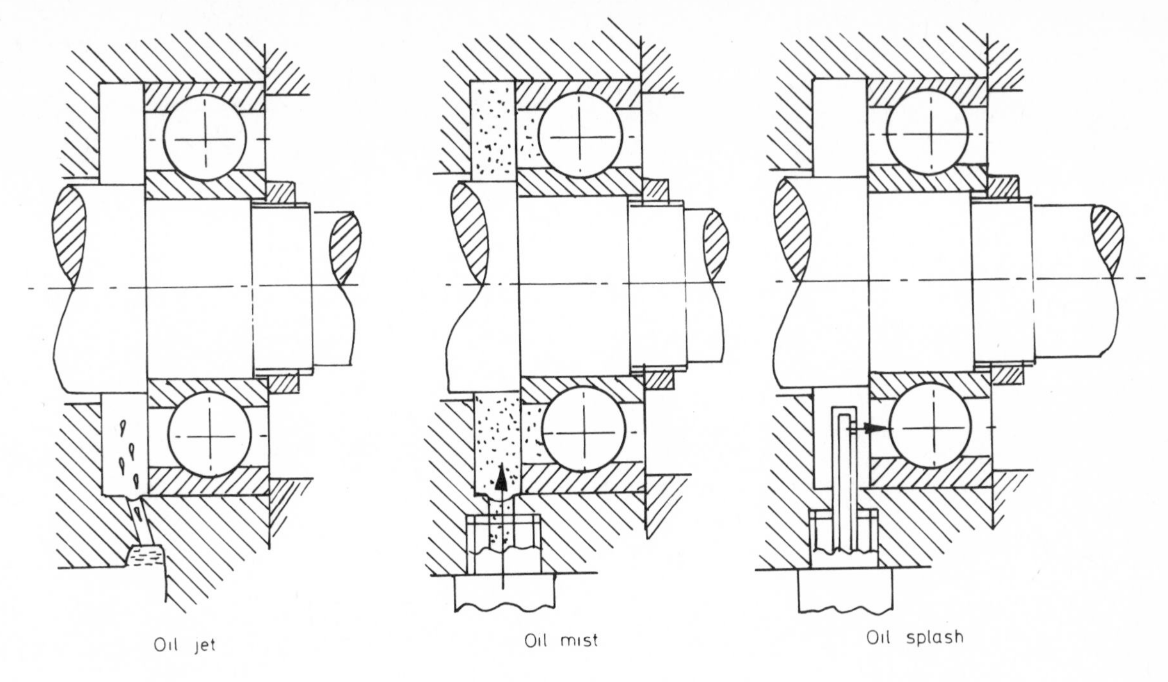

Figure 1.205 *Bearing lubrication*

1.9 ENGINEERING DESIGN FEATURES

In addition to the many standard components encountered in engineering there is a large number of features which are integral with them. These often have unusual and sometimes rather curious names with the same name being given to several items of quite different appearance. The following describe in alphabetical order the more common features to be found.

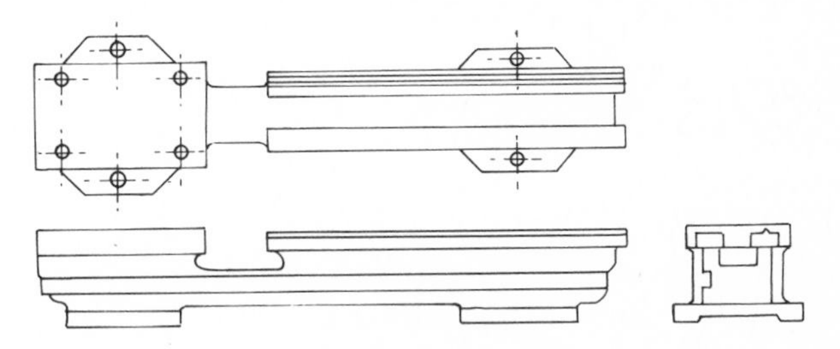

Figure 1.206 *Bedplate (for lathe)*

BEDPLATE, BED

A bedplate is a welded or bolted fabrication, or a casting, usually attached to the floor, on which machines, engines and machine tools etc. are mounted.

BODY

This is a term used for the main part of an assembly to which other smaller parts are attached. For example, the main part of a valve in which the spindle, seating, etc. are located.

BOX (*see* Casing)

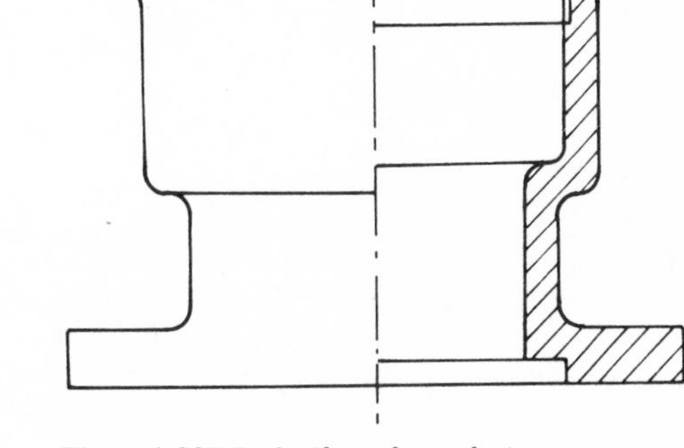

Figure 1.207 *Body (for safety valve)*

BOSS

A boss is a short, usually cylindrical, projection (on a machine part) which often has a central hole in which a pin, shaft or bolt, etc. is located. It is used on castings to give a flat seating for a bolt head or nut, or on levers to give a longer bearing.

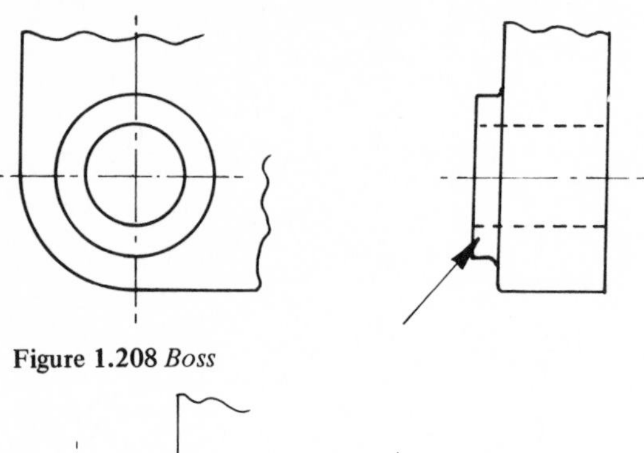

Figure 1.208 *Boss*

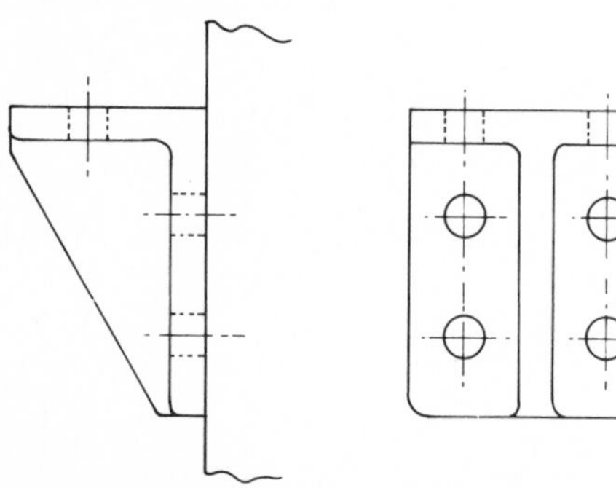

Figure 1.209 *Bracket*

BRACKET

A bracket is a support for machine parts often attached to a wall or vertical surface by bolts, rivets or welding.

BUSH

A bush is a cylindrical sleeve which fits into a hole and acts as a bearing for rotating or reciprocating shafts or rods. The bush is often made of material different from the part into which it is fitted, e.g. a brass bush in a steel part (*see* Sleeve).

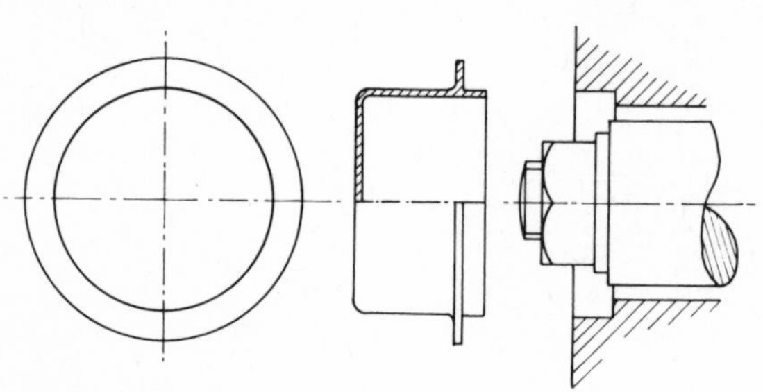

Figure 1.210 *Cap*

CAP

A cap is a metal or plastic cover bolted or pressed into position and used to retain oil or grease, or to protect, and sometimes to improve, the appearance of a machine part. The removable half of a journal bearing housing is also referred to as a cap.

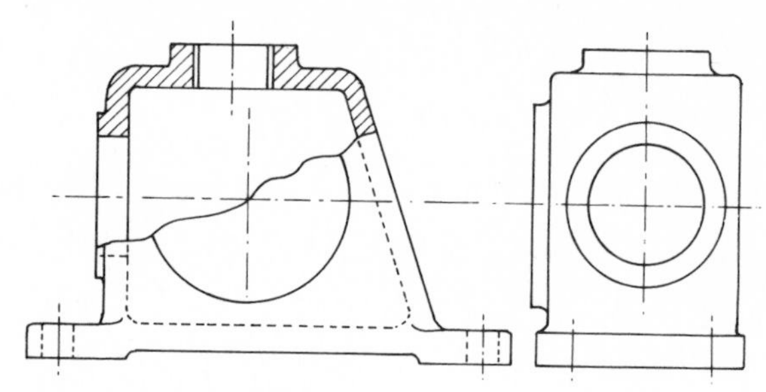

Figure 1.211 *Casing (or box)*

CASING (BOX)

A casting, forging or weldment in the form of a box or container which holds machine parts, such as those of a pump or turbine, is called a 'casing'.

CASTING

A casting is a metal or plastic article formed by pouring liquefied material into a suitably-shaped mould and then allowing it to solidify before being removed from the mould.

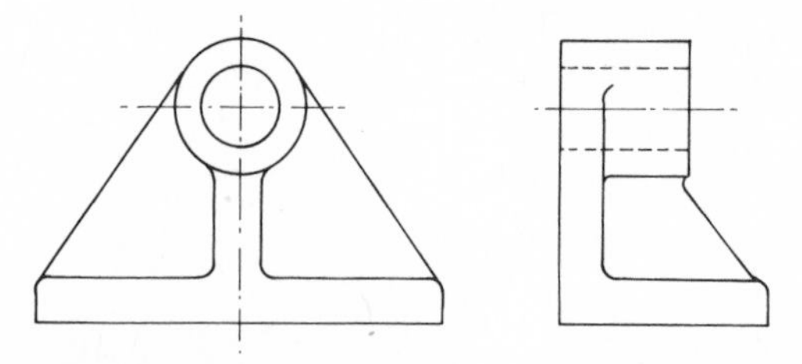

Figure 1.212 *Pedestal casting*

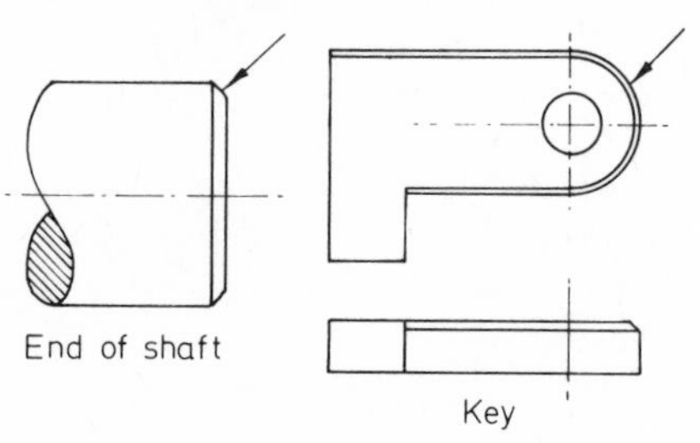

Figure 1.213 *Chamfer*

CHAMFER

The profile obtained by bevelling an edge or corner. It is usual to chamfer the corners produced by sudden changes in diameter on a shaft. This reduces the possibility of damage and eases the fitting of parts such as bearings, seals, collars, etc.

COLUMN (*see* Pillar)

COVER (COVERPLATE)

A cover is a plate, usually flat, which is bolted, riveted, welded or pressed into position to cover a cavity in a casing, etc.

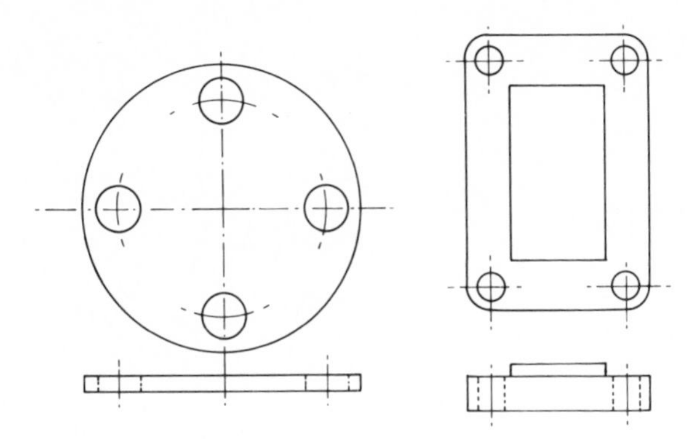

Figure 1.214 *Covers (coverplates)*

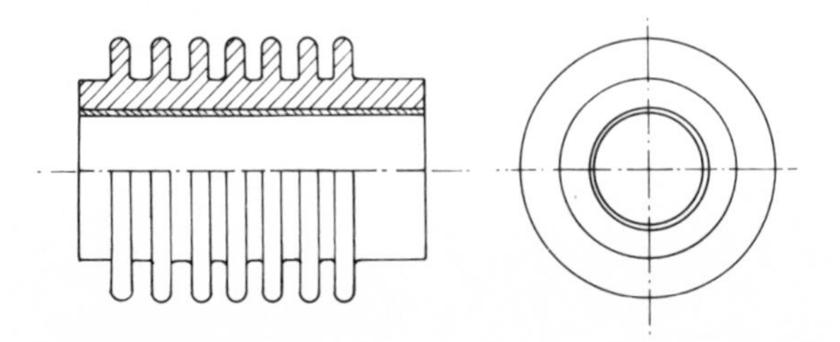

Figure 1.215 *Cylinder (with cooling fins and liner)*

CYLINDER

A cylinder is a circular tube in which a piston or plunger slides, e.g. as in pumps, engines or hydraulic rams. It is also a tubular container for liquids and gases.

DISTANCE PIECE

Any piece of material which is placed between two parts to maintain them at a fixed distance apart is termed a *distance piece*. It may be a plate or, as in the case of a shaft, a cylindrical sleeve (*see* Spacer).

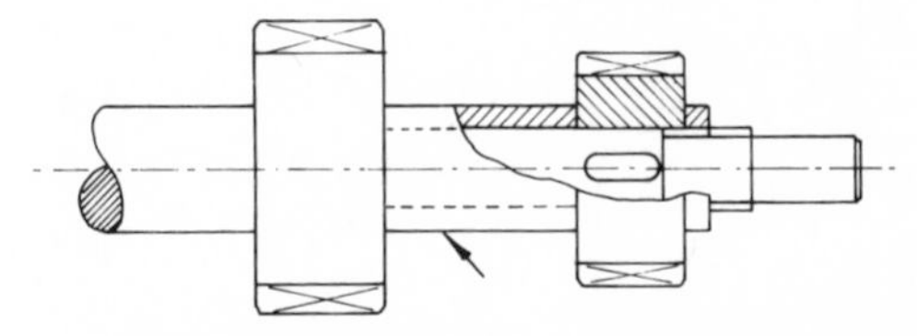

Figure 1.216 *Distance piece*

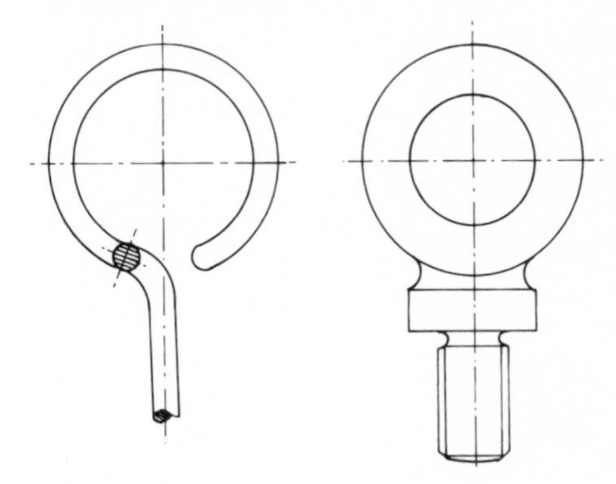

Figure 1.217 *Eye (wire and eye bolt)*

EYE

An eye is a loop formed at the end of a metal rod or wire by bending, or a ring which has been machined, cast, or forged on a component.

FACE

A face is a flat surface produced on a component by hand-filing or machining to which other parts may be attached, or on which they may slide, as opposed to the rough surface of a casting, forging etc.

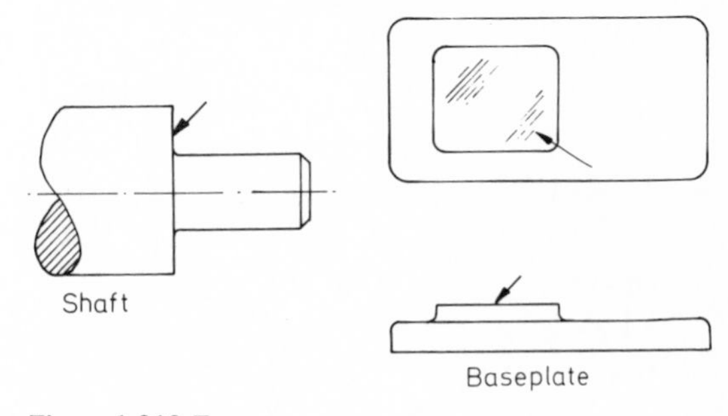

Figure 1.218 *Face*

FAUCET (RECESS)

A faucet is a circular recess into which a matching *spigot* fits, as in the case of a pipe joint.

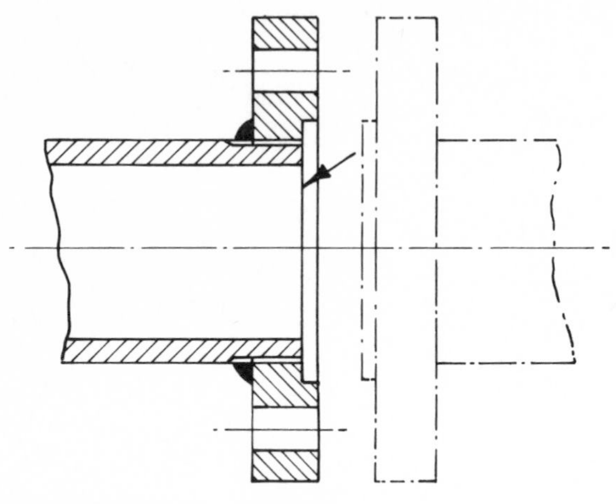

Figure 1.219 *Faucet (or recess)*

FILLET

This is a radius in a corner formed by two flat surfaces, and it is used to improve the quality of castings and the strength of machined parts (*see* Radius).

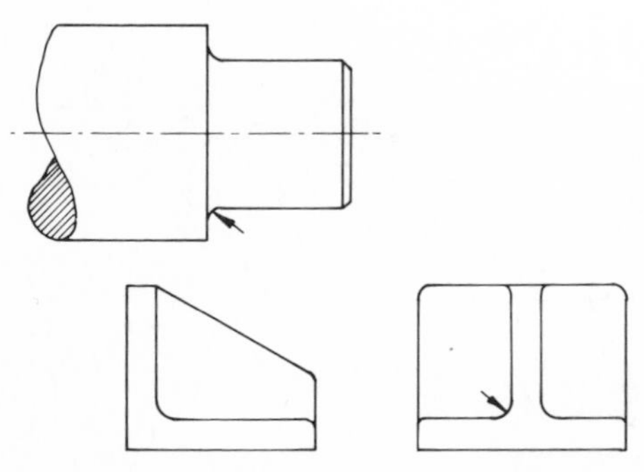

Figure 1.220 *Fillet*

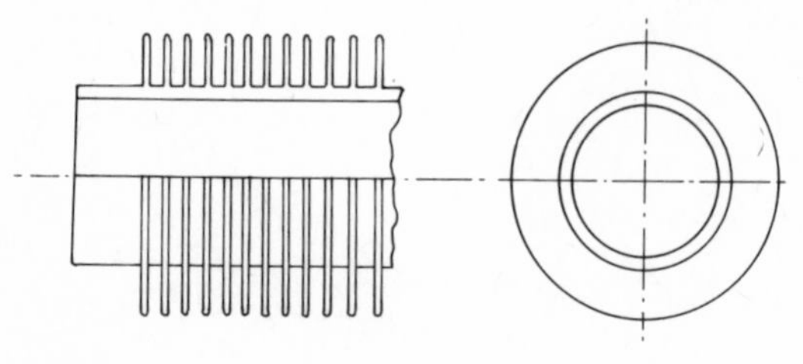

Figure 1.221 *Fins (on pipe)*

FIN

A fin is one of a number of thin ribs on the outer surface of engine cylinders, gear units, coolers, etc., used to dissipate heat to the surrounding air.

FLANGE

A flange is a projecting rim or lip, such as the rim of a wheel which runs on rails, the top and bottom parts of an I-section beam or channel section, the disk-like projection at the end of a pipe, or a bolted shaft coupling etc.

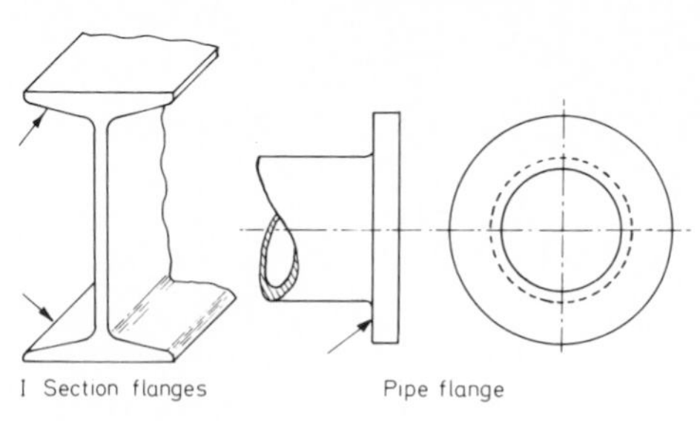

Figure 1.222 *Flange*

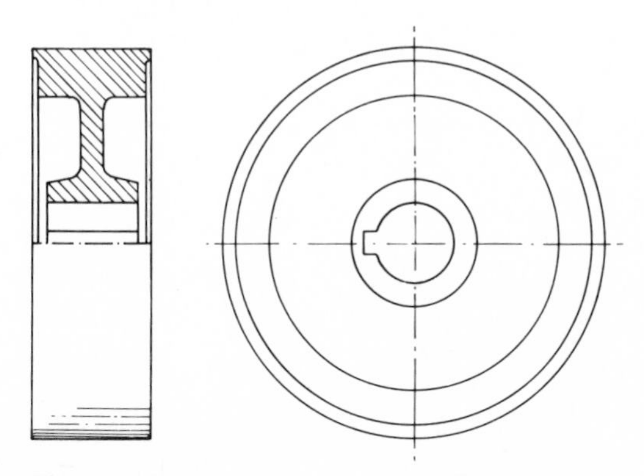

Figure 1.223 *Flywheel*

FLYWHEEL

A flywheel is a rotating disk with most of its mass concentrated at the rim. It is used for storing rotational energy and hence smoothing out vibrations.

FOOT

A foot is a projection on a casting, forging or weldment by which any of these is supported on a usually horizontal surface.

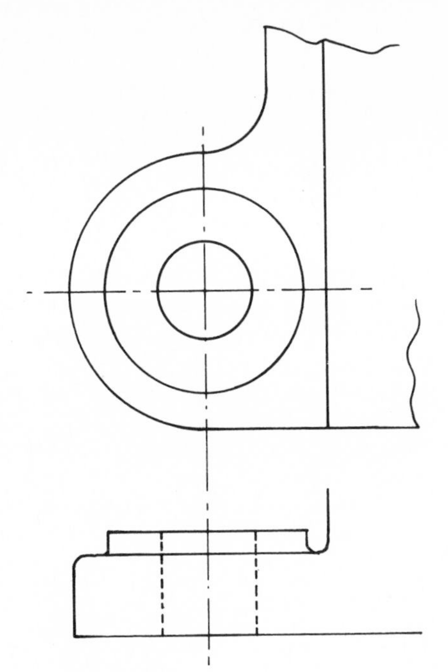

Figure 1.224 *Foot*

FORGING

A part made by hammering or pressing hot malleable metals either by hand or machine is known as a forging.

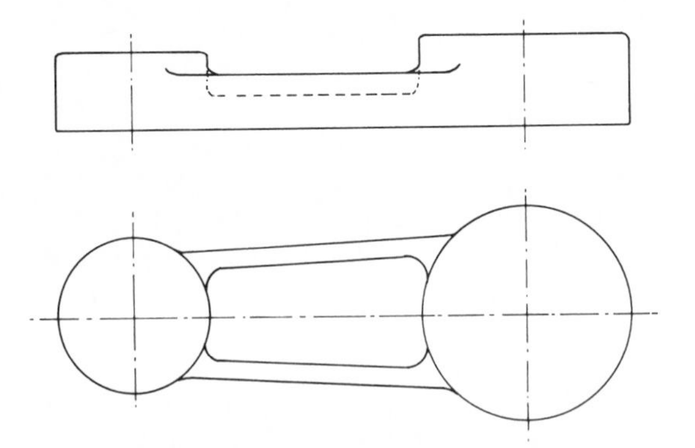

Figure 1.225 *Forging (for lever)*

FORK, FORK END

This is a feature at the end of a rod or lever consisting of two prongs which may have holes in them to take a pin.

HANDLE

A handle is a bar or lever shaped to give a good hand grip while applying straight or rotational motion.

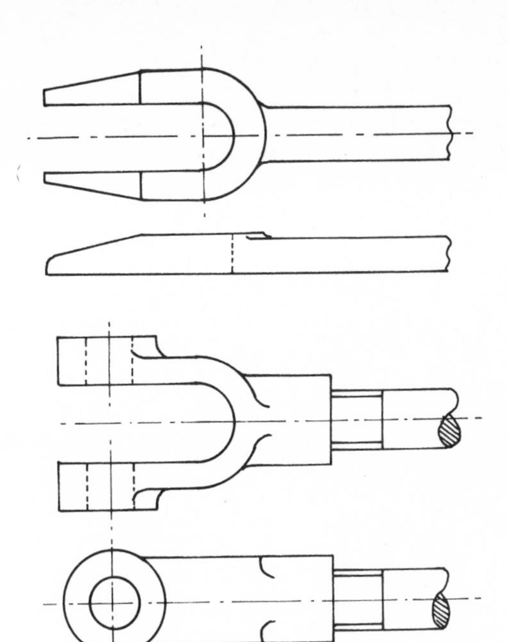

Figure 1.226 *Forks*

HANDWHEEL

This is a wheel with a heavy rim designed to provide a good hand grip when operating valve spindles, machine tool controls, steering gear, etc. Sometimes a handle is fitted to the rim to improve control.

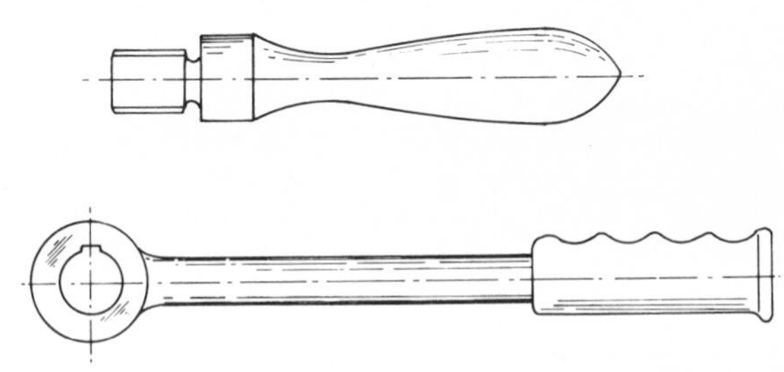

Figure 1.227 *Handles*

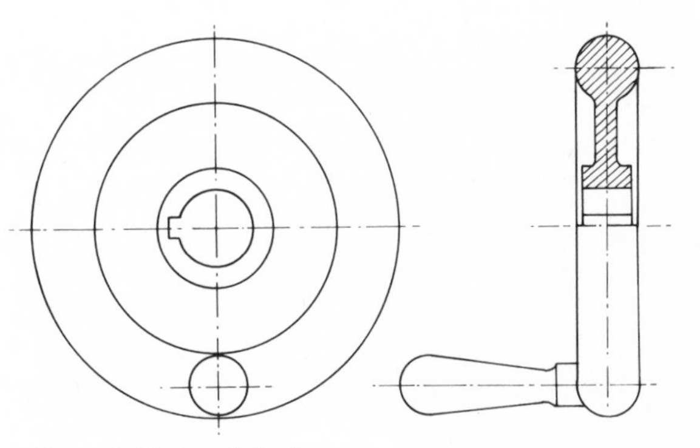

Figure 1.228 *Handwheel*

HOLES

In engineering components holes may be produced by numerous methods including casting, forging, punching, drilling and boring, and they may be reamed, tapped, countersunk, etc.

The following describes some of the types of hole most frequently encountered.

Bored hole A bored hole is produced by means of a single point boring tool on a lathe or boring mill. Greater accuracy is obtained than with a drill and larger holes can be produced.

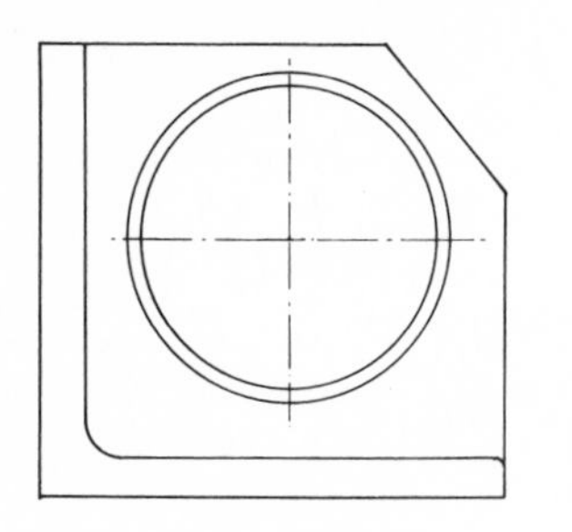

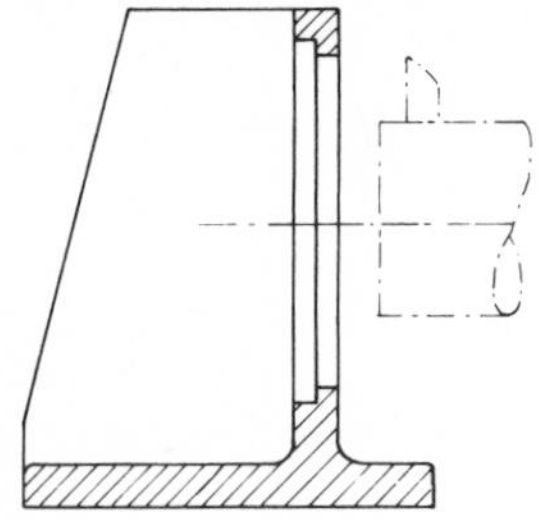

Figure 1.229 *Bored hole*

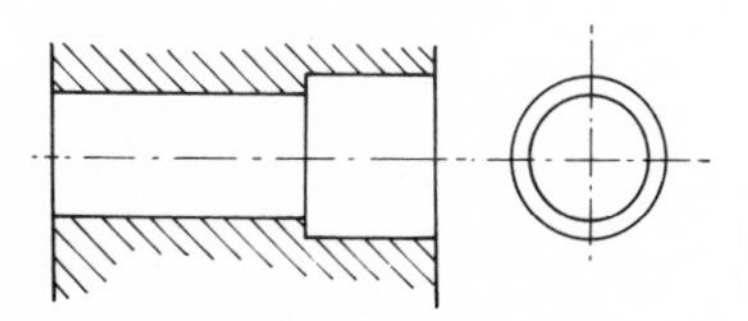

Figure 1.230 *Counterbored hole*

Counterbored hole A counterbored hole has its diameter increased for part of the depth, e.g. to provide a recess for a screw head.

Countersunk hole A countersunk hole has a conical section at the entrance to take the head of a countersunk screw, or a bolt or rivet.

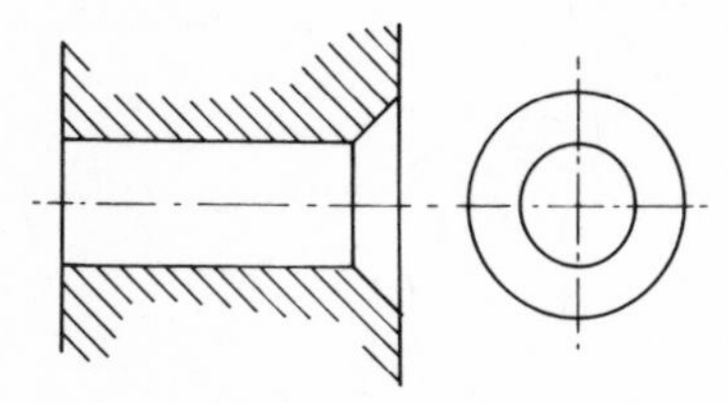

Figure 1.231 *Countersunk hole*

Drilled hole A drilled hole is produced by a rotating twist drill and it may be either a 'through' hole or a 'blind' hole.

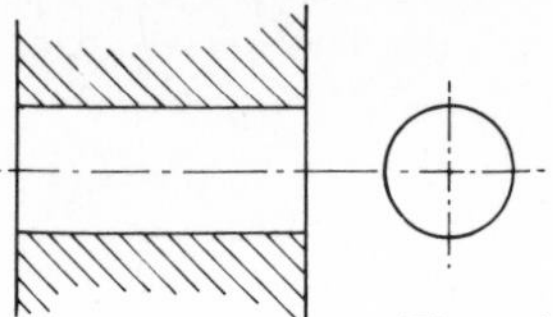

Figure 1.232 *Drilled through hole*

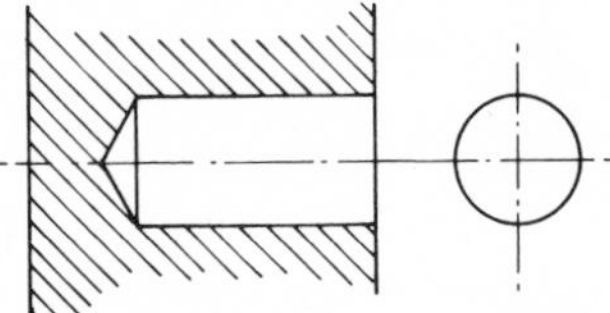

Figure 1.233 *Drilled blind hole*

Elongated hole An elongated hole is produced from a hole initially circular which has been extended into a slot by filing, or by joining two adjacent circular holes.

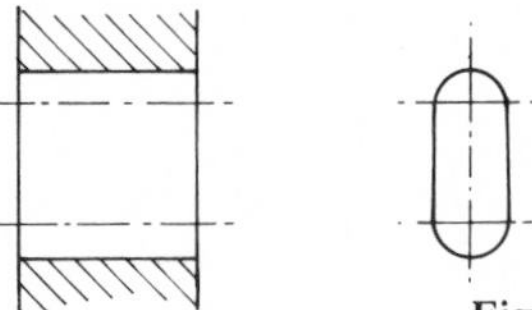

Figure 1.234 *Elongated hole*

Flat bottomed hole A drilled blind hole generally has a conical bottom but this can be made flat with a special tool to produce a 'flat-bottomed' hole.

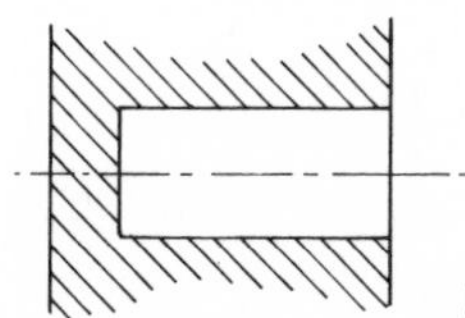

Figure 1.235 *Flat-bottomed hole*

Punched hole This is a hole of any shape produced in a sheet of metal by a hand- or machine-operated punch. A piece of metal the shape of the punch is forced out by shearing action.

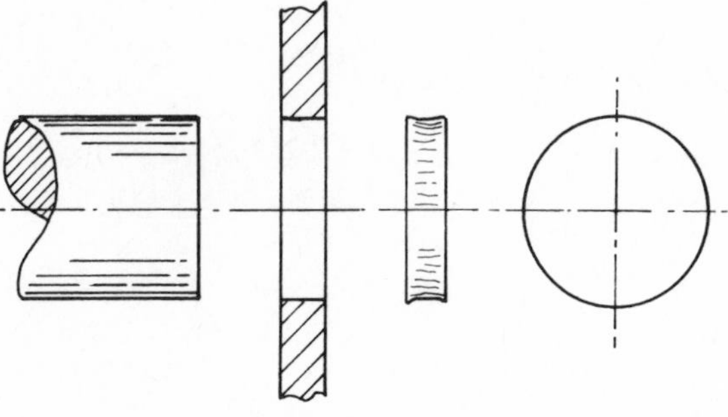

Figure 1.236 *Punched hole*

Reamed hole A reamed hole is an accurately-sized hole made by slightly enlarging a drilled hole by means of a fluted cutter called a *reamer*.

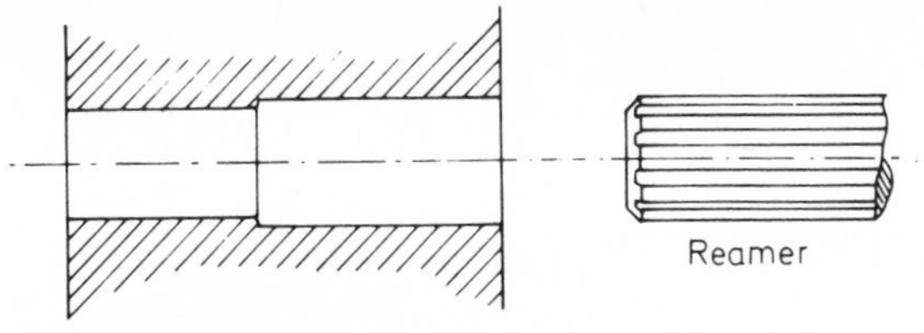

Figure 1.237 *Reamed hole*

Spotfaced hole (knifed hole) A spotfaced hole has a flat circular face cut at the entrance to take the head of a bolt etc. This is necessary when the surface is initially rough.

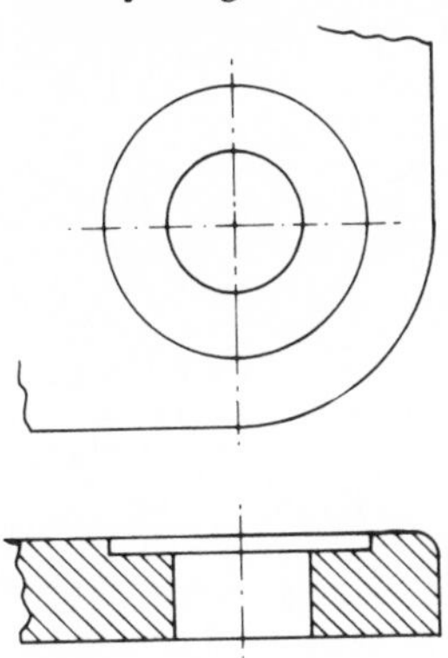

Figure 1.238 *Spotfaced hole (knifed hole)*

Square hole A square hole, or a hole of any non-circular shape, may be produced by hand filing or with a special tool called a *broach*.

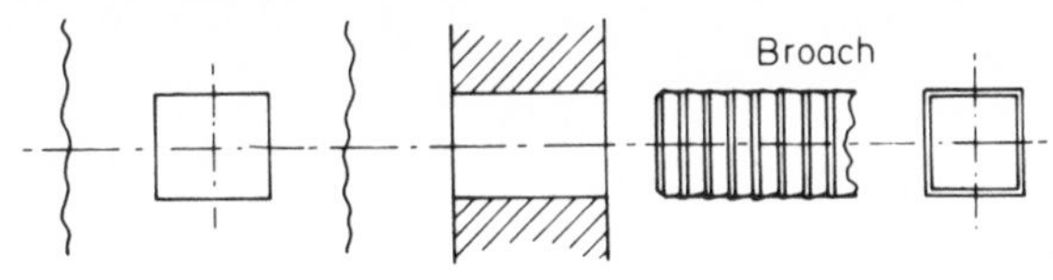

Figure 1.239 *Square hole (using a broach)*

Tapped hole This is a circular hole in which a screw thread has been cut for all or part of its length.

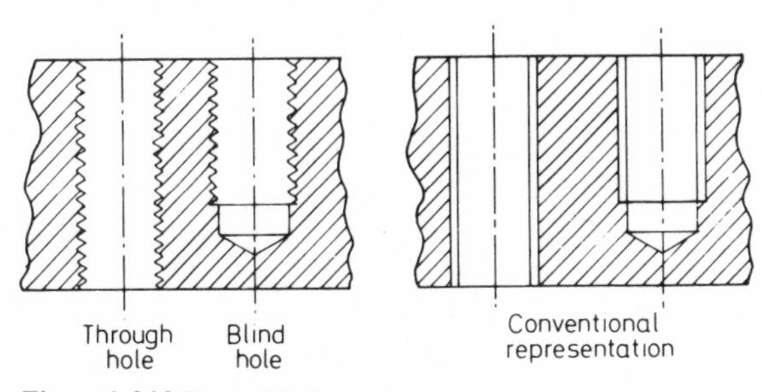

Figure 1.240 *Tapped holes*

HOUSING

A component which contains or 'houses' other components is known as a *housing*.

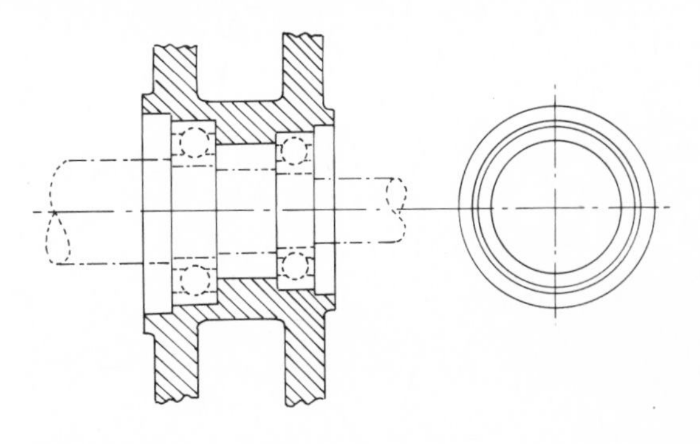

Figure 1.241 *Housing (for bearings)*

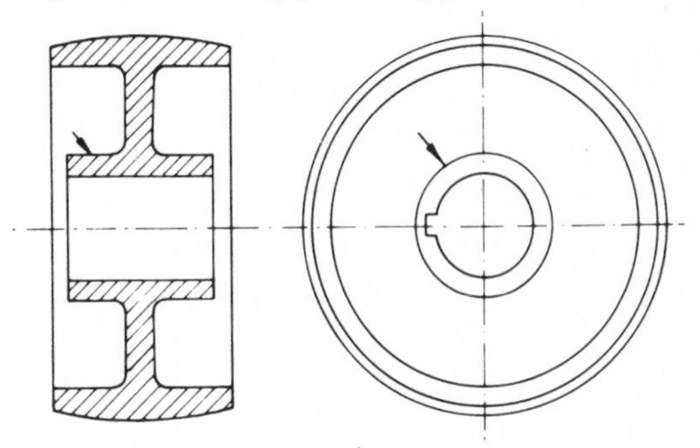

Figure 1.242 *Hub (of pulley)*

HUB

A hub is the heavy central section of a wheel, disk or pulley which usually has a hole for mounting on a shaft.

KNURLING

Knurling consists of serrations formed on the cylindrical surfaces of levers, handles, circular nuts, etc. to ensure a good hand grip.

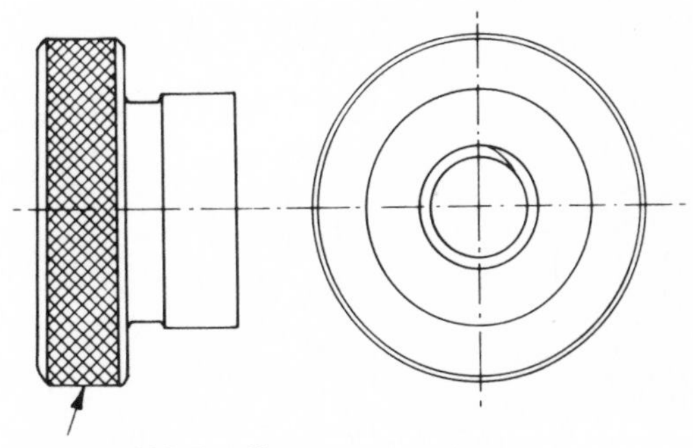

Figure 1.243 *Knurling*

LUG

A lug is an ear-shaped projection on a casting or forging, etc., often pierced by a hole.

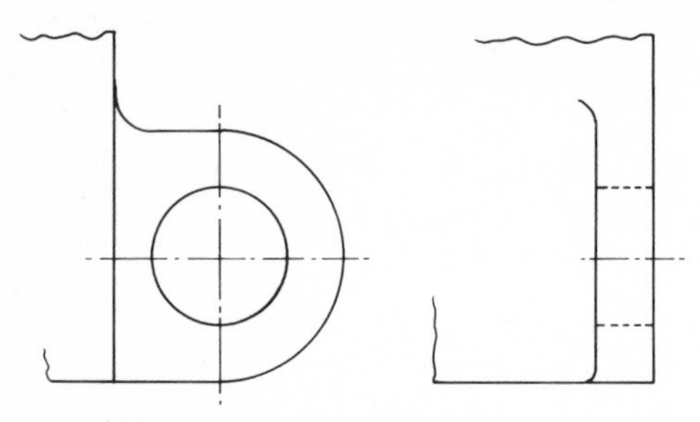

Figure 1.244 *Lug*

PEDESTAL

A support for other components, such as a shaft, mounted on a horizontal or vertical surface.

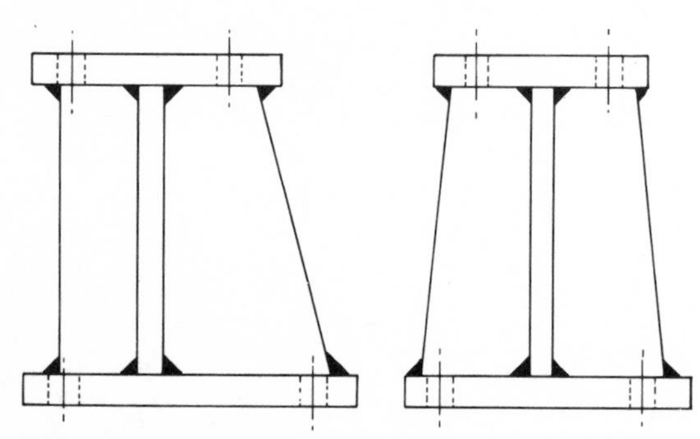

Figure 1.245 *Pedestal*

PILLAR

This is a bar or rod usually circular and vertical which holds two components apart. It is also called a *column.*

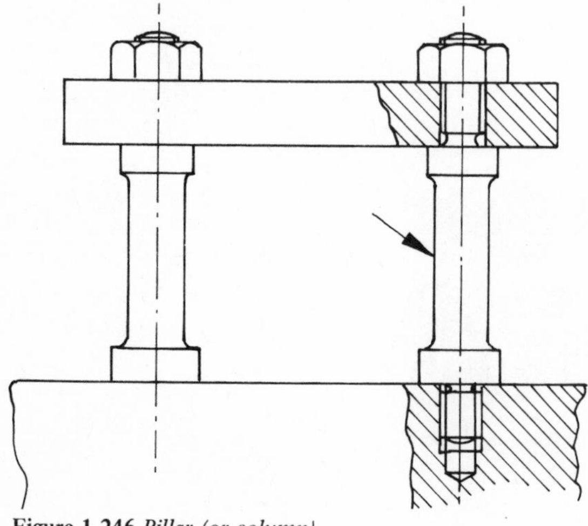

Figure 1.246 *Pillar (or column)*

PISTON

A piston is a cylindrical object which slides in a cylinder filled with a gas or liquid, as in an engine or pump. The piston is connected to a piston rod or connecting rod and is fitted with sealing rings (*see* Piston rings).

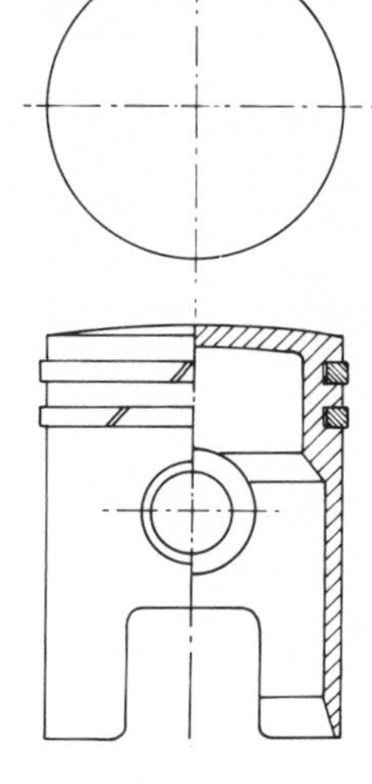

Figure 1.247 *Piston (for auto engine)*

PLATE

A plate is a piece of thin flat material, or any part which is generally flat in shape.

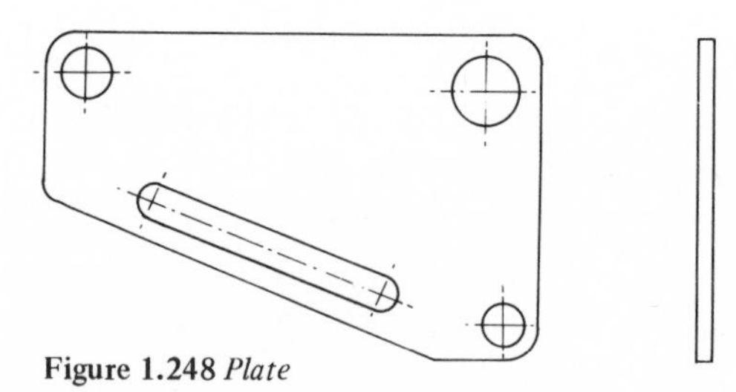

Figure 1.248 *Plate*

PLUNGER

Another name for a piston which is usually applied to small pump pistons.

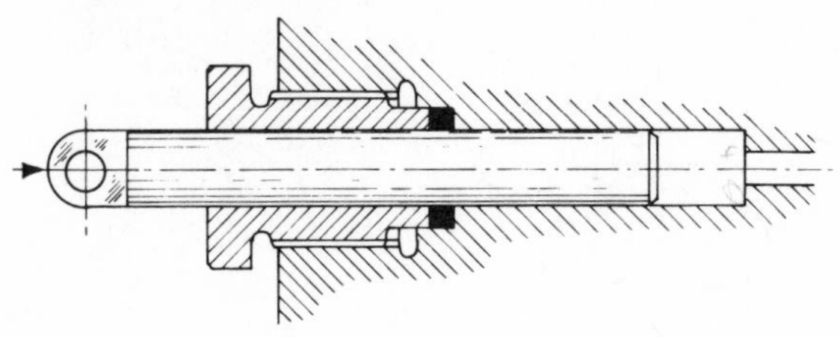

Figure 1.249 *Plunger (for pump)*

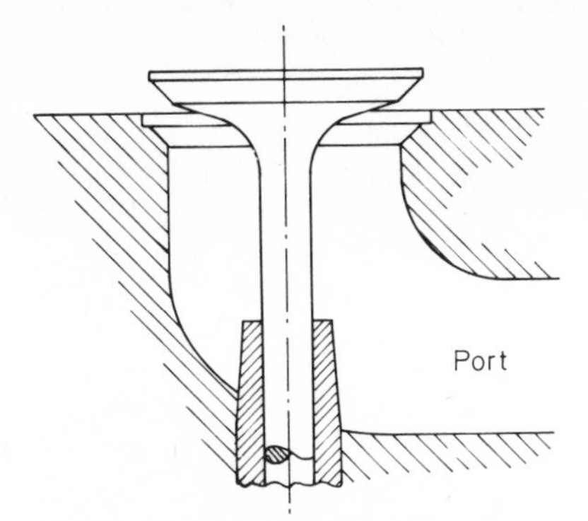

Figure 1.250 *Port (for IC engine valve)*

PORT

A port is a hole of any shape through which fluids or gases flow in engines, pumps, etc. They are often variable in size and are used to control the flow.

RADIUS

A radius is a modification to a sharp internal or external corner on a component to round it off with part of a circular arc for reasons of appearance, strength and safety (*see* Fillet).

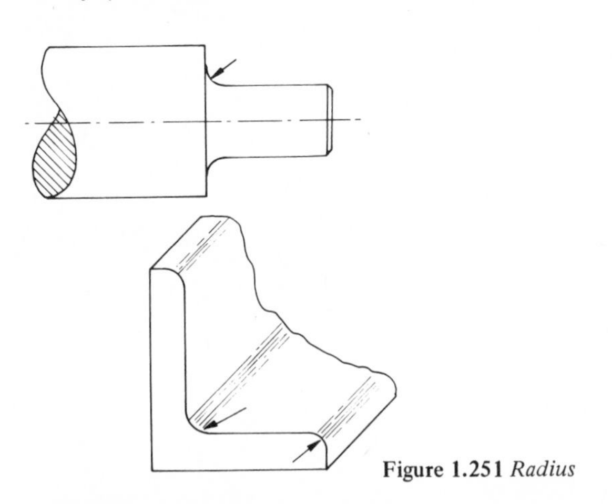

Figure 1.251 *Radius*

RECESS (FAUCET)

A recess is a depression or hollow in the surface of a part into which another part may be fitted.

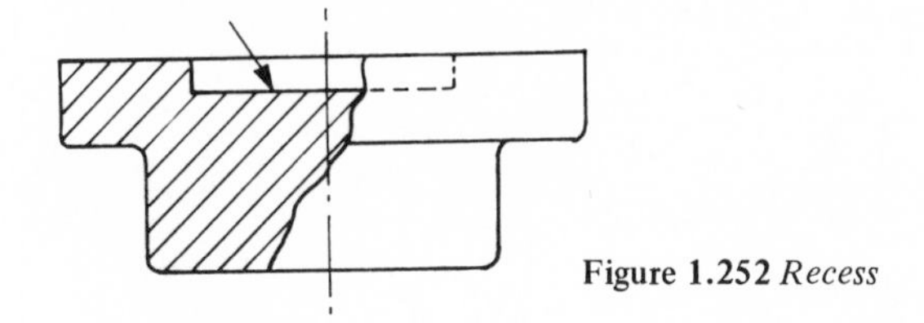

Figure 1.252 *Recess*

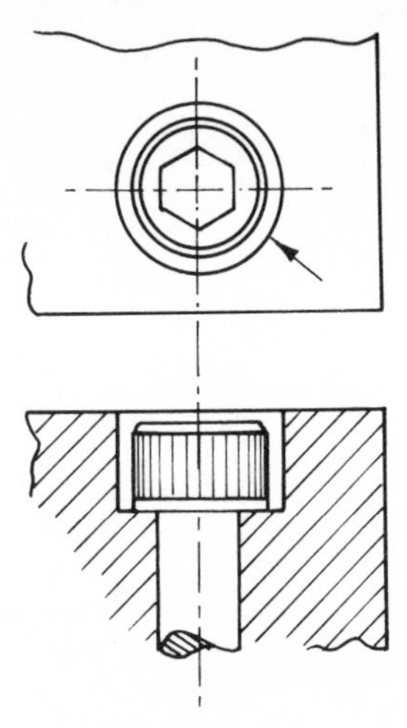

Figure 1.253 *Recessed socket head screw*

RIB

A rib is a raised thin section on the surface of a casting, forging, weldment, etc., used for strengthening and stiffening. It is also one of a series of members built into aircraft wings to which the skin is attached.

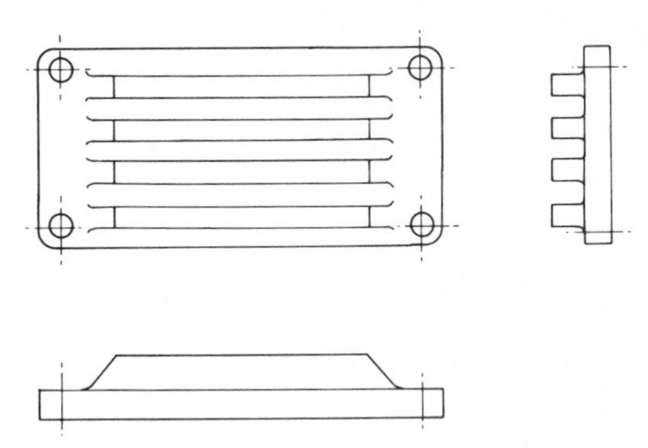

Figure 1.254 *Ribbed plate*

ROTOR

A rotor is a disk or drum mounted on a rotating shaft, e.g. turbine rotor, electric motor rotor. The term is also applied to a system of aerofoils such as those supporting a helicopter.

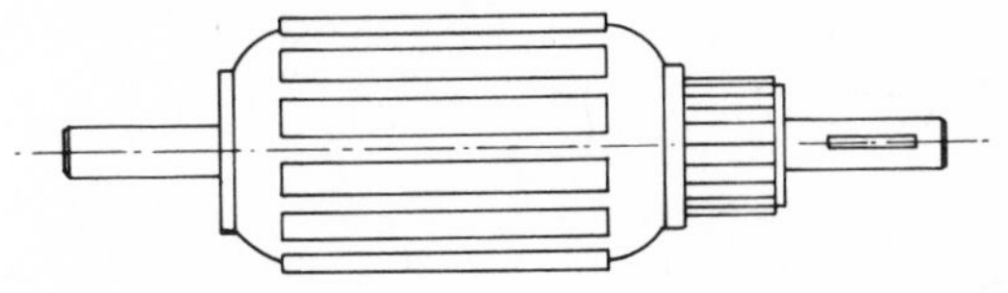

Figure 1.255 *Rotor (for electric motor)*

SLEEVE

This is a thin circular tube machined on the inside and outside.

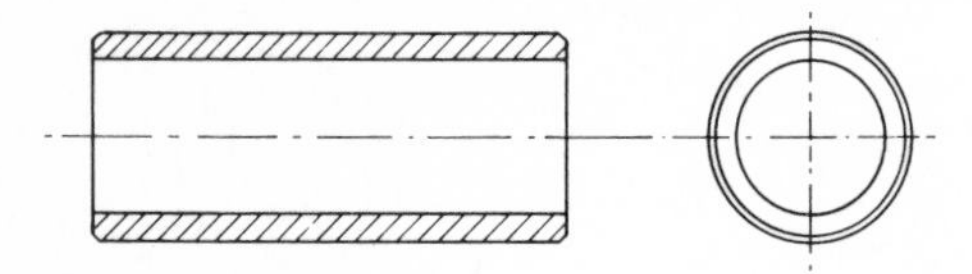

Figure 1.256 *Sleeve*

SLOT

A slot is a long groove or aperture, straight or curved, in a machine part in which another part slides or is mounted.

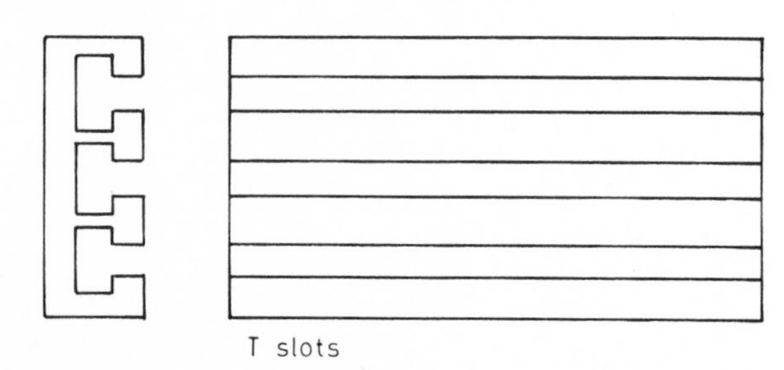

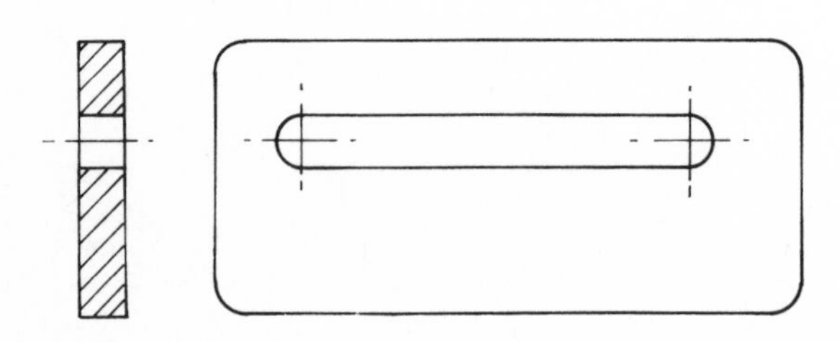

Figure 1.257 *Slots*

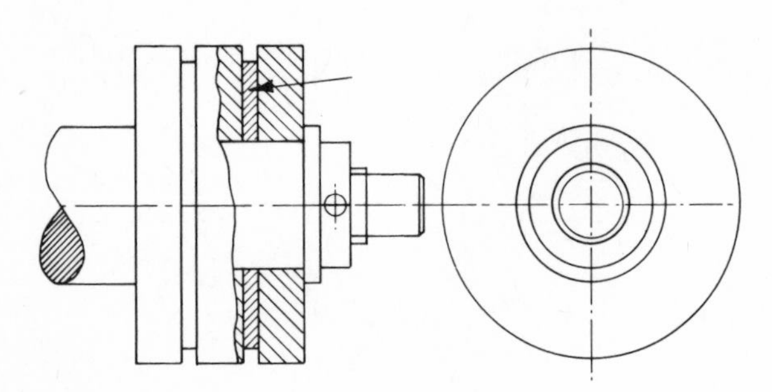

Figure 1.258 *Spacer*

SPACER

A spacer is another name for a *distance piece* but it usually refers to a thin plate.

SPIGOT

This is a raised part on the face of a circular flange on a pipe or shaft coupling which fits accurately into a corresponding recess (*faucet*) in the mating flange.

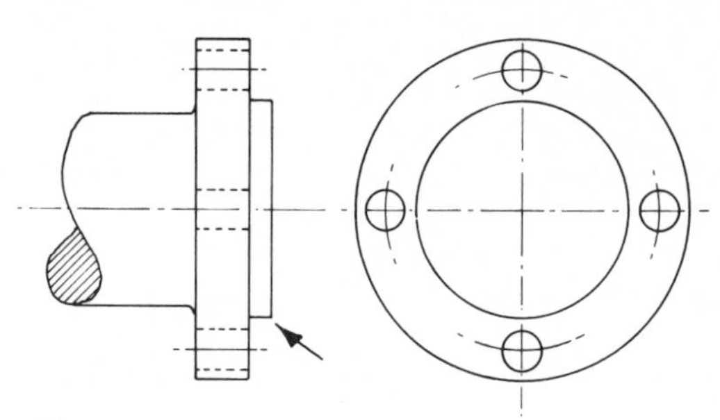

Figure 1.259 *Spigot*

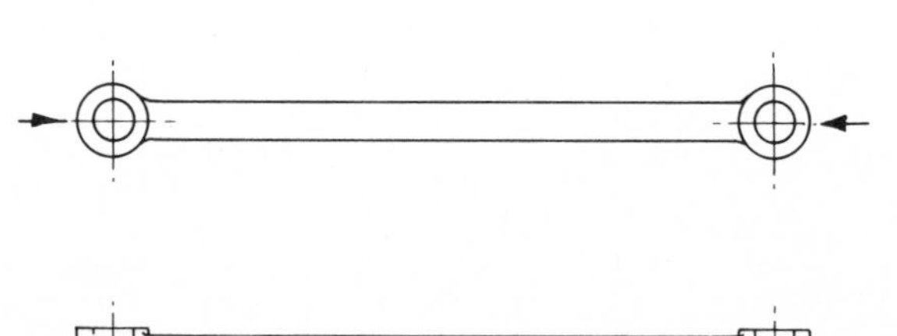

Figure 1.260 *Strut*

STRUT

A light structural member which takes a compressive load.

WEB

A web is a relatively thin part of a casting, forging or weldment joining two thicker parts, e.g. the central section of a channel or I beam. The thin disk joining the hub and rim of a wheel or pulley is also known as a web.

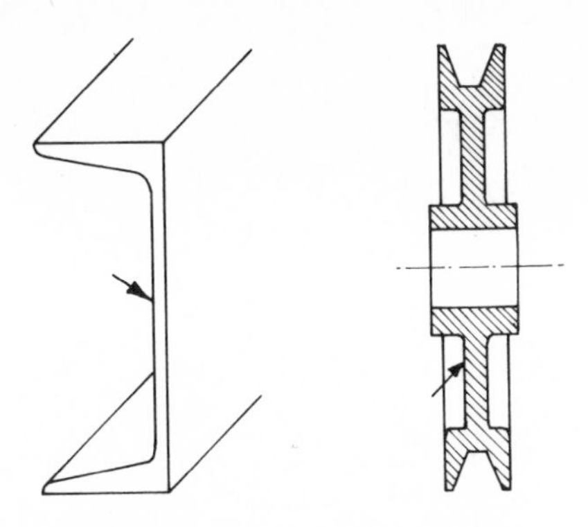

Figure 1.261 *Web (of channel section and pulley)*

WELDMENT

This refers to any welded assembly, usually fabricated from steel plate, bar, tube, etc.

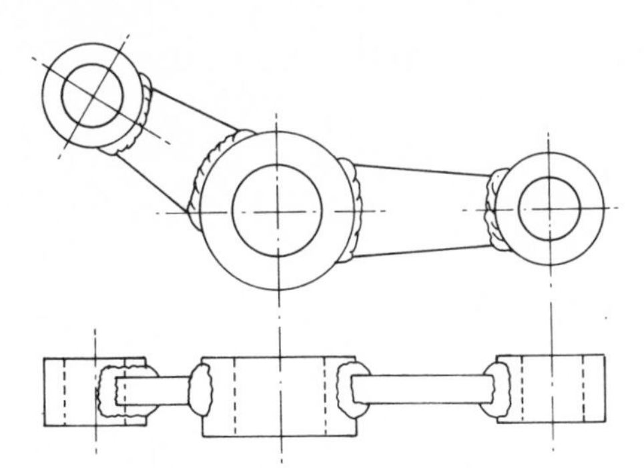

Figure 1.262 *Weldment (lever)*

WHEEL

This is the name given to a wide variety of rotating disk-shaped objects, such as flywheels, gearwheels and handwheels.

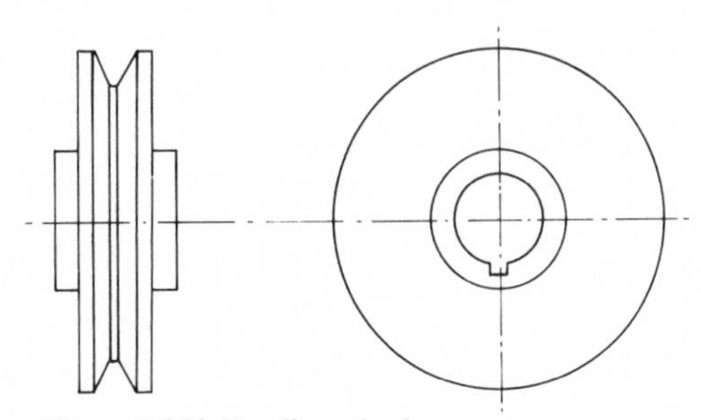

Figure 1.263 *V pulley wheel*

1.10 STOCK MATERIALS

STEEL SHEET

The term 'sheet' refers to thicknesses of less than 5mm ($^{3}/_{16}$ in.). When made it is rolled into coils and then cut into standard-sized pieces for sale.

Sheet is usually made in low carbon steel cold rolled to give a good finish and it may be given a protective coating of tin, zinc (galvanised), or plastics such as PVC. Various kinds of corrugated sheet are produced.

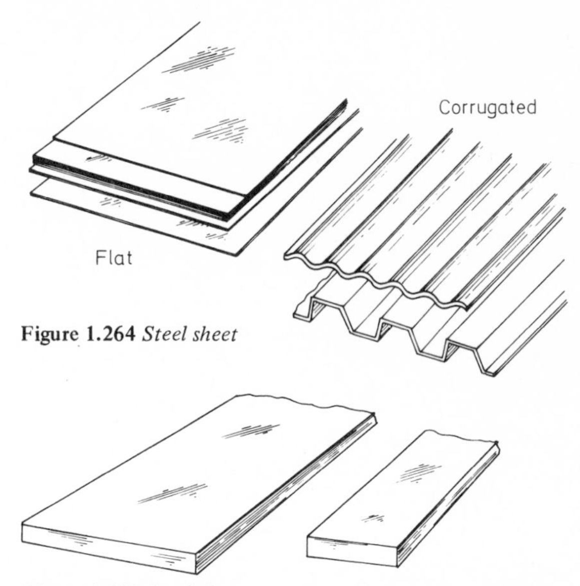

Figure 1.264 *Steel sheet*

Figure 1.265 *Steel plate*

STEEL PLATE

This is steel from 6mm (¼ in.) thick up to 150mm (6 in.) thick. Steel plate is produced in various grades and in sizes up to 2.5m (8 ft.) in width.

STEEL STRIP

This is narrow plate or sheet made in carbon, alloy and stainless steel.

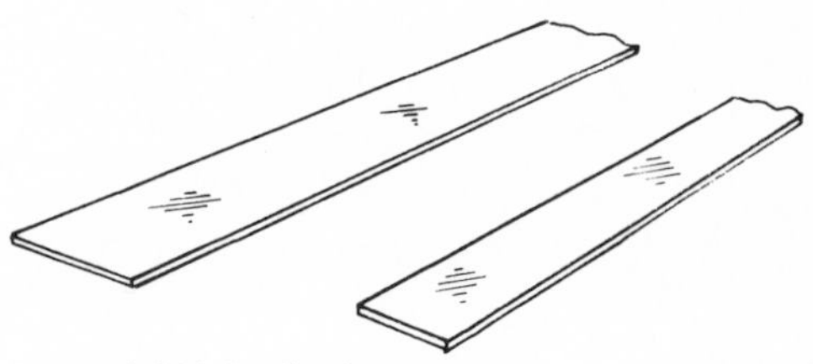

Figure 1.266 *Steel strip*

HOT-ROLLED STEEL SECTIONS

The following sections are produced by hot rolling using specially-shaped rollers: I beam, angle, channel and T for structural work; round, rectangular and hexagonal bar, and sheet for stamped, drawn and punched parts.

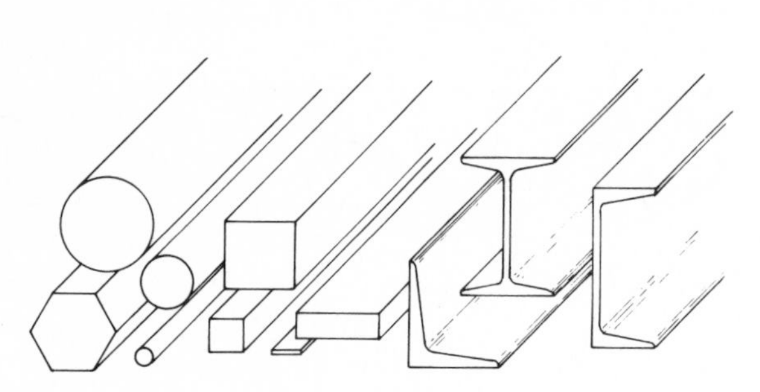

Figure 1.267 *Hot rolled steel sections*

COLD-ROLLED STEEL SECTIONS

Cold rolling of the above sections produces a smooth surface which can be plated or coated.

BRIGHT STEEL BAR

Bar produced by hot rolling has a rough oxidised surface and is referred to as 'black' bar. 'Bright' bar, of higher accuracy, is produced by the drawing process in sizes up to 40mm (1½ in.) diameter.

Square, rectangular and hexagonal bright bars are used extensively for the production of small machined parts.

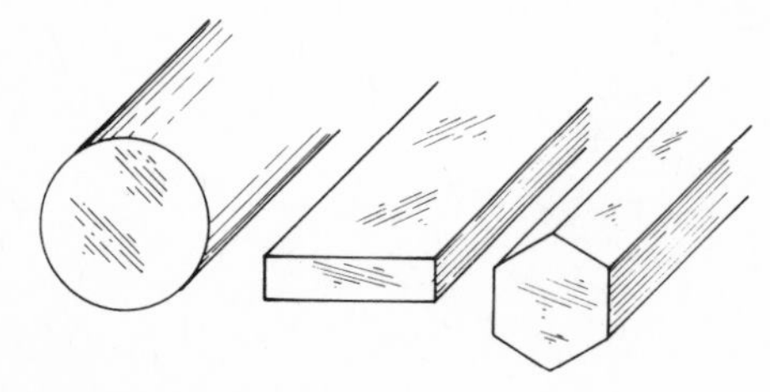

Figure 1.268 *Bright steel bar*

HOLLOW STEEL SECTIONS

Hollow round sections in small diameters are used for small machined parts. Large hollow round and hollow rectangular sections are of great value in all kinds of structural work. Rectangular sections range in size from a few millimetres to 400mm (16 in.).

Figure 1.269 *Hollow steel sections*

STEEL CHEQUER PLATE

Chequer plate is used for flooring and it has a raised pattern to give a good foothold. It is used in ships' engine rooms, power stations, etc.

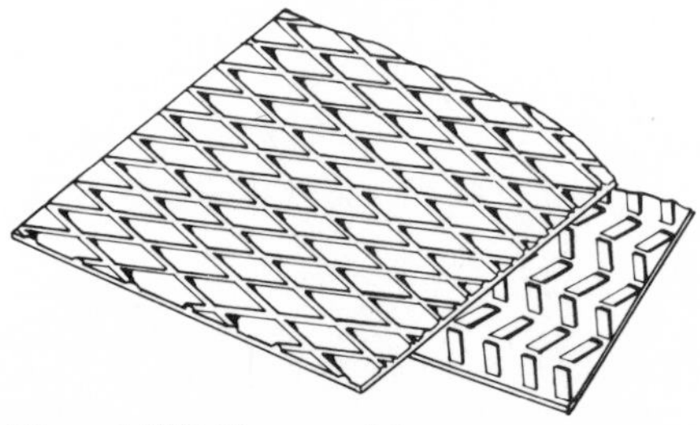

Figure 1.270 *Chequer plate*

WIRE

High strength carbon and alloy wire is used for wire ropes and small springs, while wire of lower-grade steel is used for wire mesh. Copper wire is made in a large range of diameters and is often insulated with varnish or a plastic coating. Tinned copper wire is also made.

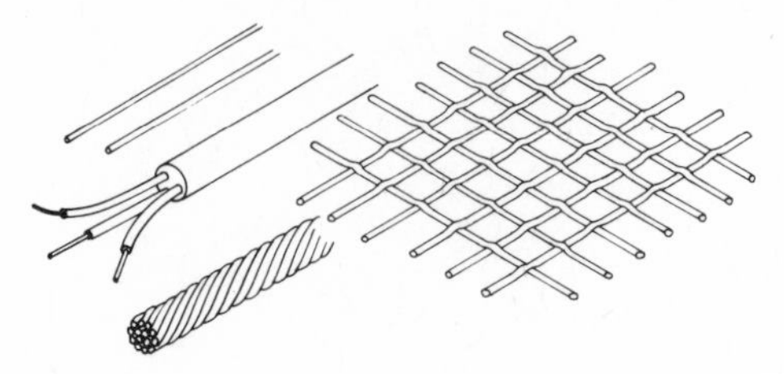

Figure 1.271 *Wire*

NON-FERROUS METALS

Brass, bronze, copper, aluminium and aluminium alloys are used to make solid and hollow round bar, rectangular bar and hexagonal bar. These metals are also used for a wide range of gauges of sheet and plate.

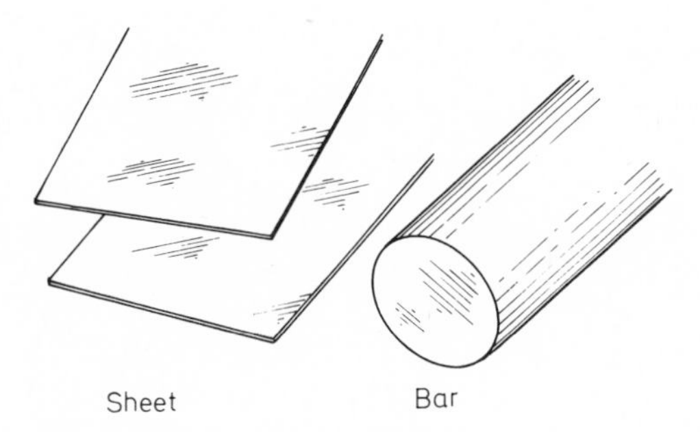

Figure 1.272 *Non-ferrous metals*

TUBE

Light gauge metal hollow sections are referred to as *tubes* and these are made in mild steel, high-strength alloy steel, stainless steel and aluminium alloys.

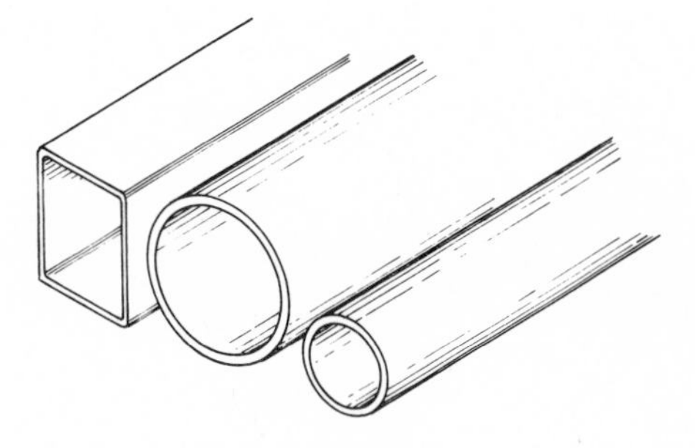

Figure 1.273 *Light gauge tube*

2. Power Transmission Elements

2.1 BRAKES AND CLUTCHES

BRAKES

A brake is a device which applies a resistive force to a moving body in order to retard or stop it. It may also be used to absorb and/or measure power. In most cases the motion is rotational.

Disk brake A brake in which a segmental block, or an annular flat ring of friction material, is forced against the face of a rotating disk. Automobile disk brakes employ two segmental blocks (or pads) on opposite sides of the disk operated by hydraulic pistons located in a *calliper*.

Disk brakes are less prone than drum brakes to 'fading', i.e. a fall in efficiency due to prolonged application.

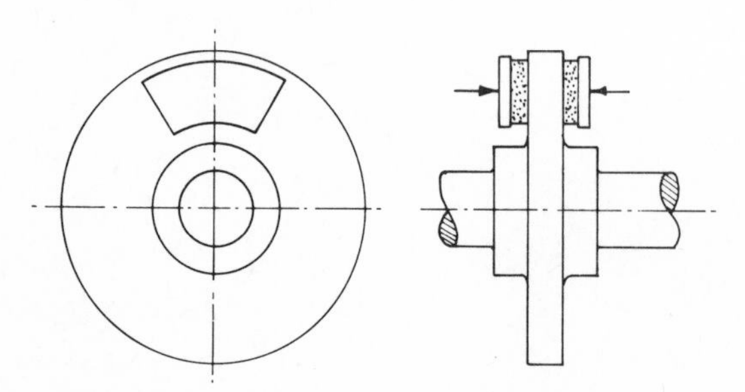

Figure 2.1 *Disk brake*

Single block brake This is a brake in which a block made from, or lined with, a material of high coefficient of friction is held against the rim of a rotating wheel in order to cause retardation of the wheel. The force may be applied manually, by a spring or by other means.

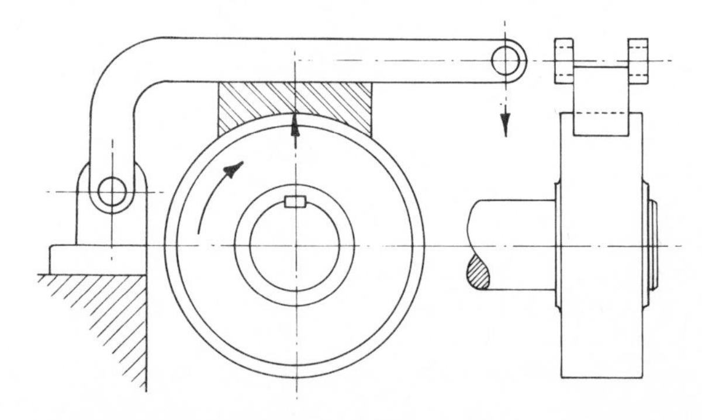

Figure 2.2 *Single block brake*

Double block brake In this brake two blocks situated on opposite sides of a wheel or drum are actuated simultaneously by a bell crank lever.

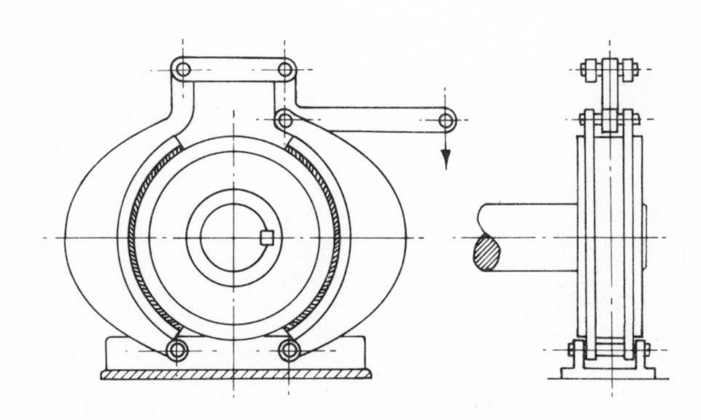

Figure 2.3 *Double block brake*

Spring-set brake This is a double block brake in which the blocks, or shoes, are normally held in contact with the drum, thus preventing its rotation. A compressed spring applies the load and the operating lever compresses the spring still further to release the drum. The lever may be operated by hand, electric solenoid, or by a hydraulic or pneumatic cylinder. This type of brake is used in lifts since it is 'fail-safe'.

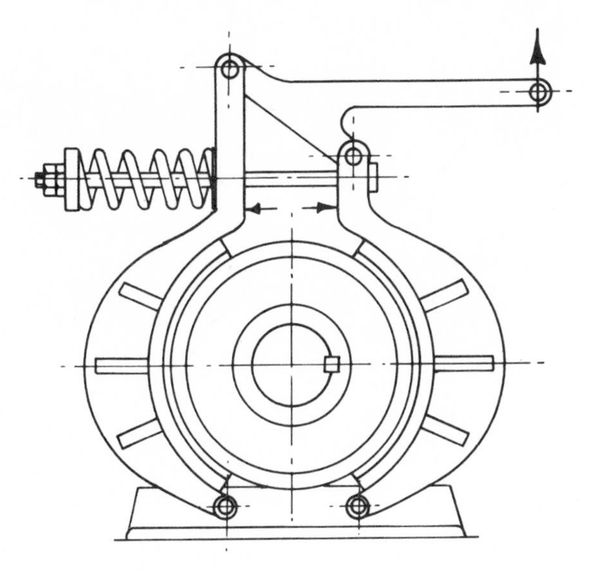

Figure 2.4 *Spring set brake*

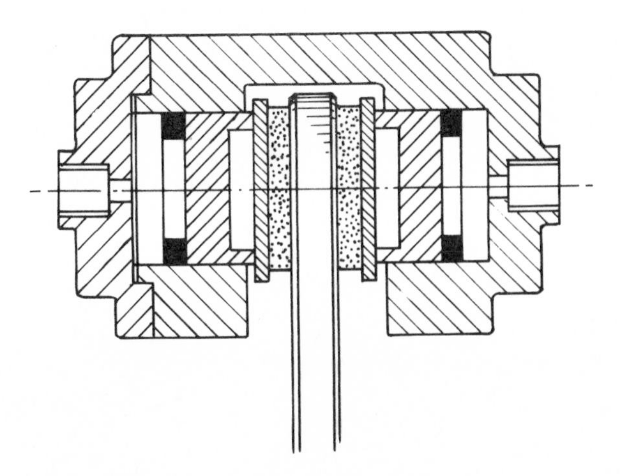

Figure 2.5 *Automobile disk brake calliper*

Multi-plate (disk) brake This type comprises several annular friction disks interleaved with steel disks. The steel disks run on a splined shaft, and the friction disks are prevented from rotating by pins. The brake is actuated by compressing the disks.

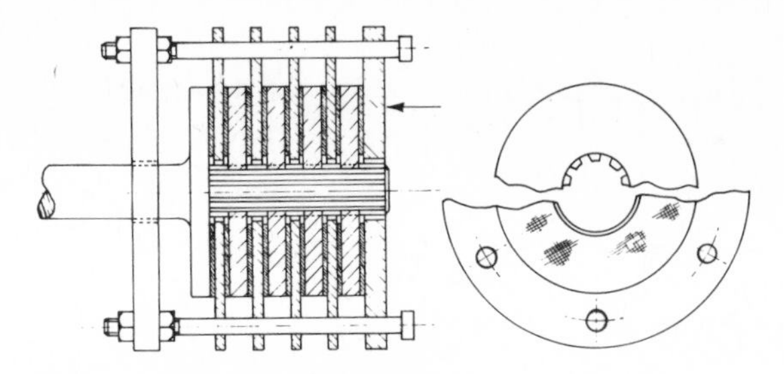

Figure 2.6 *Multi-plate (disk) brake*

Centrifugal brake In a centrifugal brake, shoes are thrown outwards by centrifugal force against the action of springs. The speed at which the brake operates is determined by the spring force.

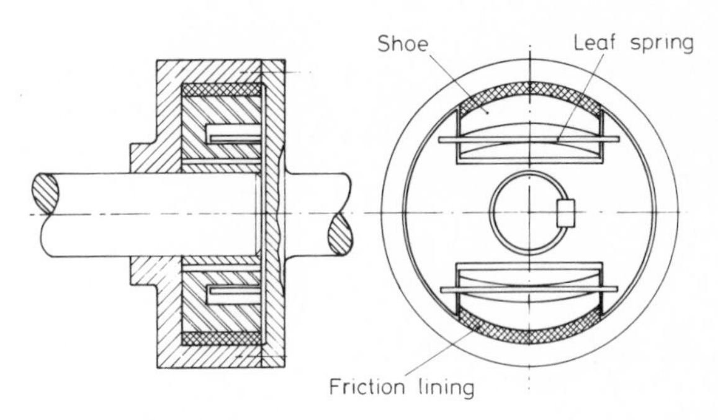

Figure 2.7 *Centrifugal brake*

Internal expanding shoe brake (drum brake) A brake in which two curved shoes are forced outwards against the inside of the rim of a rotating drum. The shoes are lined with friction material, known as brake linings, riveted or bonded to their outer surface.

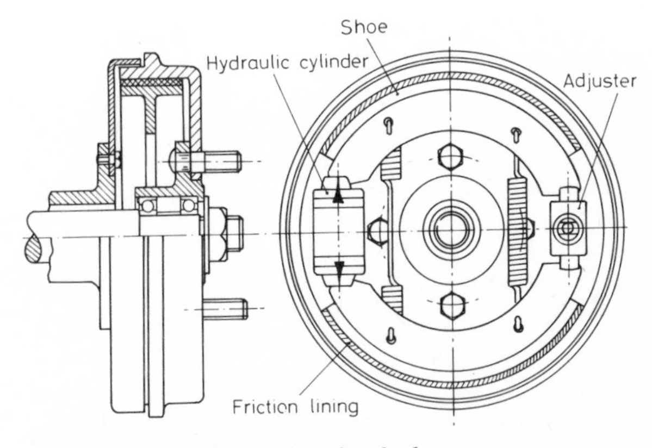

Figure 2.8 *Internal expanding shoe brake (automobile-type drum brake)*

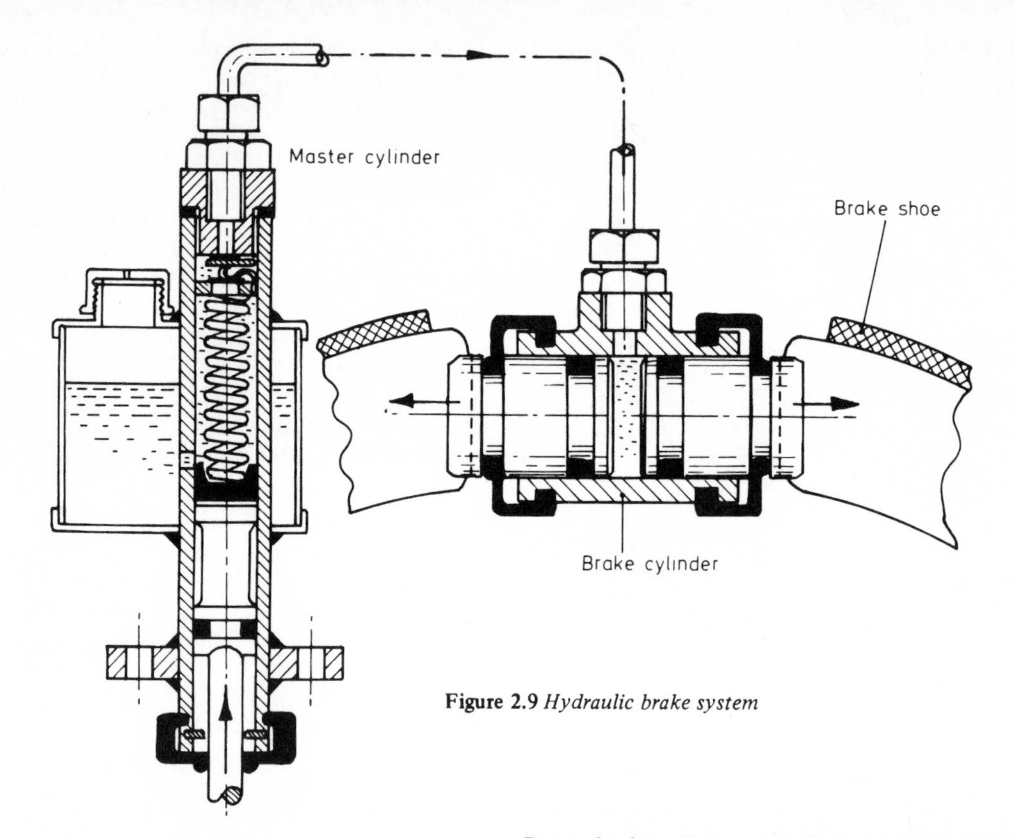

Figure 2.9 *Hydraulic brake system*

Power brake Brakes may be energised by electric solenoids, or by pistons using hydraulic or pneumatic pressure or a vacuum. In automobile brakes foot pressure applied to a master cylinder pressurises the brake fluid and this actuates pistons in contact with the shoes or pads.

Power absorption brake or dynamometer Brakes are used in the testing of engines to absorb and usually measure the power of a rotating shaft. These brakes, or *dynamometers* as they are called, may be of the friction type, hydraulic or electrical.

Rope brake or dynamometer (band brake) Rope of one or more strands, or a flexible belt, is looped around a drum and tightened to provide a friction force on the drum. The torque can be found by measuring the tangential force with a spring balance attached to the rope or belt.

Prony brake The Prony brake is used for the measurement of power in which friction blocks run on the outside of a drum. The torque on the block carrier is balanced by weights and a spring balance, or alternatively, by a load cell.

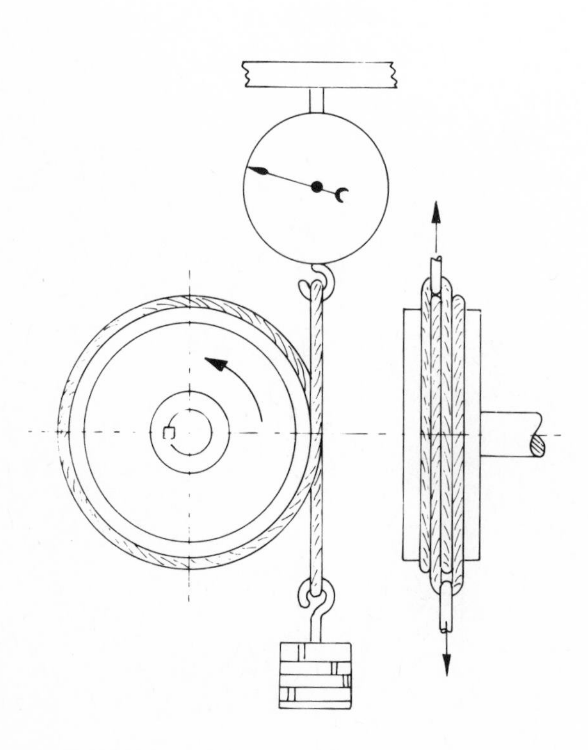

Figure 2.10 *Rope brake*

Figure 2.11 *Prony brake*

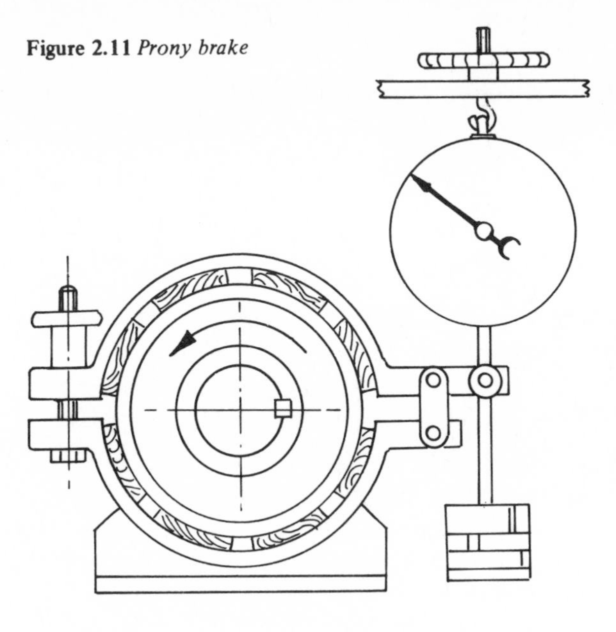

CLUTCHES

A clutch is a device which enables two shafts or rotating elements to be connected or disconnected while at rest or in relative motion.

Friction clutch In a friction clutch power is transmitted from one rotating element to another by means of the frictional force between them.

Single-plate friction clutch (disk clutch) This is a friction clutch in which the contacting surfaces consist of flat annular rings held together with sufficient force to prevent slipping when power is transmitted through the clutch. The force is usually supplied by one or more springs and the clutch is disengaged by a lever.

Clutch plate (clutch disk) A clutch plate is one of the plates in a friction clutch which is lined with a material having a high coefficient of friction when in contact with a metal surface. The friction material is either riveted or bonded to a metal backing plate.

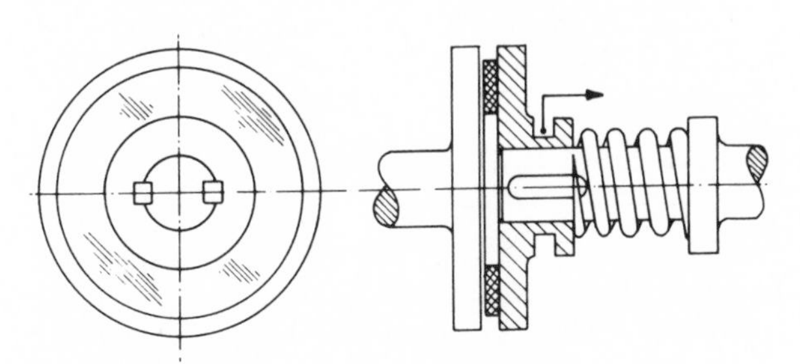

Figure 2.12 *Single-plate (disk) friction clutch*

Automobile friction clutch This clutch employs a plate with friction material on both sides which is clamped between two steel plates when the clutch is operated. The friction plate is carried on splines or keys on the output shaft so that it can slide axially, and one of the steel plates is attached to the input shaft. The other steel plate rotates with the input shaft and is spring loaded so that it normally holds the clutch in the engaged position. The clutch is disengaged by a lever moving a release sleeve on the shaft.

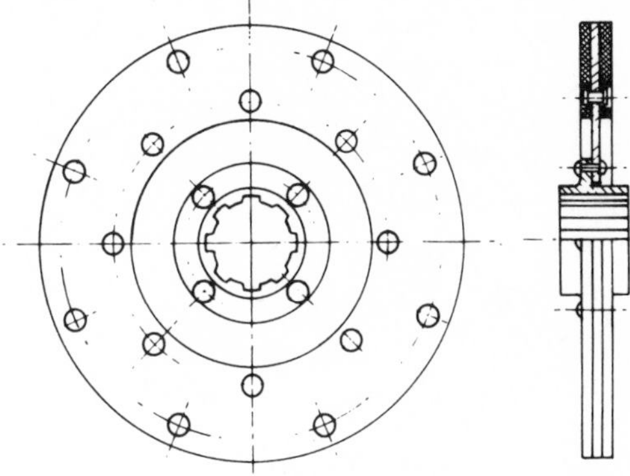

Figure 2.13 *Automobile-type clutch plate (disk)*

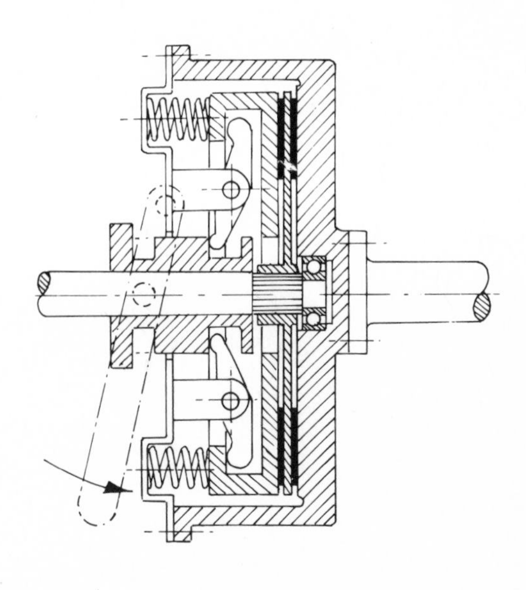

Figure 2.14 *Automobile friction clutch*

Multi-plate (disk) friction clutch The multi-plate automobile clutch has evolved from the single-plate clutch. Here several friction plates are keyed to one shaft and rotate with it. Interleaved with them are steel pressure plates keyed to the other shaft. All the plates are compressed together by a spring and released by a lever-actuated sleeve.

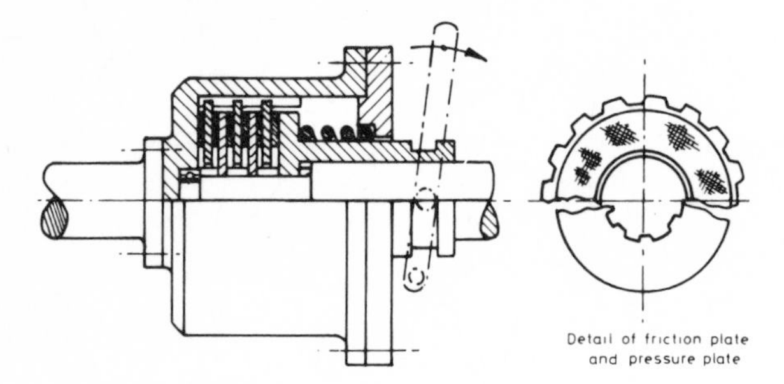

Figure 2.15 *Multi-plate (disk) friction clutch*

Cone clutch This has two conical mating surfaces one of which may be lined with a high-friction material. The torque capacity of a cone clutch is higher than that of a flat plate clutch of the same diameter. This increases as the angle of the cone to the axis decreases.

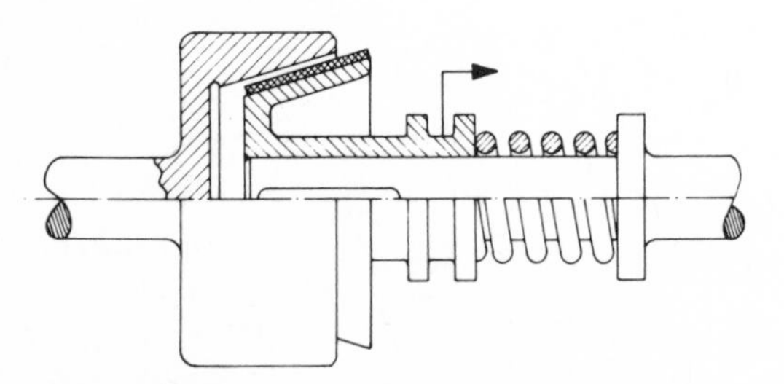

Figure 2.16 *Cone clutch*

Dog clutch (claw clutch) One half of this clutch is fastened permanently to one shaft while the other half slides on a feather key, or on splines, and is moved by a lever. Mating teeth on each half engage with one another and transmit the drive. The clutch can be operated only when stationary or moving at very low speeds.

Freewheeling or over-running clutch A freewheeling, or over-running, clutch permits a shaft to be driven in one direction of rotation only. It slips when the speed of the driven shaft exceeds that of the driving shaft.

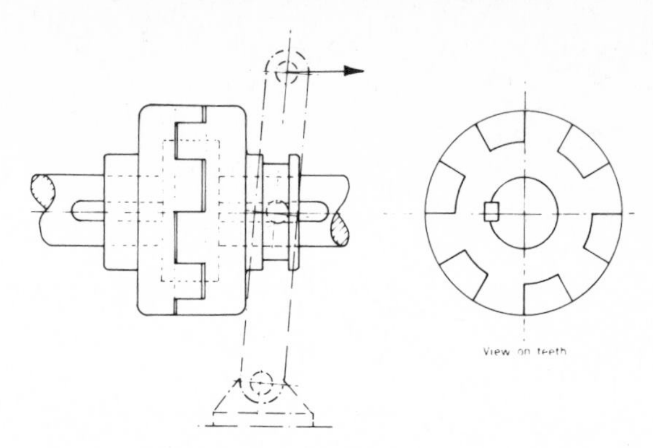

Figure 2.17 *Dog, or claw, clutch*

Roller freewheeling clutch Each roller is located in a wedge-shaped space between the inner and outer races. In one direction of rotation the rollers run up the wedge and lock to give a drive. In the other direction the rollers lie at the bottom of the ramp and the clutch slips.

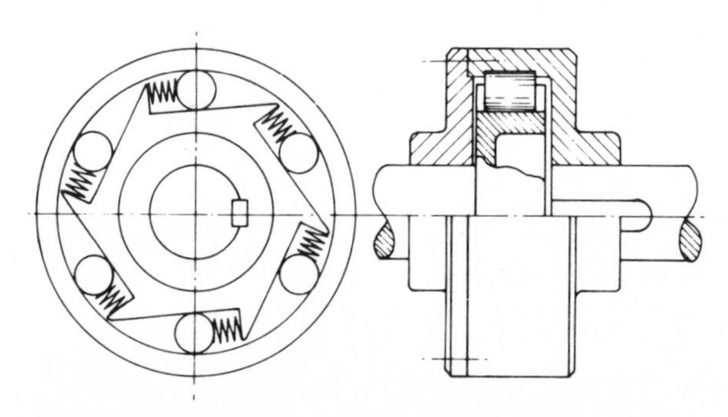

Figure 2.18 *Roller freewheeling clutch*

Sprag clutch Inner and outer races are connected to the input and output shafts. Wedge-shaped objects called *sprags* are situated in the annular space between the races. The sprags are shaped so that in one direction of rotation they wedge between the two races and the clutch is engaged. In the other direction the sprags tilt so that they are freed and the clutch slips.

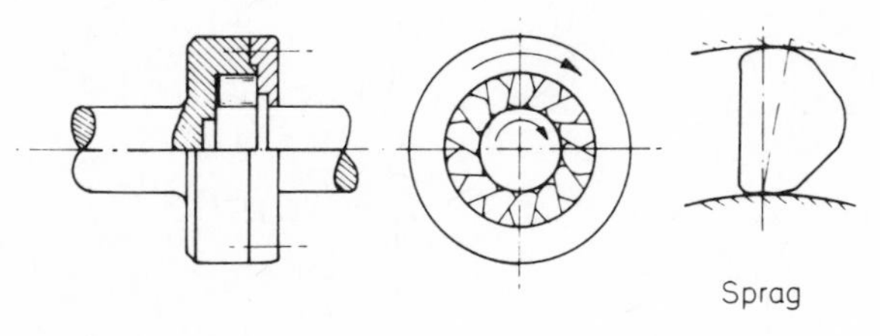

Figure 2.19 *Sprag clutch*

Centrifugal clutch A centrifugal clutch is used when the engagement of a prime mover with a load is to be achieved at a predetermined rotational speed. A typical design has spring-loaded weights mounted in radial slots in a member connected to the driving shaft.

The outer faces of the weights, which are faced with friction material, engage with the inner surface of a drum attached to the driven shaft at a speed which is determined by the tension on the springs (*see* Figure 2.8).

Dry powder clutch This is a type of centrifugal clutch in which metal particles, such as steel shot, are compacted under the action of the centrifugal force produced by rotation. The particles are contained in a hollow driving member in which a disk attached to the driven member rotates.

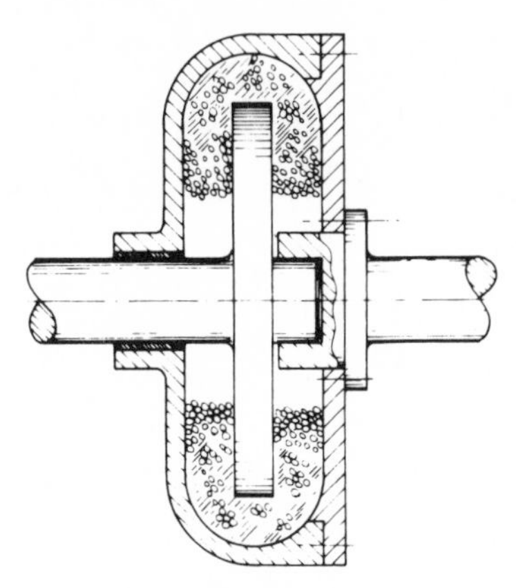

Figure 2.20 *Dry powder clutch*

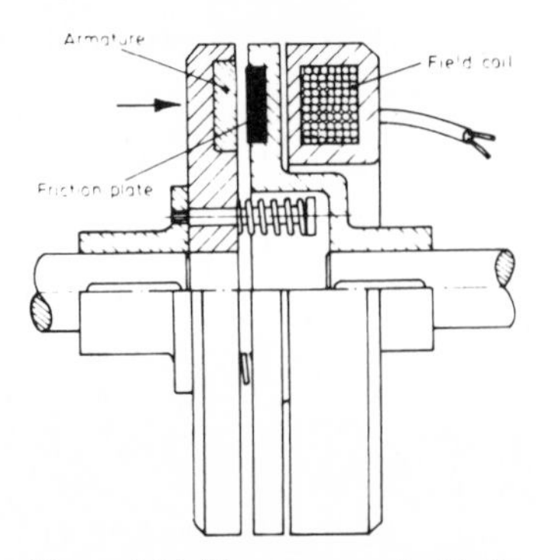

Figure 2.21 *Electromagnetic friction clutch*

Electromagnetic friction clutch In this clutch the output shaft carries a rotor with a friction facing. An armature in the form of a disk is driven by the input shaft and can move axially against springs. A field coil, which is either fixed or free to rotate with the output shaft, is energised to engage the clutch by producing a magnetic field which draws the rotor and armature together.

Fluid coupling (fluid flywheel) In a fluid coupling both input and output shafts carry impellers which have radial vanes. The vane spaces are filled with oil which circulates in the vanes when the coupling rotates. The input wheel acts as a pump and the output wheel as a turbine so that power is transmitted. There is always a loss of speed due to slip.

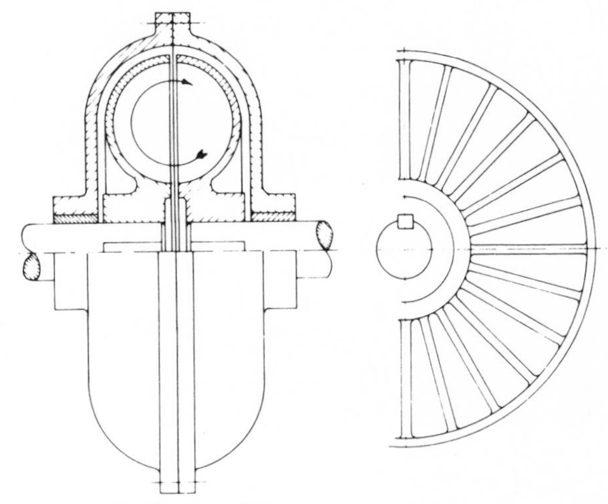

Figure 2.22 *Fluid coupling*

FRICTION MATERIALS FOR BRAKES AND CLUTCHES

Most brake and clutch linings are made of asbestos in a resin binder or rubber compound which will take a moderately high pressure. Powder metal on a steel backing is suitable for higher pressures and cork is used for light duty.

The coefficient of friction depends upon whether the lining is wet (with oil) or dry. Typical values are listed in Table 2.1.

Table 2.1

Material on Steel	*Coefficient of Friction*	
	Dry	*Wet*
Cork	0.3	0.1
Asbestos in rubber compound	0.3–0.4	0.1
Asbestos in resin binder	0.3–0.4	0.1
Powdered metal	0.2–0.4	0.05–0.08

2.2 SHAFT COUPLINGS

A shaft coupling is a device which is used to connect two shafts together either rigidly, or flexibly when misalignment may be present.

SOLID BOLTED FLANGED COUPLING

Flanges on the shafts are rigidly connected by bolts. The flanges may be keyed to the shafts or integral with them. The shafts must be accurately lined up. Location is achieved by means of a spigot on one flange which fits into a recess in the other, or by using fitted bolts.

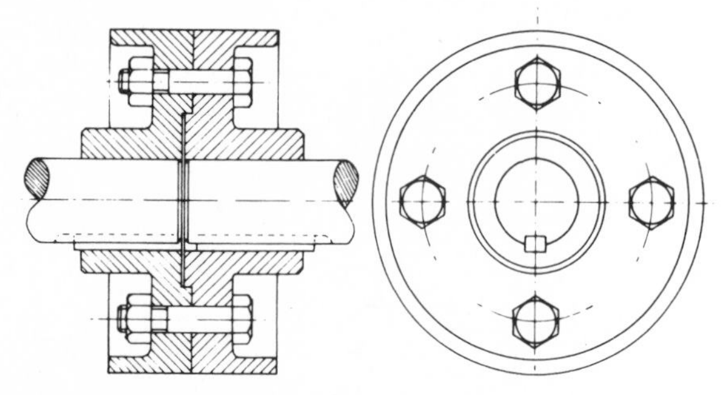

Figure 2.23 *Solid bolted flanged coupling*

MUFF COUPLING

Shafts may be rigidly connected by a muff coupling consisting of a sleeve halved longitudinally with one half keyed to both shafts. The halves of the sleeve are bolted together.

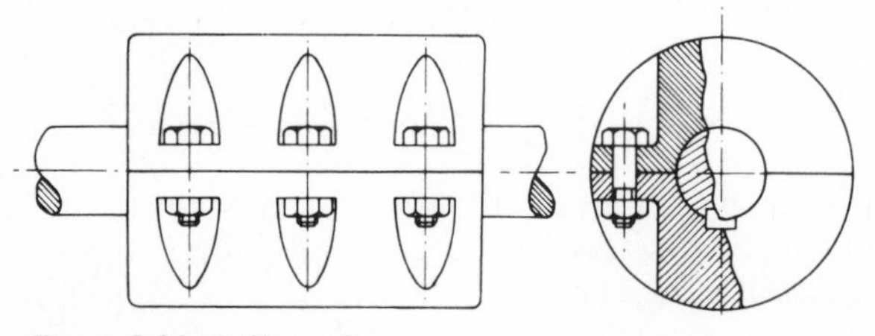

Figure 2.24 *Muff coupling*

COMPRESSION COUPLING

A split, double conical sleeve fits tightly over the shafts (which must have the same diameter) and is compressed onto the shafts by bolted flanges. The connection is made by friction between the sleeve and the shafts, and keys are unnecessary. This type of coupling can easily be dismantled without disturbing the shafts.

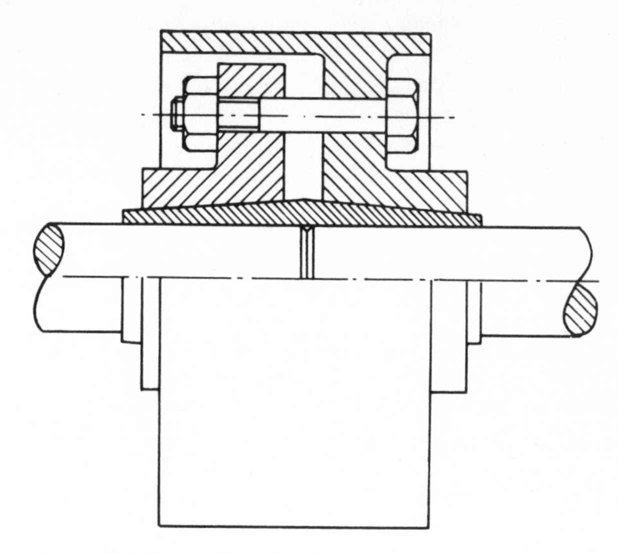

Figure 2.25 *Compression coupling*

CLAW COUPLING

Flanges keyed to the shafts have mating teeth cut on their faces which engage to give a drive.

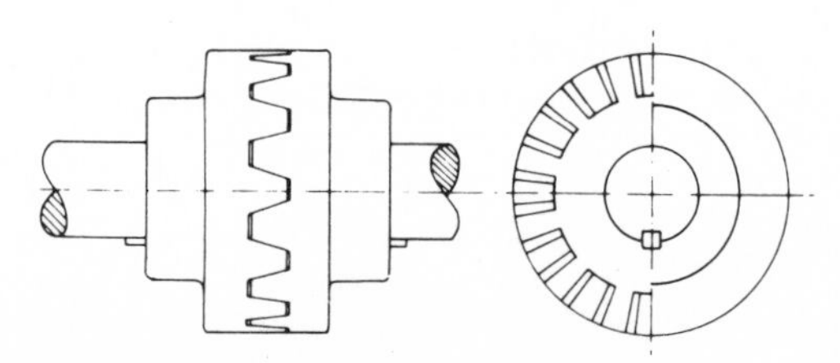

Figure 2.26 *Claw coupling*

SLEEVE COUPLING

This is a simple type of coupling consisting of a sleeve fitted over the two shafts and fastened to them by set screws or pins. It is used for light drives.

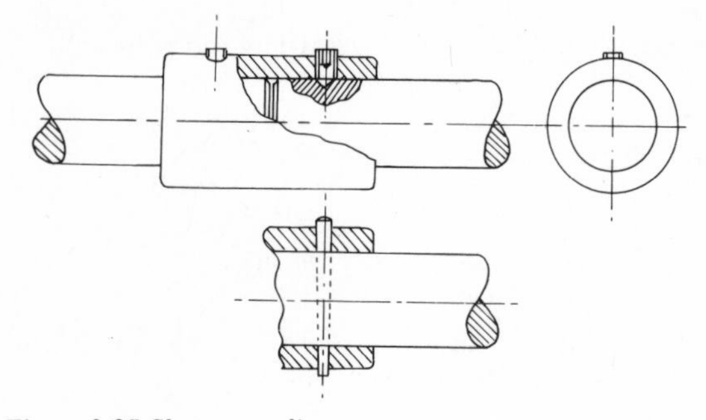

Figure 2.27 *Sleeve coupling*

FLEXIBLE SHAFT COUPLINGS

These couplings are designed to accommodate misalignment of shafts and also to help reduce torsional vibrations and absorb sudden torque variations.

Coupling design depends upon which of the following types of misalignment is present:–

Angular When the axes of the shafts are at an angle to one another

Parallel When the shafts are parallel but the axes are not coincident

Axial When the axes are coincident but there is relative axial movement.

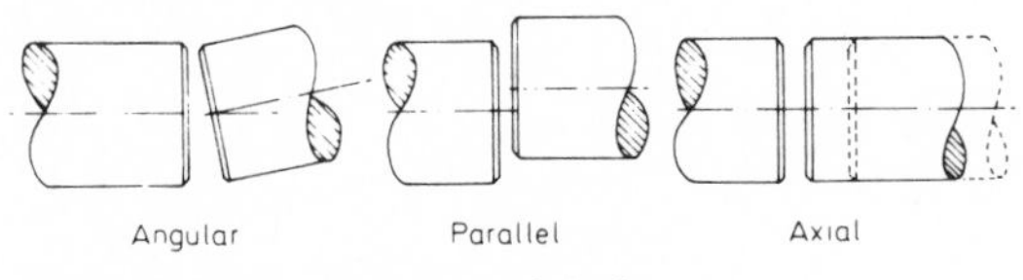

Figure 2.28 *Misalignments of shafts*

BONDED RUBBER COUPLING

A simple type of coupling for light loads in which steel sleeves, keyed to the shaft and locked with screws, are bonded to a rubber or synthetic rubber section.

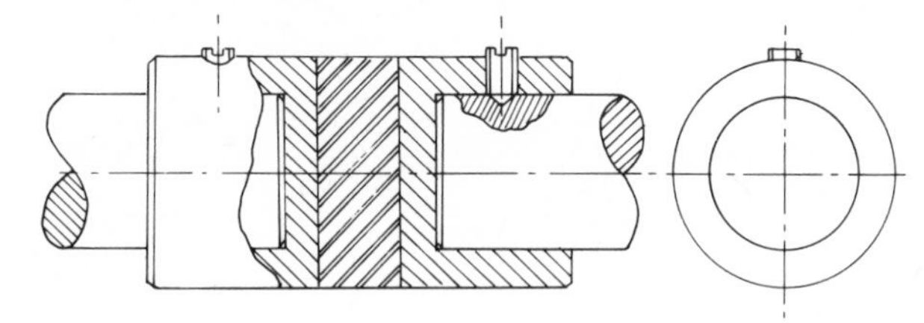

Figure 2.29 *Bonded rubber coupling*

RUBBER-BUSHED PIN-TYPE COUPLING

This is a bolted flange coupling where the bolts are rigidly attached to one flange but pass through rubber bushes set in the holes in the other flange. It is used mainly for angular misalignment.

DISK-TYPE FLEXIBLE COUPLING

A flanged coupling which has a rubber disk, bonded between two steel disks, bolted to the flanges through alternate holes.

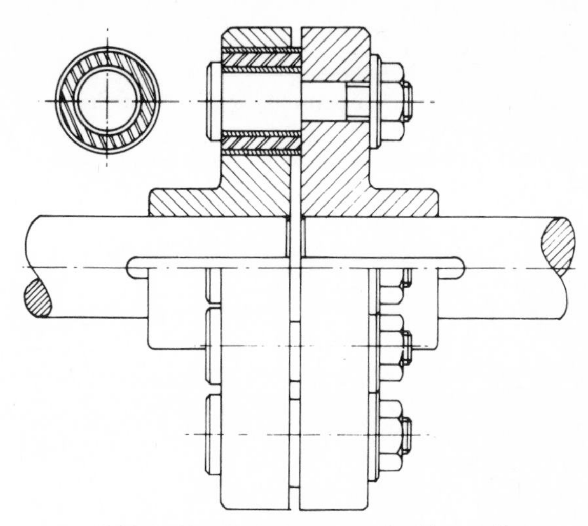

Figure 2.30 *Rubber-bushed pin-type flexible coupling*

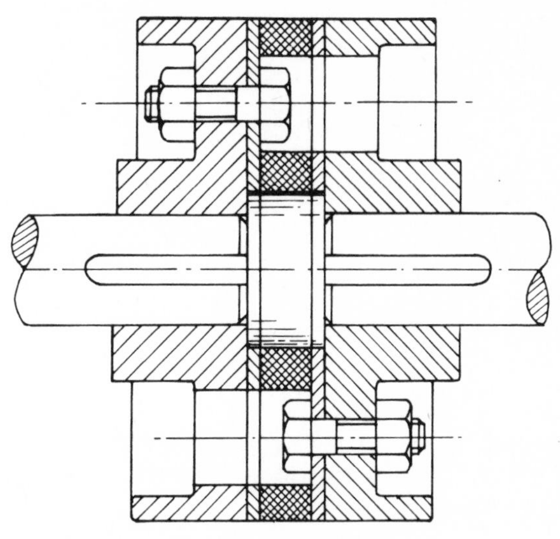

Figure 2.31 *Disk-type flexible coupling*

MOULDED RUBBER INSERT COUPLING

Flanges keyed to the shafts have projections which fit into moulded recesses in a rubber insert through which the drive is transmitted.

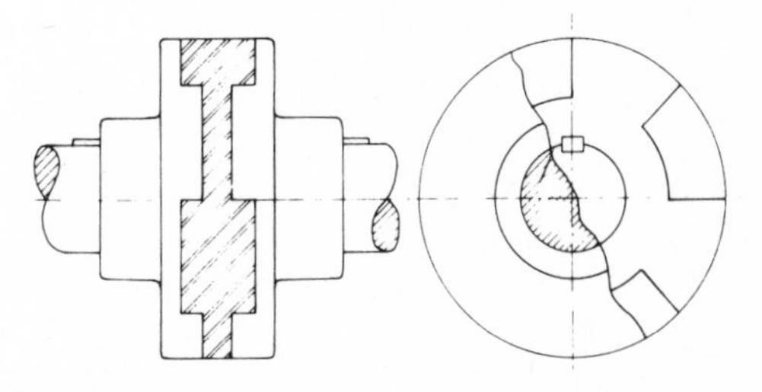

Figure 2.32 *Moulded rubber insert coupling*

RUBBER-TYRE-TYPE FLEXIBLE COUPLING

In this coupling the flanges on the shafts are connected by a rubber tyre clamped to each flange. The coupling, which is made under the names Fenaflex and Periflex, gives high flexibility and shock-absorbing capacity.

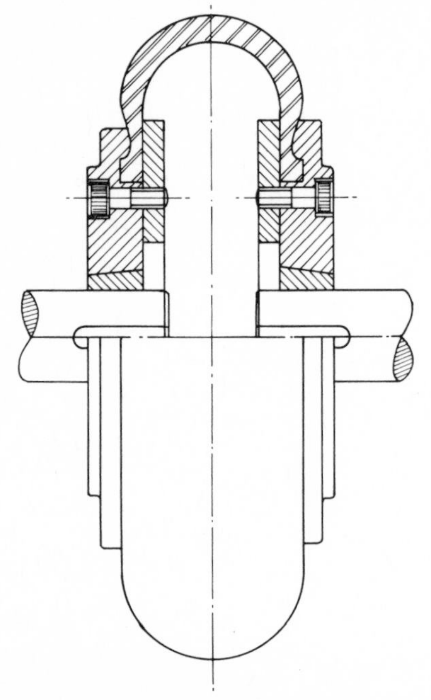

Figure 2.33 *Rubber-tyre-type flexible coupling*

GEAR COUPLING

Flanges keyed to the shafts have involute teeth cut on their periphery which engage with mating internal teeth at each end of a sleeve packed with lubricant.

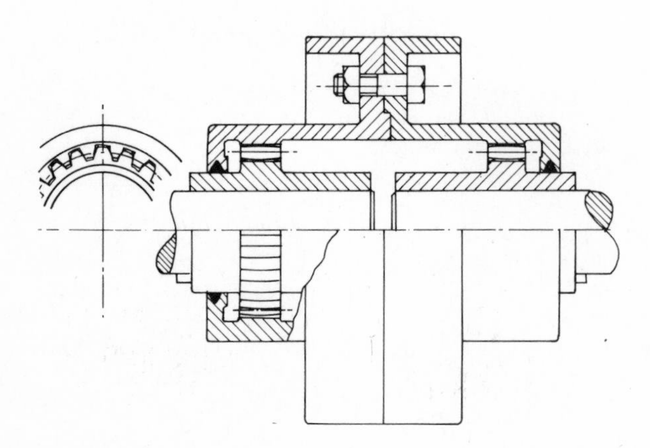

Figure 2.34 *Gear coupling*

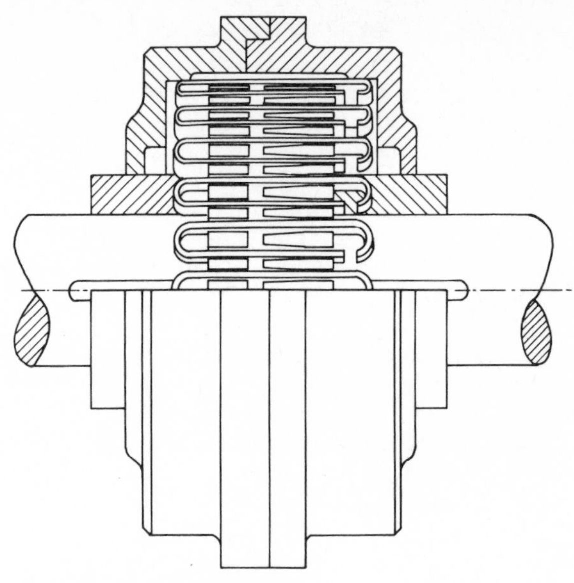

Figure 2.35 *Metal spring coupling*

Parallel and angular misalignment are accommodated but there is no torsional flexibility.

METAL SPRING COUPLING

Loops of spring steel, set in axial slots in the shaft flanges, transmit the drive and provide angular and torsional flexibility.

OLDHAM COUPLING

Steel flanges keyed to the shafts have diametral keys on their faces which mate with two corresponding slots set at right angles to one another on a disk between them. The disk is usually made of brass. This coupling is suitable for parallel misalignment only.

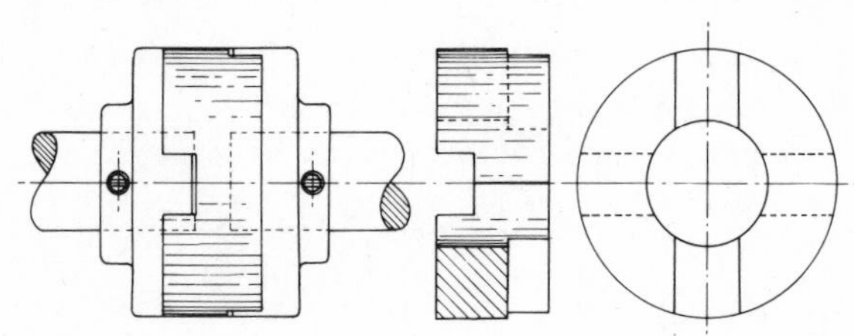

Figure 2.36 *Oldham coupling*

METAFLEX COUPLING

This is a flexible coupling in which the shaft flanges are connected through sets of thin steel laminations which provide longitudinal and angular flexibility but not flexibility in torsion. Parallel misalignment can be accommodated if two sets of laminations are used.

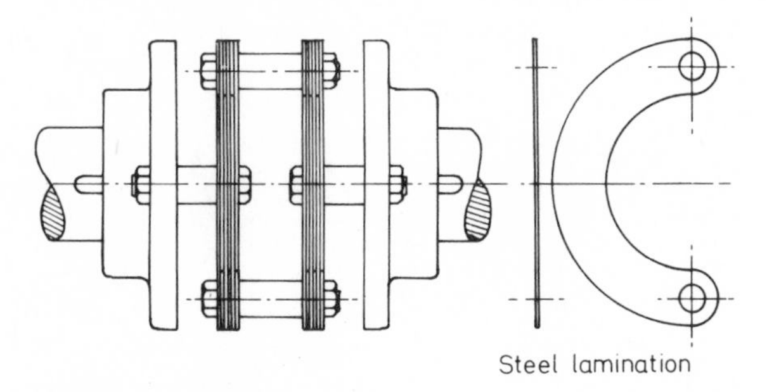

Figure 2.37 *Metaflex coupling*

HOOKE'S-TYPE UNIVERSAL JOINT

This joint provides a coupling which will accept up to about 20° of angular misalignment. It consists of a fork on each shaft joined by a cross-piece with bearings. Two joints, one at each end of a shaft, will accommodate a large parallel misalignment.

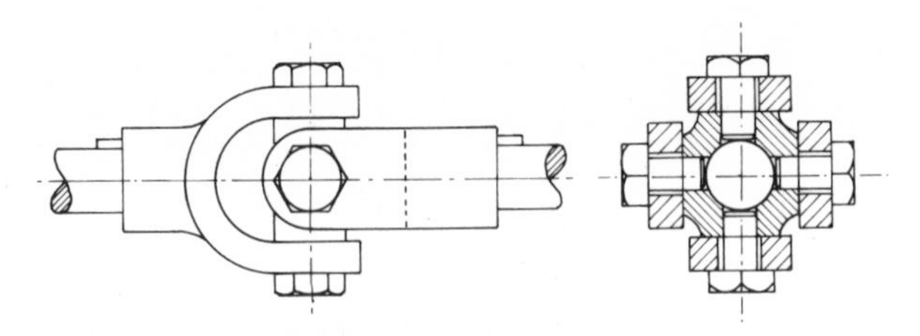

Figure 2.38 *Hooke's-type universal joint*

CONSTANT-VELOCITY UNIVERSAL JOINT

The Hooke's joint suffers from the disadvantage of speed fluctuations which increase with angular misalignment. Constant-velocity joints, of which there are several types, overcome this problem. In the type shown the inner and outer races have circular arc grooves which are curved and in line with the shaft axis. A ball in each groove transmits the drive and allows angular misalignment of the shafts.

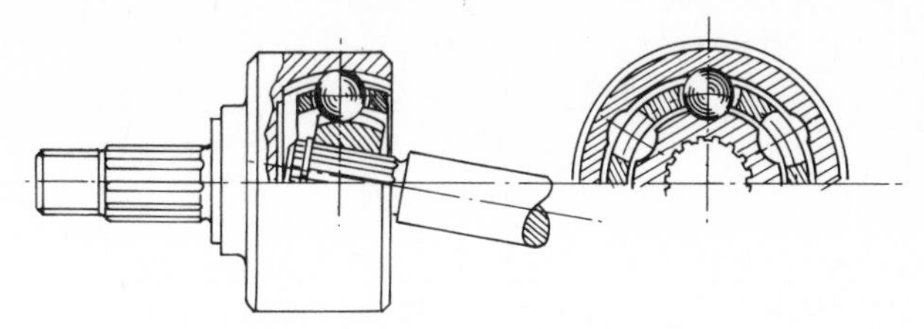

Figure 2.39 *Constant-velocity universal joint*

AUTOMOBILE-TYPE UNIVERSAL JOINT

This is a development of the Hooke's joint which is used in pairs to transmit power to the road wheels of vehicles. The bearings have needle rollers and the forks are mounted on splined shafts to allow for changes in length between joints.

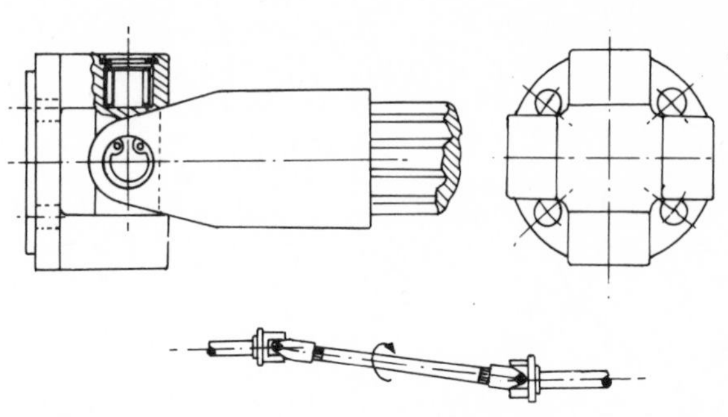

Figure 2.40 *Automobile-type universal joint*

CHAIN COUPLING

The flanges are provided with sprockets which take a ring of duplex (or double) roller chain which connects the flanges. A rubber cover is usually fitted.

This coupling has only a slight amount of flexibility.

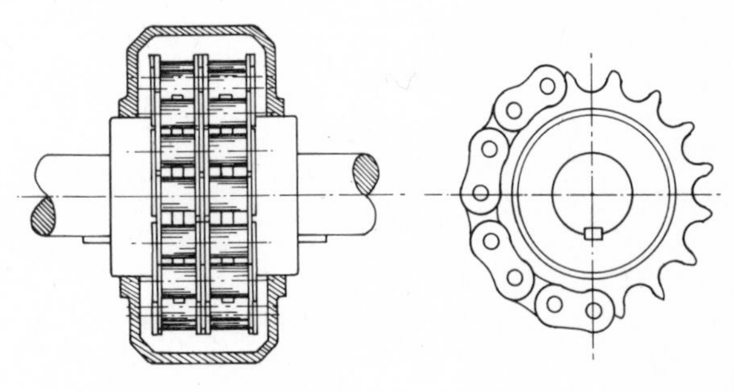

Figure 2.41 *Chain coupling*

2.3 BELT, ROPE AND CHAIN DRIVES

BELT DRIVE

A belt drive is used to transmit rotation from one shaft to another by means of a flexible belt running on pulleys on the shafts. The belt is usually flat or of V section, and it is tensioned to prevent slipping. In general, the pulleys have different diameters so that either an increase or a decrease in speed is obtainable.

FLAT BELT DRIVE

Flat belts are made of leather, reinforced rubber, impregnated canvas or woven fabric and belt speeds of 30 m/sec are possible. To prevent the belt from slipping sideways off the pulley, the latter may be cambered or have flanges. A flat belt may be twisted to give a drive through a right angle or a reversal of the direction or rotation.

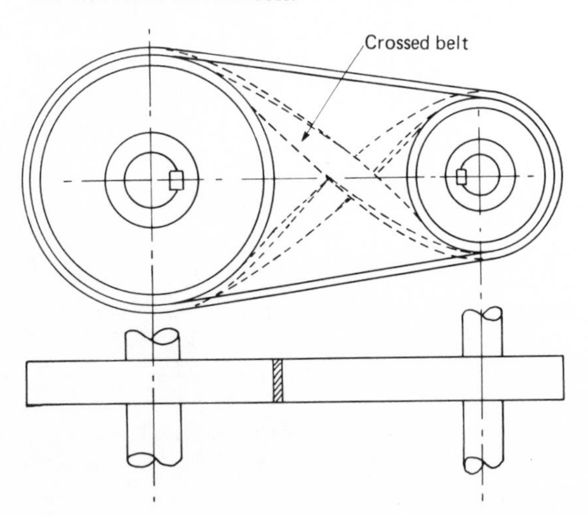

Figure 2.42 *Flat belt drive*

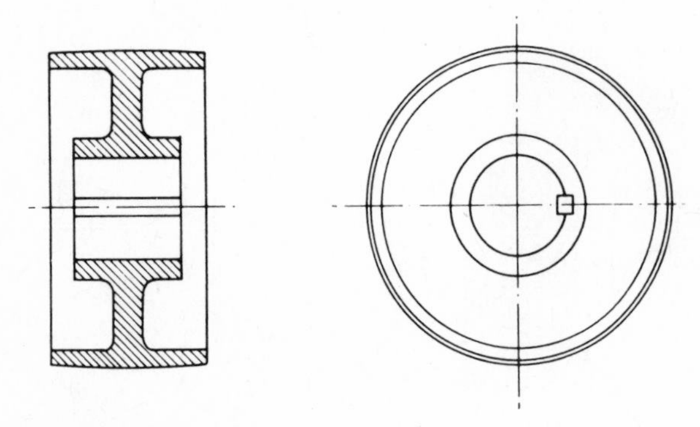

Figure 2.43 *Cast pulley for flat belts*

STEPPED PULLEY DRIVE

Stepped pulleys are used in pairs to provide a selection of speed ratios. In effect, each of the two pulleys consists of several pulleys of different diameters joined together, with the two pulleys being mounted in opposite ways on the shafts. The speed ratio can be changed while running.

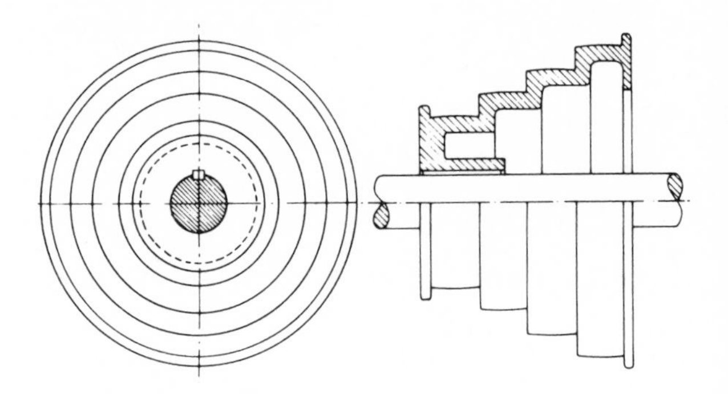

Figure 2.44 *Stepped pulley (flat belt) drive*

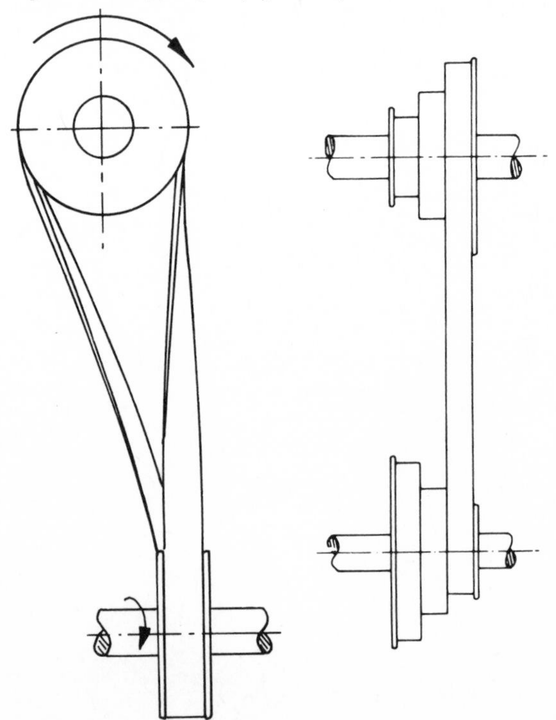

Figure 2.45 *Crossed belt drive (left), and stepped pulley drive*

V BELT DRIVE

A V belt has certain advantages over the flat belt. It is more compact than the flat belt and because of its wedge action it can transmit about three times the power for the same belt strength. It has a tapered cross-section with an angle of about 40° and this fits into a groove of the same shape in the rim of the pulley. V belts are made of rubber in which are embedded nylon cords encased in rubber-impregnated woven cotton. They are used for electric motor drives, automobile fan belts, etc.

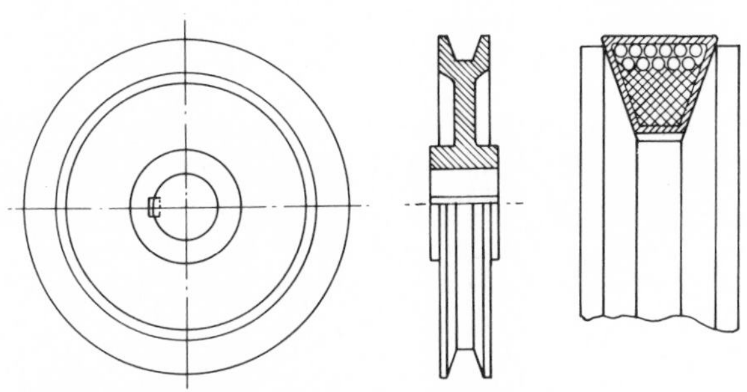

Figure 2.46 *V pulley and section through V belt*

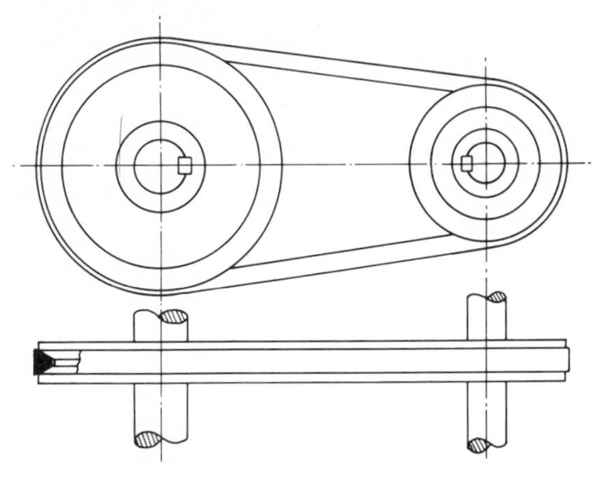

Figure 2.47 *V belt drive*

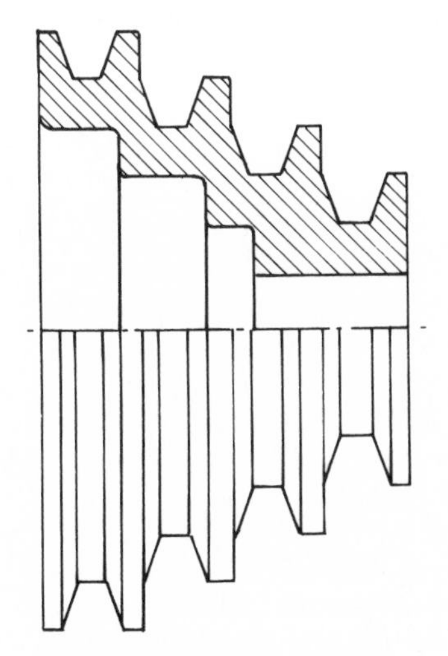

Figure 2.48 *Stepped V pulley*

Stepped V belt drive Stepped V pulleys are available to permit speed selection, but to allow alteration of the belt position the drive must be stopped.

Multiple V belt drive To permit higher powers to be transmitted the multiple V belt drive is used. In this type each pulley has several grooves of the same diameter with a belt in each groove, and this variation is safer in the event of belt failure.

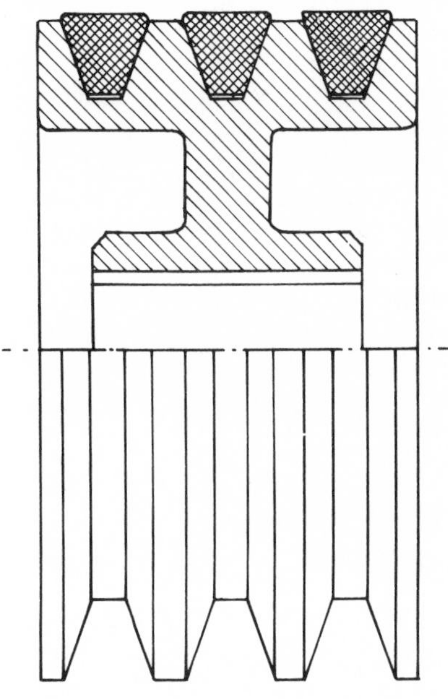

Figure 2.49 *Multiple V pulley*

Ribbed belt drive This is an alternative to the multiple V belt in which a single belt with longitudinal triangular cross-section ribs is employed.

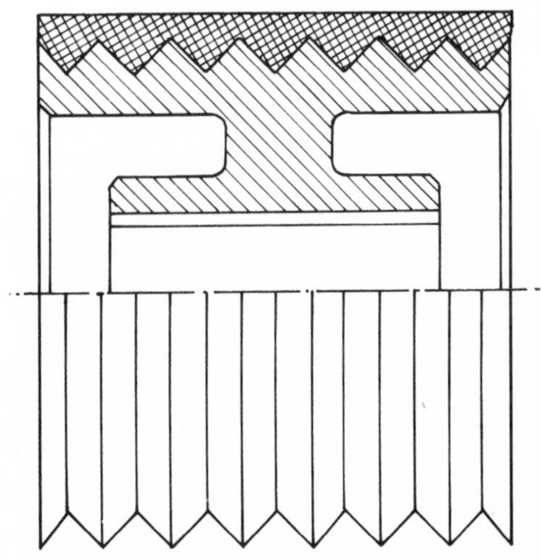

Figure 2.50 *Ribbed belt drive*

VARIABLE SPEED BELT DRIVE

This is a parallel belt drive in which the speed ratio can be altered while running by changing the effective diameters of the pulleys. Each shaft carries two coned pulleys with the narrow ends of the cones facing one another. One cone of each pulley slides on keys on the shaft and a wide V belt connects the pulleys. The speed is varied by moving one pair of cones closer together and the other pair further apart, or vice versa. The pulleys may be grooved to prevent possible slip.

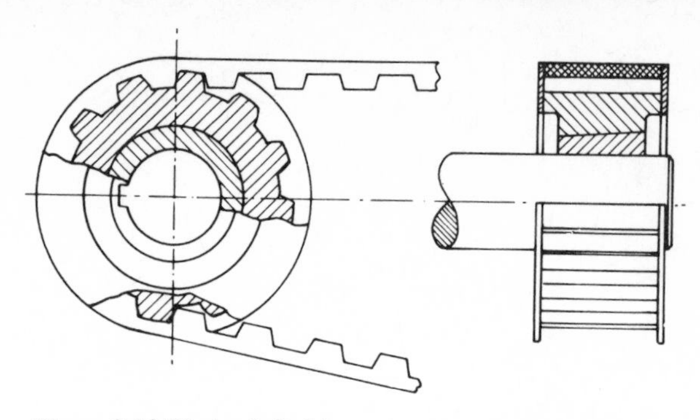

Figure 2.52 *Timing belt drive*

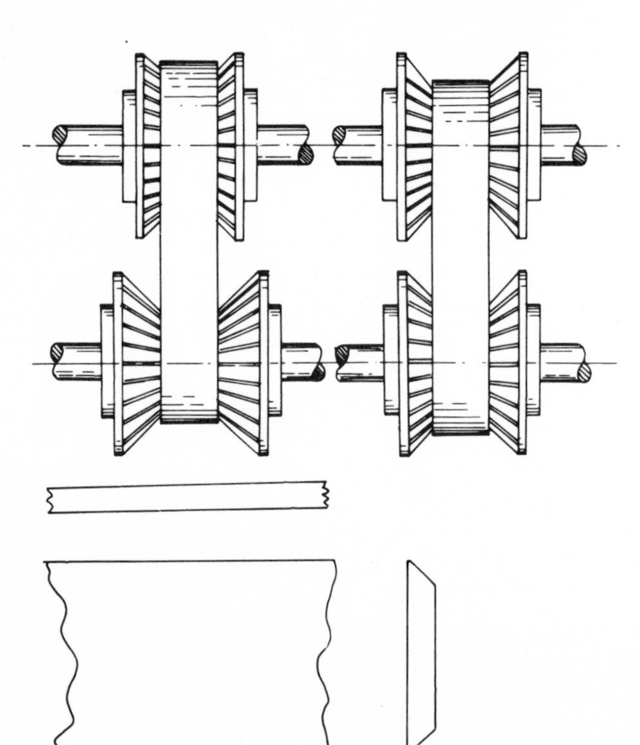

Figure 2.51 *Variable-speed belt drive and belt*

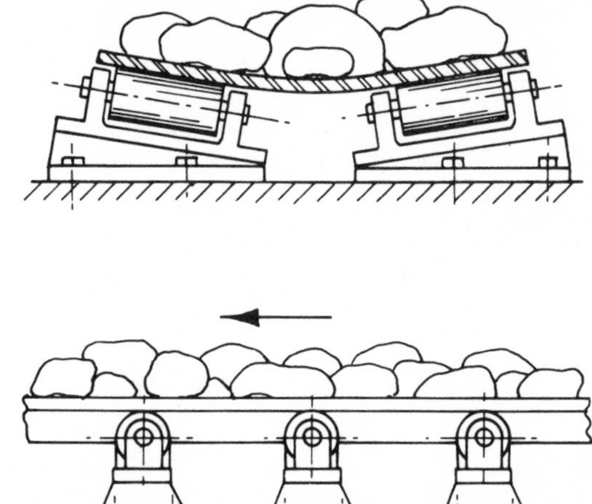

Figure 2.53 *Belt conveyor*

TIMING BELT DRIVE

A timing belt has transverse teeth on the inside surface which mate with grooves on the pulleys. The belt has steel wire reinforcement which enables it to transmit about three times the power at three times the speed of a conventional belt. There is no slip and exact speed ratios are maintained.

BELT CONVEYOR

This is a device for transporting loose material and machine parts using a wide flat belt running on rollers.

ROPE DRIVE

Rope drives are used extensively for lifting and transporting gear. Manilla rope is satisfactory for relatively light loads but steel wire rope is used for heavy loads.

Pulleys have V grooves with a large radius at the bottom of the groove, and the large diameter of the pulleys limits bending stress in the wire. Wire rope is made of several strands, each consisting of a number of smaller wires twisted about a core of hemp saturated with lubricant.

Ropes are used in lifts, hoists and earth-moving machines, etc. One application is in a *block-and-tackle* hoist in which the rope is passed around the pulleys in two *sheaves* one of which is attached to a fixed point and the other carrying a hook for the load. Each sheave has two or more pulleys running freely on the same shaft, and a load several times the pull on the rope can be lifted with this equipment.

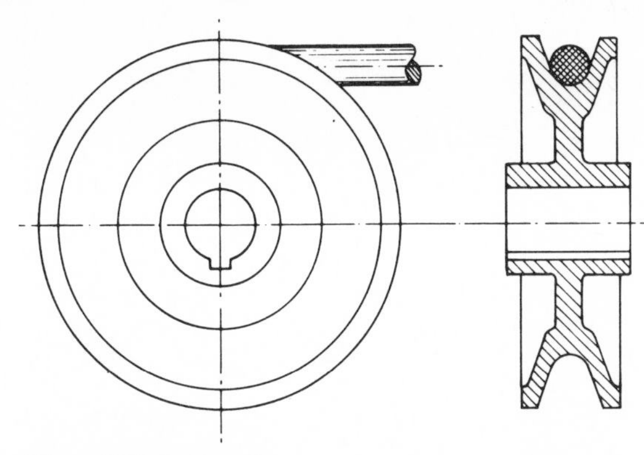

Figure 2.54 *Rope pulley*

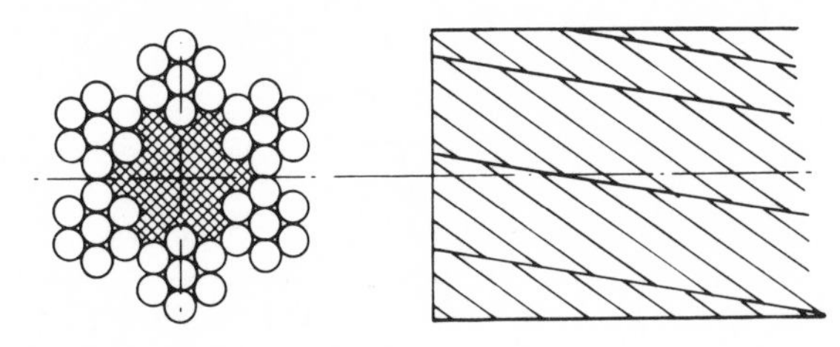

Figure 2.55 *6 x 7 wire rope*

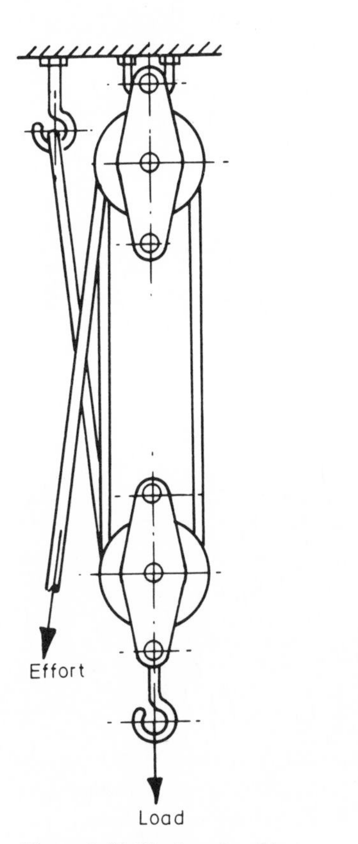

Figure 2.56 *Block-and-tackle*

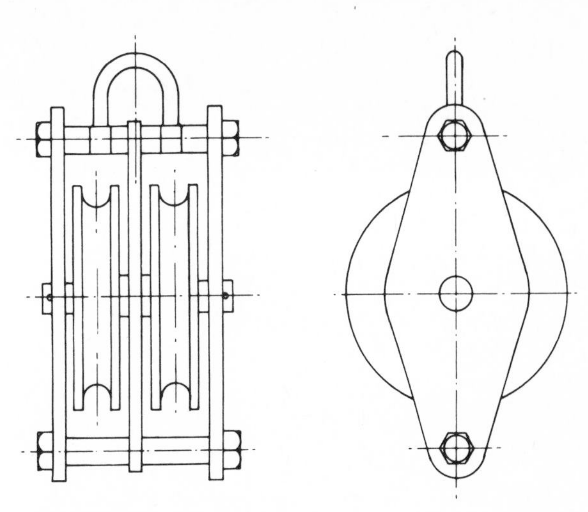

Figure 2.57 *Two-pulley sheave*

CHAIN DRIVE

A chain drive consists of a continuous series of links which engage with teeth on pulleys attached to parallel shafts. This type of drive has no slip and it will transmit much more power than belt drives.

The most common type is the *roller chain drive* as used on bicycles. This has hardened steel rollers, joined by links, which engage with toothed wheels called *sprockets*. Higher powers can be transmitted by using double or treble chains known as 'duplex' and 'triplex' chains.

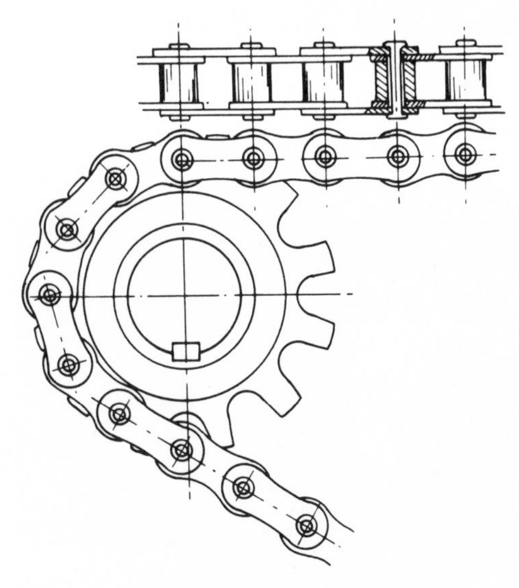

Figure 2.58 *Roller chain and sprocket drive*

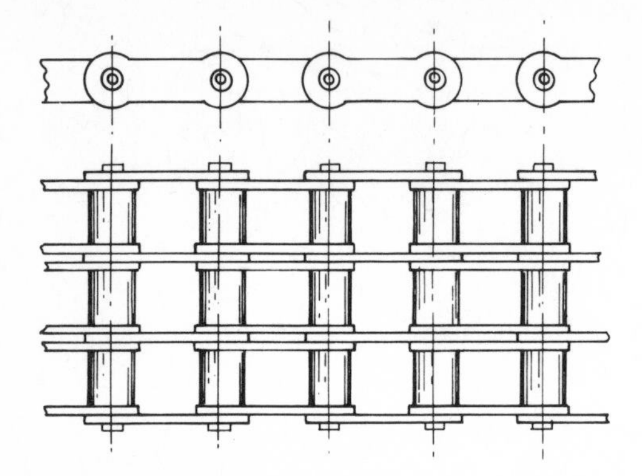

Figure 2.59 *Triplex roller chain*

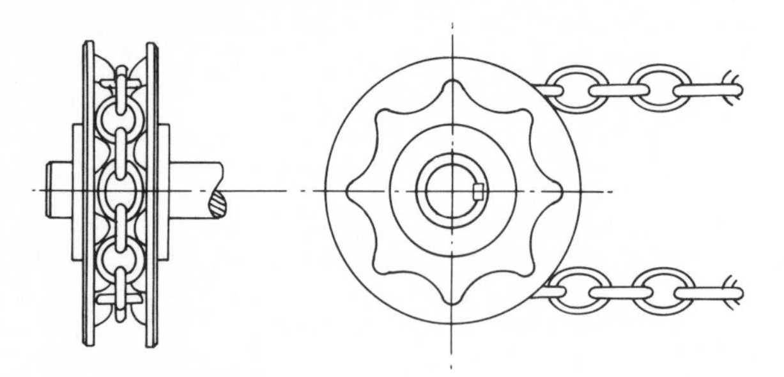

Figure 2.60 *Chain drive*

For large centre distances it is often necessary to use a tensioner to take up the slack in the chain. This tensioner consists of a free-running sprocket on a spring-loaded lever.

Another type of drive uses malleable iron links of rectangular shape which can easily be connected or disconnected when required. Known as *link belt chains* they are suitable only for low speed drives such as, for example, on agricultural machinery.

For low power drives a *bead chain* may be used. This chain has beads spaced on a wire which engage with recesses in the pulleys and it can be used for non-parallel shafts.

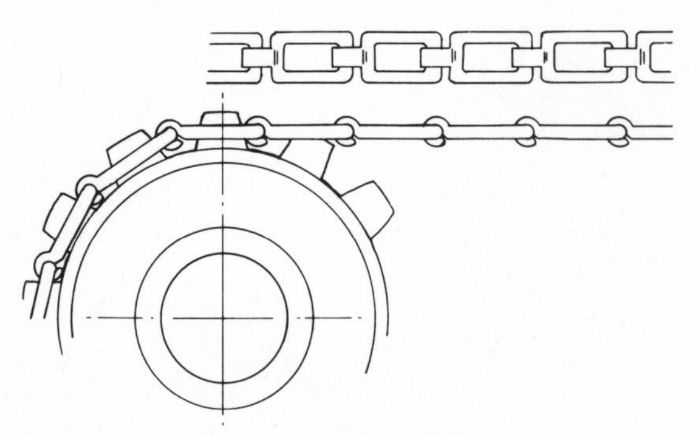

Figure 2.61 *Link belt chain drive (malleable iron)*

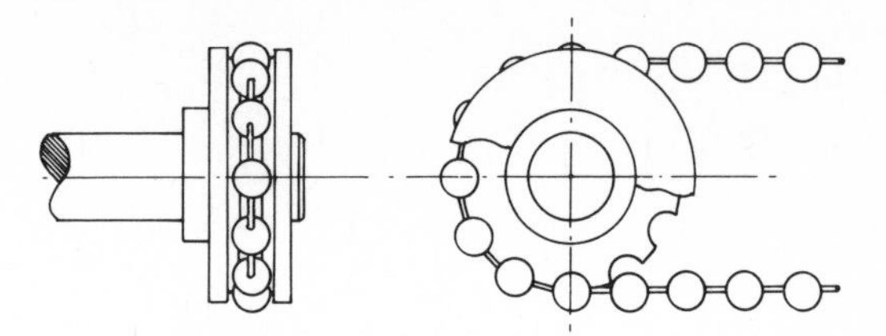

Figure 2.62 *Bead chain drive*

2.4 MECHANISMS

LEVERS

A lever is a rigid beam pivoted at a point known as the 'fulcrum', with a 'load' at another point and an 'effort' applied at a third point which balances the load. The fulcrum and the points at which the load and effort are applied have pin joints. Levers used as machine components can be of rectangular, elliptical, I-section, etc.

Levers may be of the first, second or third order: A *first order lever* has the fulcrum between the load and the effort; the *second order lever* has the load between the effort and the fulcrum; the *third order lever* has the effort between the load and the fulcrum.

The *bell crank lever* has the fulcrum at the junction of two arms which are at an angle to one another.

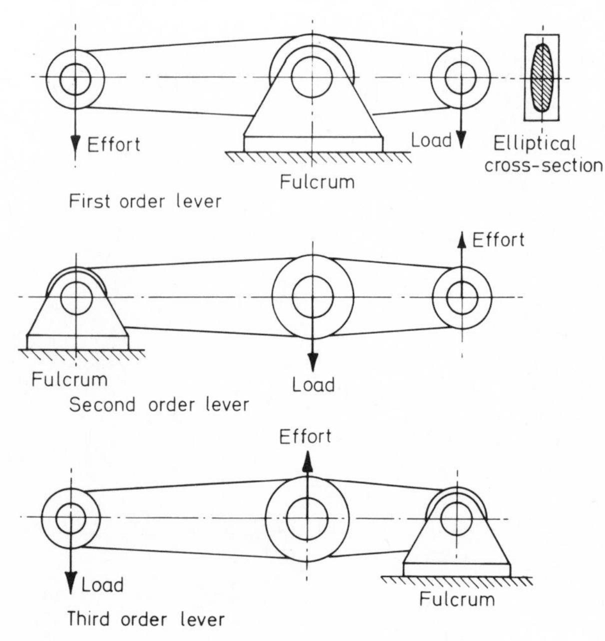

Figure 2.63 *Orders of levers*

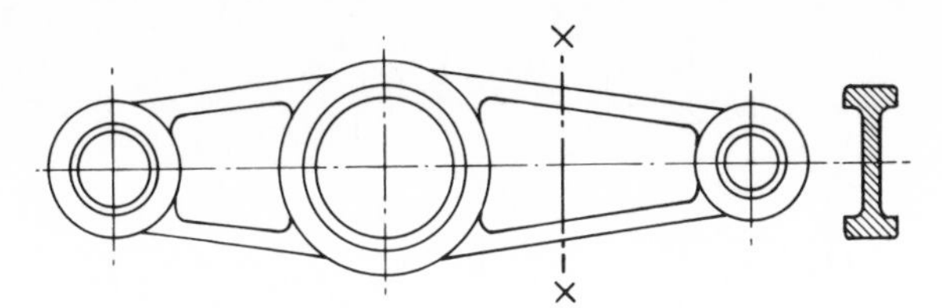

Figure 2.64 *I-section lever*

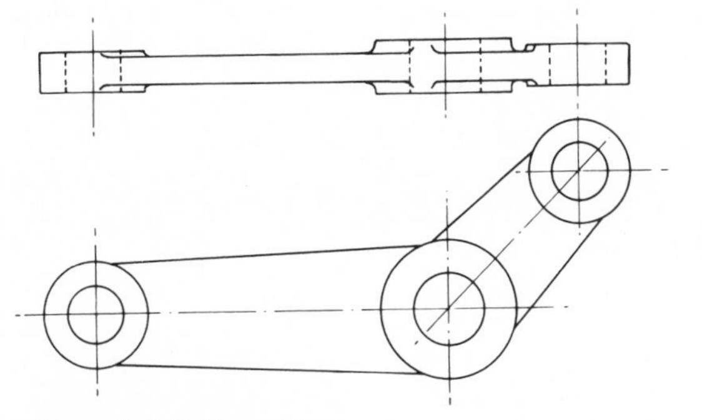

Figure 2.65 *Bell crank lever*

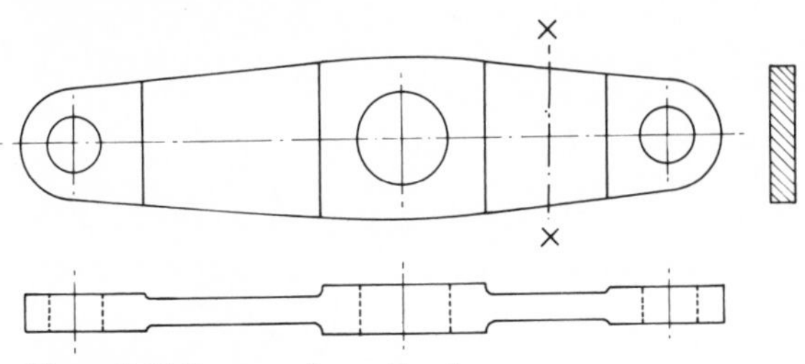

Figure 2.66 *Rectangular-section lever*

LINKAGES

Linkages are combinations of levers, rods and cranks which convert one type of motion into another, e.g. rotary to reciprocating.

Four-bar chain This consists of four links connected at their ends by pins in the form of a trapezium. One of the links may be made to rotate continuously and another link is usually part of a machine frame. The rotating link is called a *crank*.

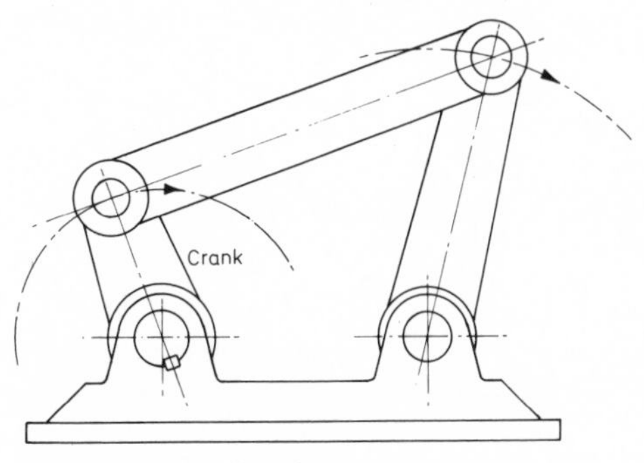

Figure 2.67 *Four-bar chain*

Crank-slider mechanism In this mechanism a link known as a *connecting rod* is connected at one end to a rotating crank and at the other end to a sliding block, or *slider*. As the crank rotates the slider moves with reciprocating motion. This mechanism is used in the IC engine.

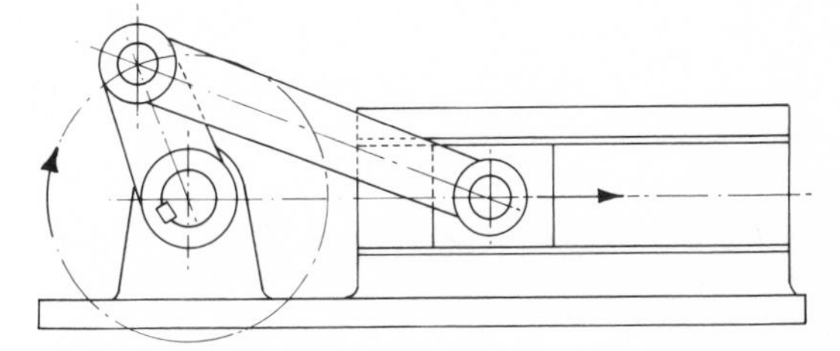

Figure 2.68 *Crank-slider mechanism*

Eccentric-crank and slider mechanism An eccentric is a crank-slider mechanism in which the crank and crank pin are replaced by an eccentric circular disk mounted on the shaft.

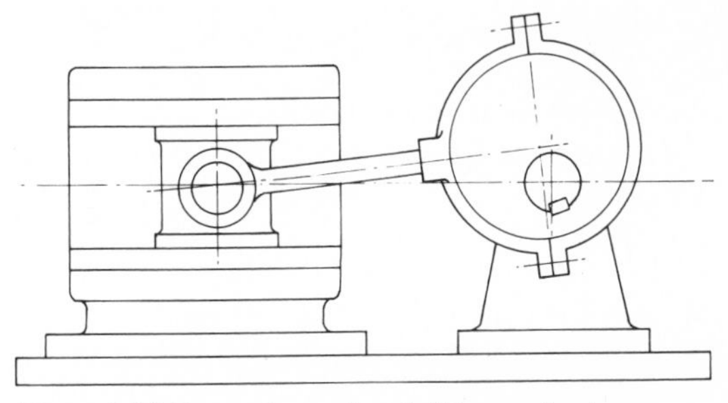

Figure 2.69 *Eccentric-crank and slider mechanism*

Parallel motion mechanism This is a four-bar chain in which opposite links are of equal length, and two opposite links rotate in the same direction. The pantograph uses a parallel linkage for the purpose of reproducing a motion to a different scale as, for example, in the scaling-up of drawings.

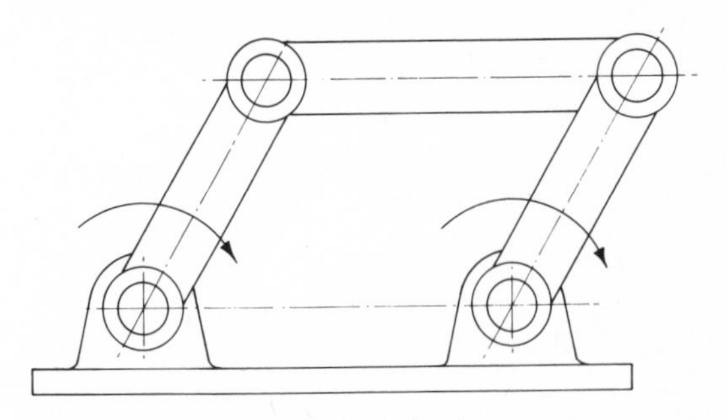

Figure 2.70 *Parallel motion mechanism*

Ratchet mechanism A ratchet mechanism produces an intermittent motion from a reciprocating or oscillating motion. It is useful for indexing in machine tools. The ratchet may be driven by a crank and connecting rod, as shown.

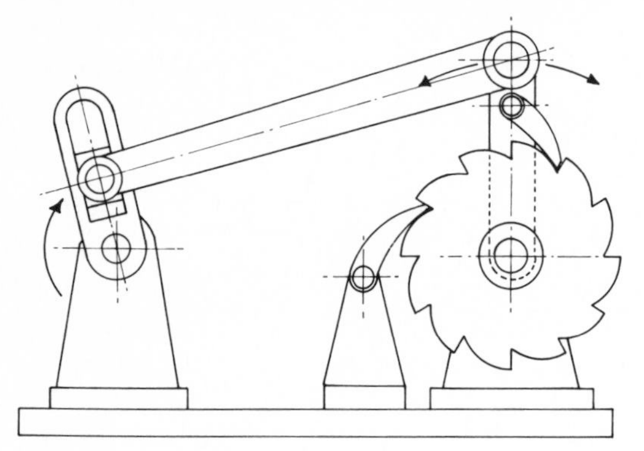

Figure 2.71 *Ratchet mechanism*

Quick-return mechanism (oscillating-crank mechanism) In this mechanism the end of a rotating crank is attached to a block which slides in an oscillating link which in turn moves a reciprocating bar. The motion of the bar is more rapid in one direction than in the other.

This motion is used in machine tools, such as a shaper, where the cutting stroke of a tool is required to be slower than the return stroke.

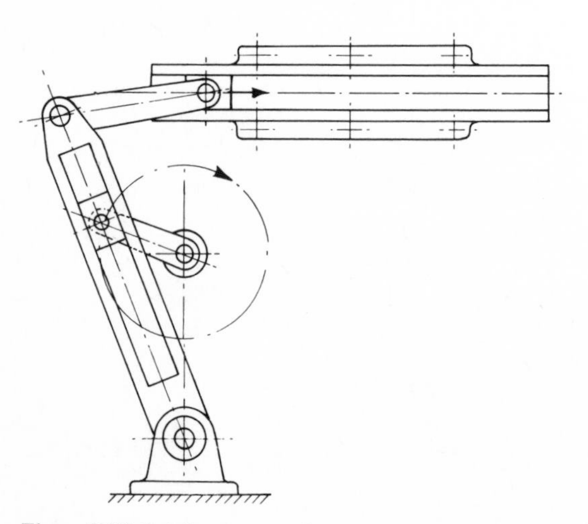

Figure 2.72 *Quick-return mechanism*

Scotch yoke mechanism A scotch yoke consists of a crank pin which slides in a slot in a crosshead attached to a reciprocating rod. The slot is at right angles to the rod. Uniform rotation of the crank produces simple harmonic motion in the rod.

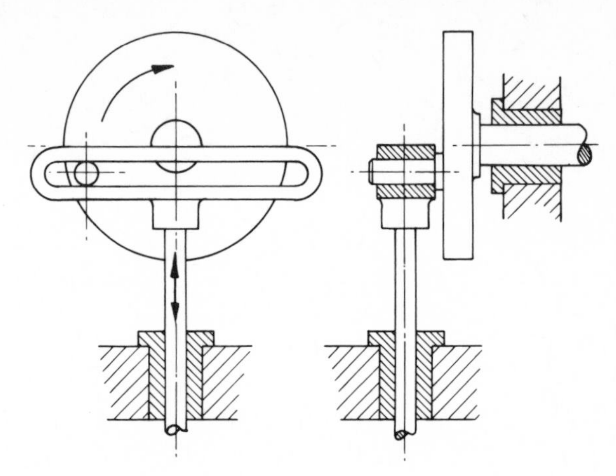

Figure 2.73 *Scotch yoke*

Geneva wheel mechanism In the Geneva wheel mechanism a rotating crank pin engages with radial slots in a disk attached to a parallel shaft to give an intermittent and opposite rotation in the second shaft. The mechanism is used in machine tools where an intermittent action is required.

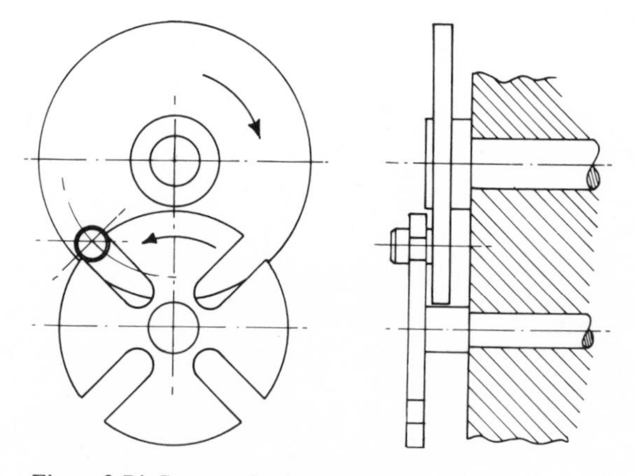

Figure 2.74 *Geneva wheel mechanism*

GOVERNORS

Governors are devices for controlling the flow of steam, gas, air or water to engines, turbines, etc., by maintaining constant speed under varying load.

Centrifugal dead-weight governor In this type of governor, weights on pivoted arm rotate and fly outwards under centrifugal force, the restoring force being the gravitational force on the weights. The movement of the weights operates the valve control.

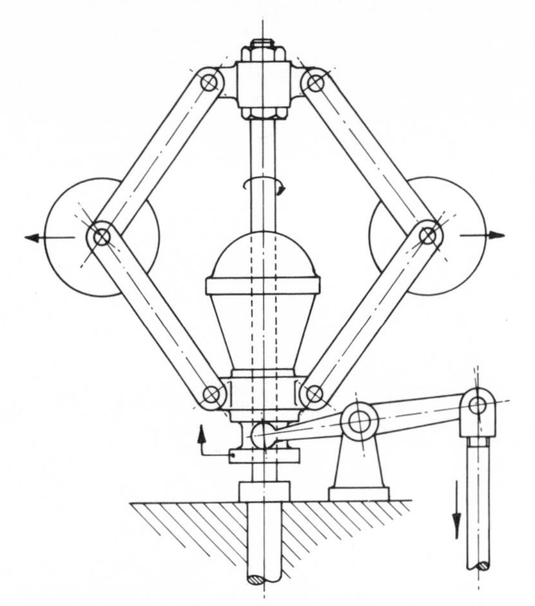

Figure 2.75 *Centrifugal dead-weight governor*

Hartnell governor (spring-loaded) In the type known as the Hartnell governor, the weights are attached to a spring which provides the restoring force. The spring force may be adjusted to control the speed at which the governor operates.

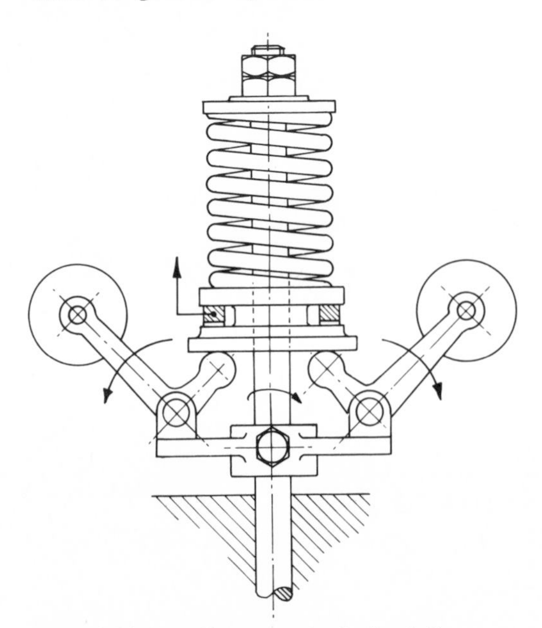

Figure 2.76 *Hartnell governor (spring-loaded)*

JACKS

Jacks are devices using levers, gears or hydraulic intensifiers to provide a large lifting force from a small manual effort.

Screw jack This has a nut rotated by bevel gears when these are turned by a handle. The nut moves a vertical screw supporting the load.

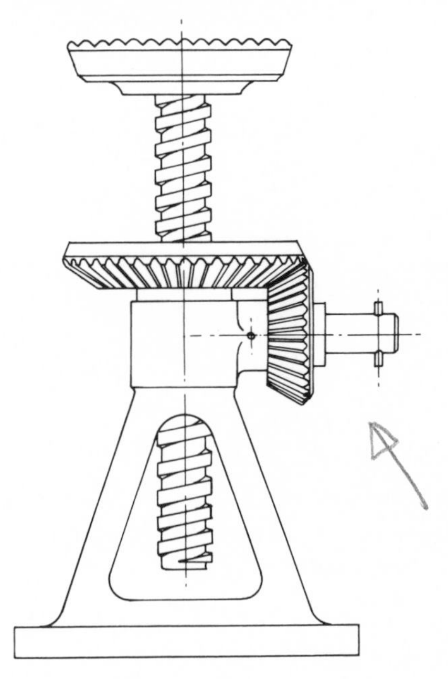

Figure 2.77 *Screw jack*

Hydraulic jack In a hydraulic jack a hand-operated lever connected to a pump with a small diameter plunger supplies oil to a large diameter ram which lifts the load. The load is proportional to the ratio of the piston areas and the handle leverage.

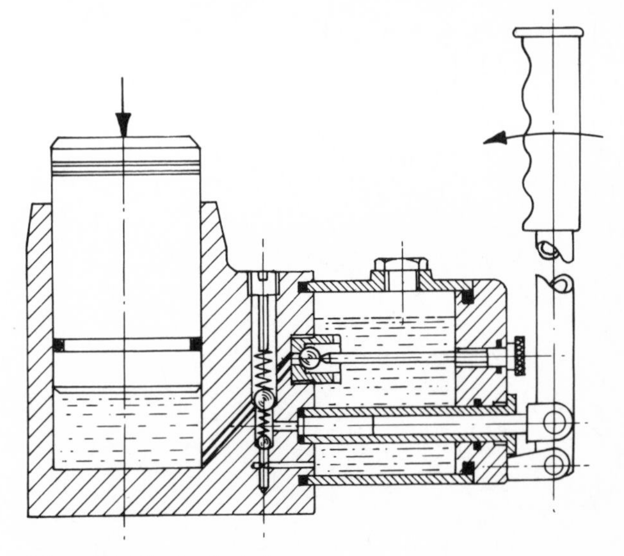

Figure 2.78 *Hydraulic jack*

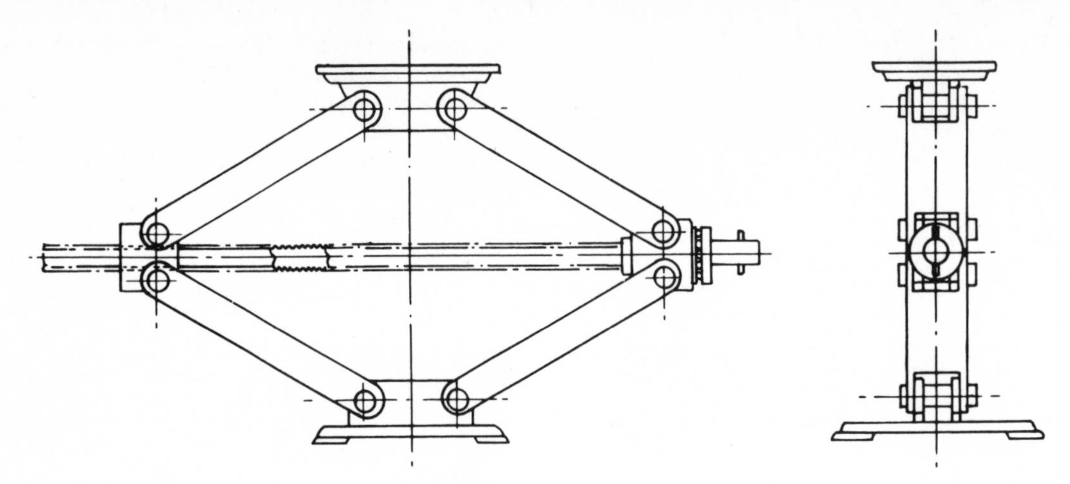

Figure 2.79 *Scissors jack*

Scissors jack A scissors jack uses a screw and nut in combination with links. Four links are arranged in the form of a parallelogram with a screw connecting two opposite corners. The other two corners are attached to the base and load-application points respectively. Turning the screw brings the first two corners together and moves apart the base and load points, thus lifting the load.

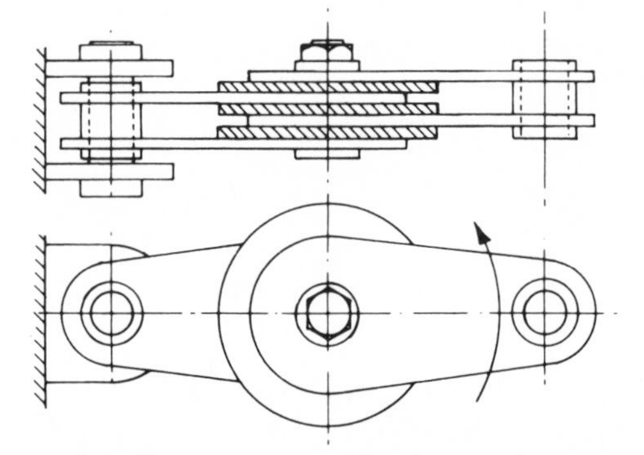

Figure 2.80 *Mechanical friction damper*

SHOCK ABSORBERS

These are devices installed between a machine and its mountings to damp out any undesirable vibrations or shock loads. They utilise mechanical or fluid friction to absorb the power.

Mechanical friction damper This has friction disks clamped between two elements which have relative motion.

Hydraulic shock absorber This has a piston inside a cylinder which forces oil through a small hole or valve orifice to provide resistance to the motion and hence retard it.

Two types are used on automobiles: the older type which has a piston connected to a lever; the telescopic type in which one tube slides inside another.

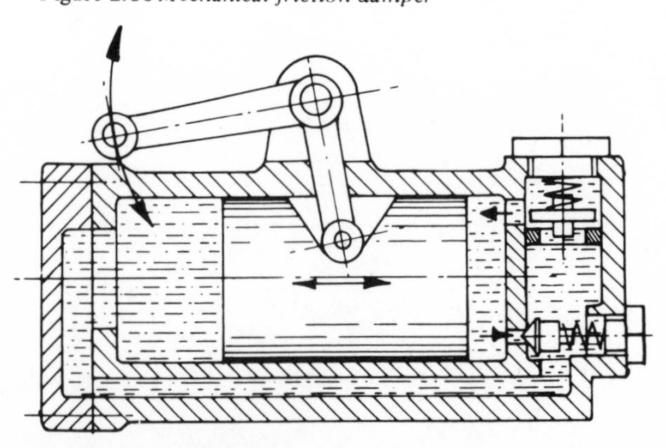

Figure 2.81 *Hydraulic shock absorber*

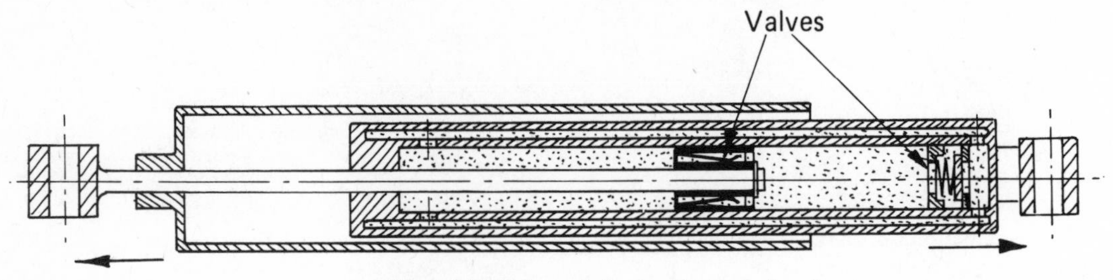

Figure 2.82 *Telescopic hydraulic shock absorber*

STEERING MECHANISMS

These are mechanisms between the steering wheel of a vehicle and the steering linkage connected to the road wheels.

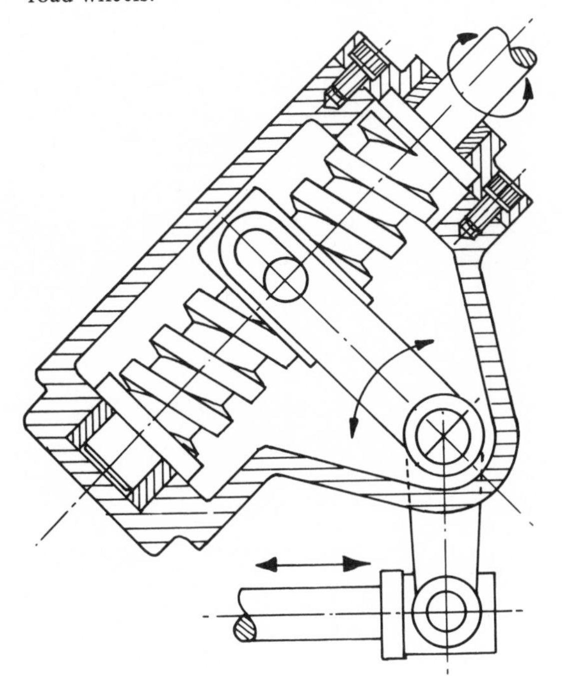

Figure 2.83 *Screw-and-nut steering*

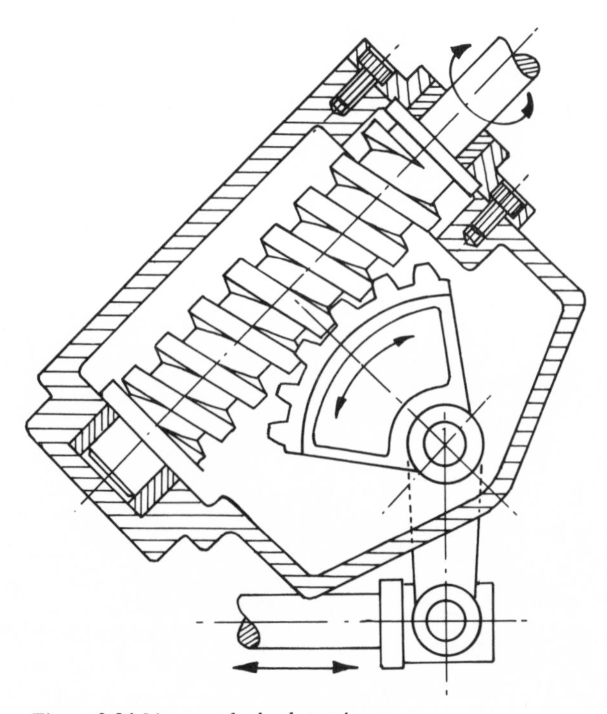

Figure 2.84 *Worm-and-wheel steering*

Screw-and-nut steering A square-threaded nut connected to the steering linkage is driven by a mating screw on the steering column.

Worm-and-wheel steering This has a worm on the steering column which engages with a toothed quadrant which has a lever connected to the steering rod.

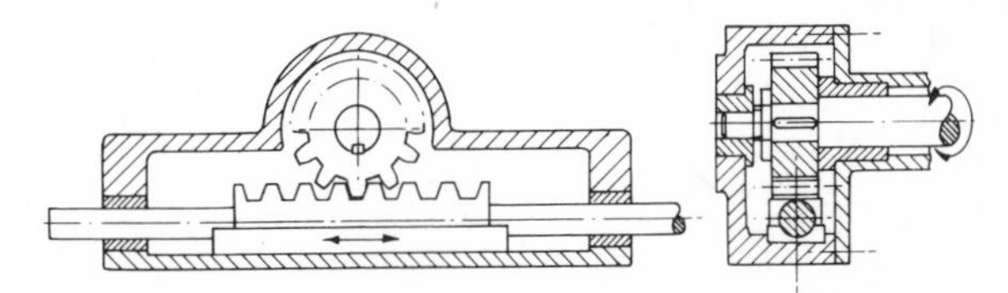

Figure 2.85 *Rack-and-pinion steering*

Rack-and-pinion steering A small gear or pinion on the steering column drives a toothed quadrant carrying a lever pinned to the steering rod.

CAM

A cam is a mechanism which involves sliding and which converts one type of motion into another, e.g. rotary to reciprocating. The cam itself may have any type of motion, rotary, reciprocating or oscillating.

RADIAL CAM (PLATE CAM)

This cam has a radial 'profile' and rotates continuously to give motion to a sliding or rocking 'follower'. The total movement of the follower is called the 'lift' and the highest point on the cam is known as the 'nose'. The profile is constructed on the 'base circle', and the period when the follower is stationary is known as the 'dwell'.

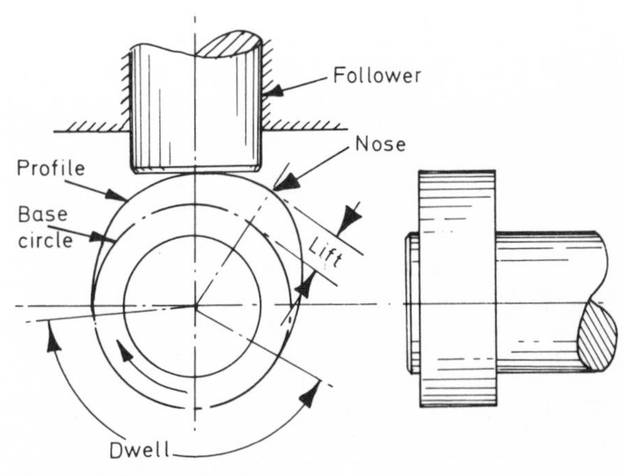

Figure 2.86 *Cam details*

CAM FOLLOWERS

That part of a cam mechanism which is driven by the cam is known as the cam 'follower'. This may have reciprocating or rocking motion and have different types of end in contact with the cam, e.g. knife-edge, flat, domed or with a roller.

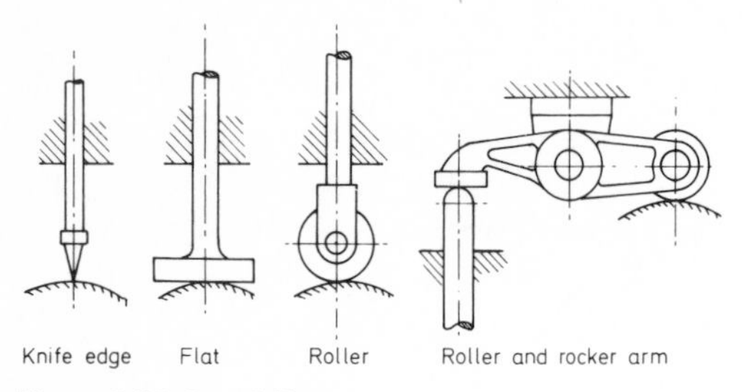

Figure 2.87 *Cam followers*

TYPES OF RADIAL CAM

The profile of the cam is designed to give the required type of motion to the follower.

Constant velocity cam A cam which produces a constant speed of the follower.

Constant acceleration/deceleration cam This is used to limit high acceleration and deceleration of the follower. For the first half of its travel the follower accelerates uniformly and for the second half it decelerates uniformly.

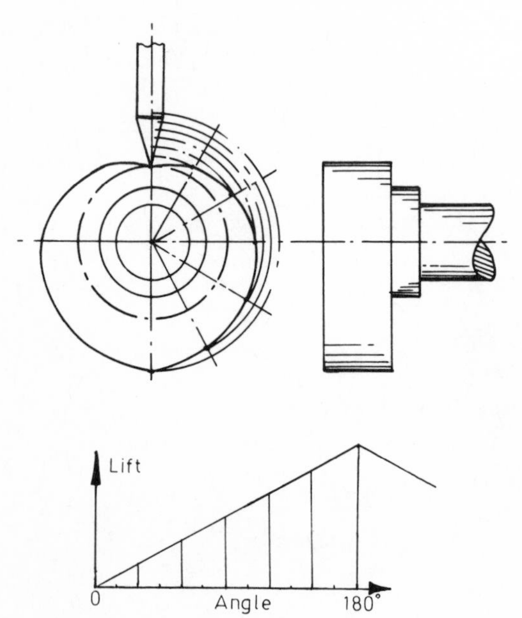

Figure 2.88 *Constant velocity cam*

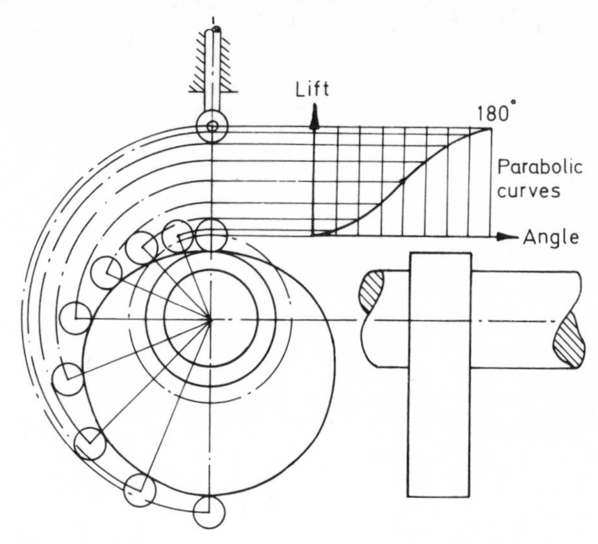

Figure 2.89 *Constant acceleration/deceleration cam*

Simple harmonic motion cam A cam which produces an oscillating motion of that type. An eccentric circle cam with a flat follower produces simple harmonic motion.

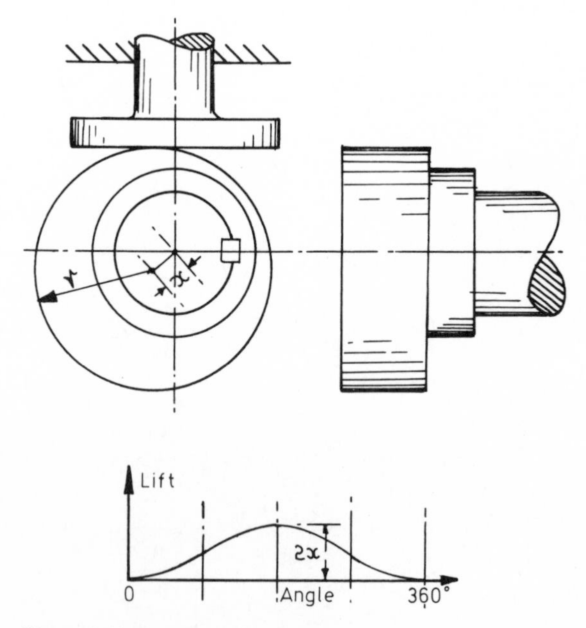

Figure 2.90 *Simple harmonic motion cam*

POSITIVE RETURN CAM

A radial type of cam where the follower ends in a side-mounted peg which fits into a slot in the face of the cam. With this cam a return spring is not required on the follower.

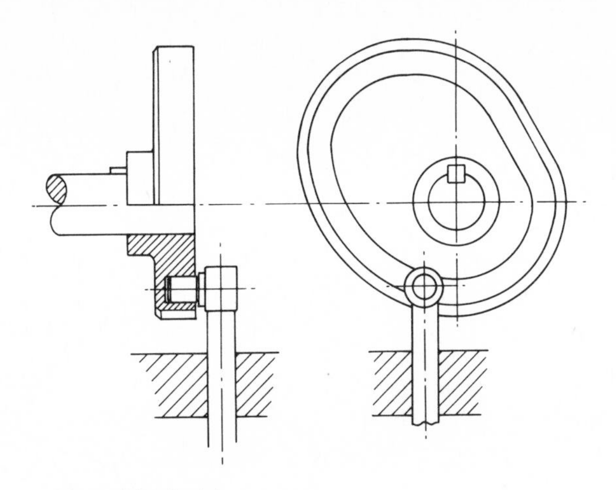

Figure 2.91 *Positive return cam*

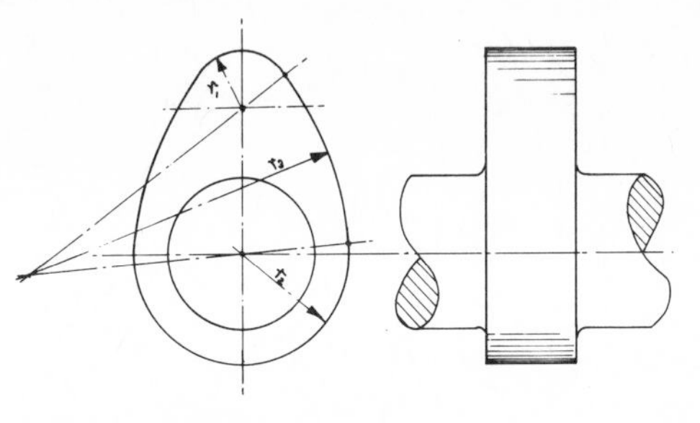

Figure 2.93 *Circular arc cam*

Some cams are named according to their shape.

Tangent cam This has a profile comprised of two circular arcs joined by tangents.

Circular arc cam The profile of this type is composed of four circular arcs.

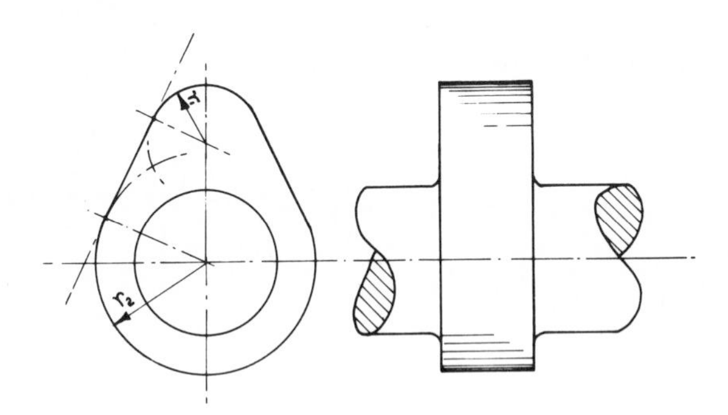

Figure 2.92 *Tangent cam*

Face cam (axial cam) The cam profile of this type is on the end of a rotating cylinder and it imparts to the follower a sliding motion parallel to the shaft axis.

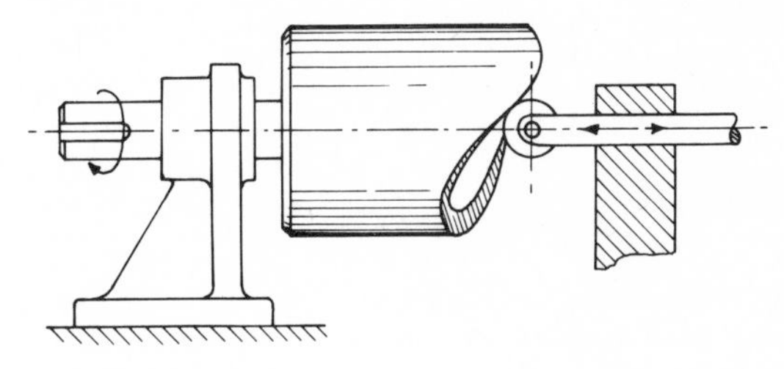

Figure 2.94 *Face cam*

Globoid cam This cam is a rotating cylinder with a concave circular arc profile (globoid). The follower, which is of the rocker type, has a peg which follows a groove cut in the cylinder.

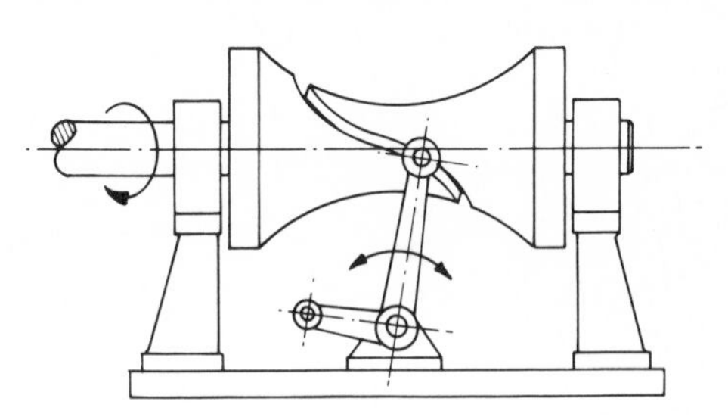

Figure 2.95 *Globoid cam*

3. Workshop Equipment

3.1 HAND TOOLS

HAND FILE

A hand file is a metal cutting tool consisting of a bar of hardened and tempered high carbon steel on which cutting teeth have been formed. It has a tapered 'tang' which fits into a handle usually made of wood. The cross-section of the bar may be rectangular, square, round, half-round, triangular, etc., and the pitch of the cutting teeth varies from fine to coarse. Files are often tapered along their length but may be parallel.

Nowadays, work is machined to such fine limits that use of the hand file is restricted. In many cases bench- and band-filing machines are used.

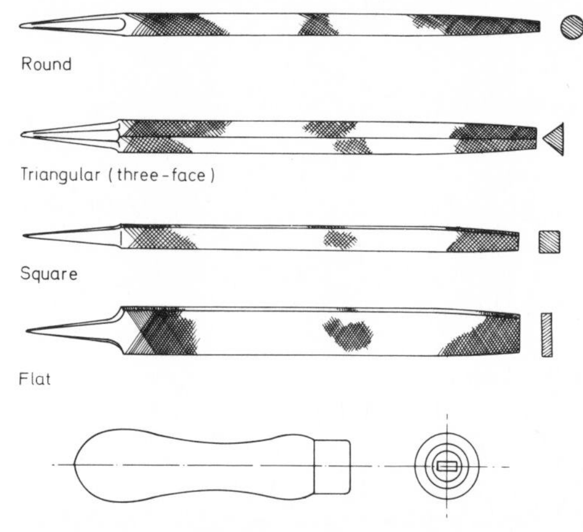

Figure 3.1 *Hand files and handle*

Needle files (pattern files) These are small, fine-tooth files with various cross-sections and sometimes with integral handles, used for diemaking and general toolroom work.

Rotary files These are short sections of hardened steel with various profiles, such as cylindrical, conical and spherical, which fit into the chuck of a hand-held power tool. They are useful for filing awkward recesses in dies, etc.

Figure 3.2 *Needle files (pattern files)*

SCRAPERS

Scrapers are hand tools consisting of bar of various cross-sections, such as rectangular, half-round and triangular, which have sharp edges for removing metal from a flat or curved surface by scraping. The blades are made of hardened high-carbon or tool steel and fit into handles.

RASP

The rasp is a very coarse file used on soft metals, such

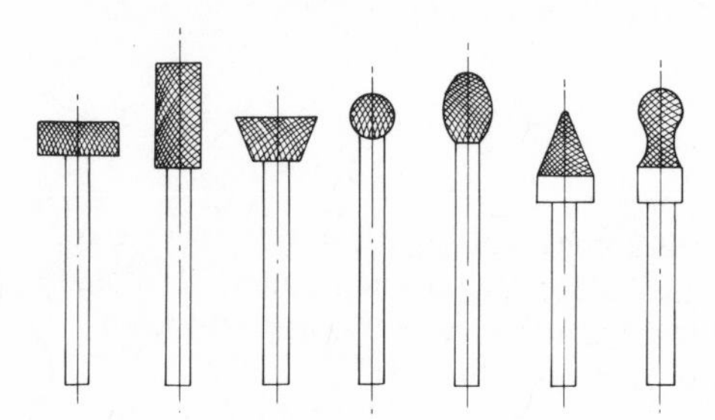

Figure 3.3 *Rotary files*

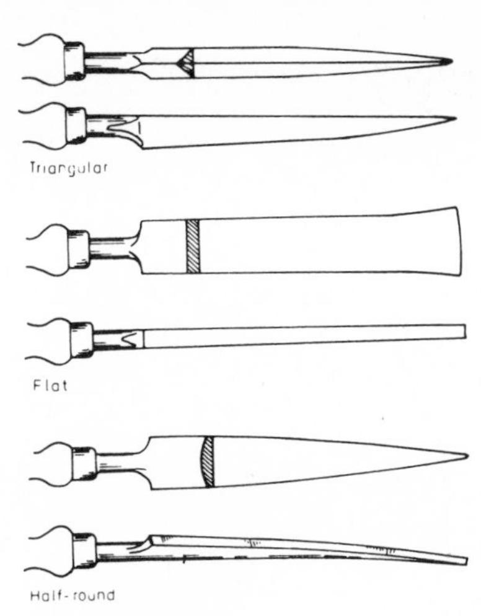

Figure 3.4 *Scrapers*

as lead-tin alloy, and non-metallic material, such as wood, hardboard and plastics.

The teeth of rasps are cut with a pointed punch which produces a series of sharp projections. The usual cross-section is half-round.

A proprietary rasp known as Surform has a thin, replaceable blade.

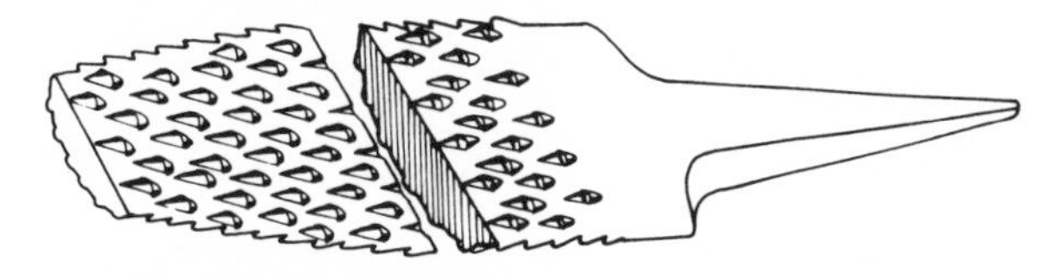

Figure 3.5 *Rasp*

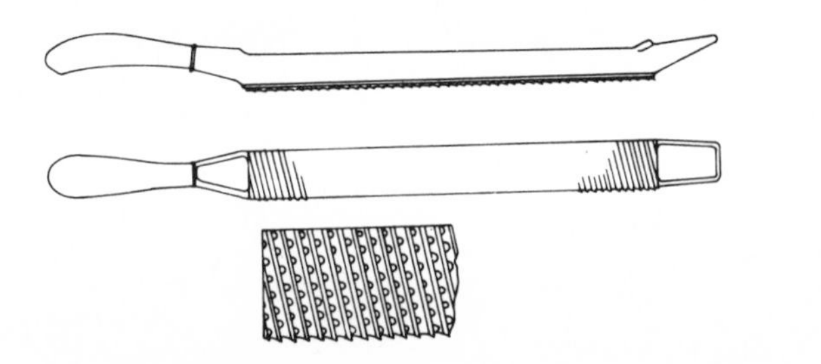

Figure 3.6 *Surform rasp*

HACKSAW

A hacksaw is a metal-cutting hand tool with a thin, narrow blade held in an adjustable frame. The blades are replaceable and the frame can accommodate blades of different lengths.

Hacksaw blades are made of carbon or high-speed steel with either the teeth or the whole blade hardened. The pitch of the teeth varies from 0.8mm ($^1/_{32}$ in.) to 1.8mm ($^1/_{14}$ in.). For general use with mild steel 16-18 teeth per inch are suitable, but fine pitch is used for thin sheet and tube and a coarse pitch for brass, copper and cast-iron.

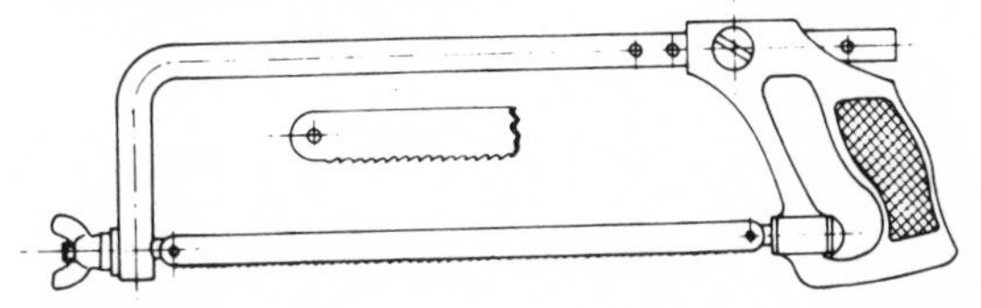

Figure 3.7 *Hacksaw*

CHISEL (SET)

Two main types of chisel, or *set*, are used by blacksmiths, the *hot chisel* for cutting hot metal and the *cold chisel* for cutting cold metal. Both are normally fitted with a handle and the chisel is held on the work and struck with a hammer. In engineering a fitter uses a shorter, hand-held cold chisel.

The most important types are the flat, the crosscut, the half-round and the diamond-pointed chisel.

Chisels are made from high carbon steel of octagonal cross-section varying in size from 10–20mm ($^3/_8$–$^3/_4$ in.), and alloy steel is also used.

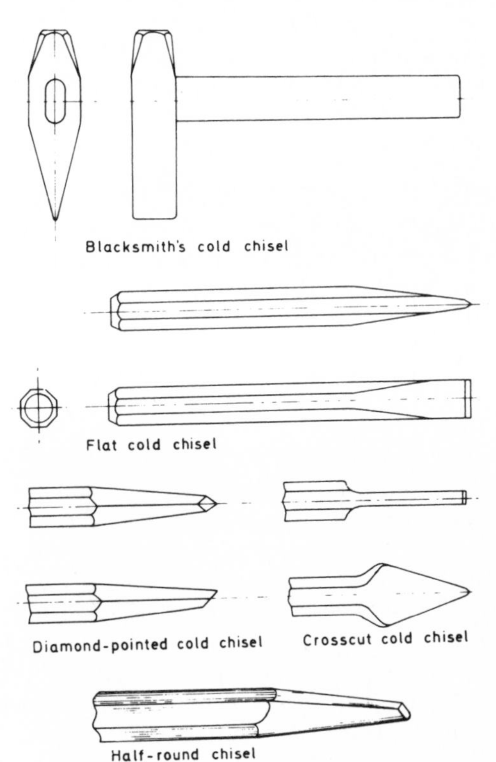

Figure 3.8 *Chisels*

CENTRE PUNCH

The centre punch is used to give small, round indentations when struck with a hammer. The marks are used in conjunction with scribed lines when marking-off for the centres of drilled holes and to provide a hole for one leg of a pair of dividers when marking off circles. Punches are made of hardened and tempered cast steel.

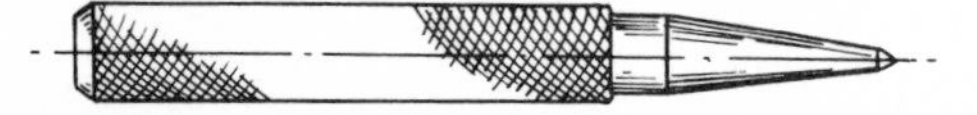

Figure 3.9 *Centre punch*

DRIFTS

Drifts are punches made of hardened and tempered tool steel with specially shaped ends used for finishing off non-circular holes, e.g. square, rectangular and hexagonal.

One type of square drift has teeth on its faces to improve the cutting action.

Pin drift A drift with a small-diameter end used for driving pins out of shafts, etc. They are made in several sizes.

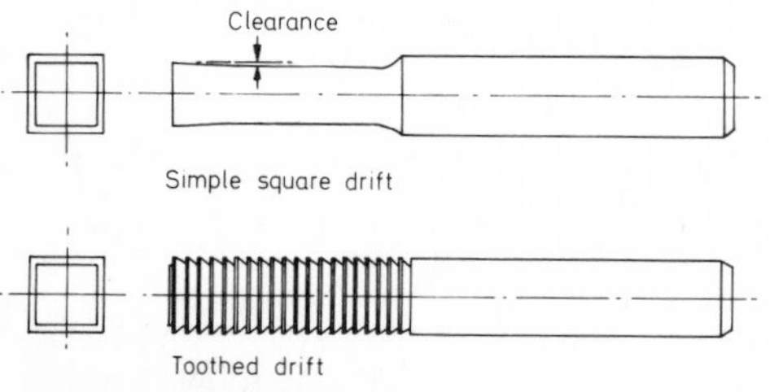

Figure 3.10 *Drifts*

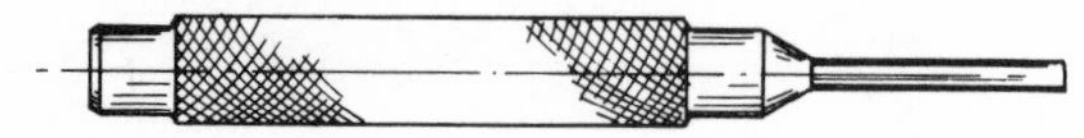

Figure 3.11 *Pin drift*

TWIST DRILL

A twist drill is a manually- or machine-rotated tool with cutting edges for producing circular holes in metal, plastics, wood, etc. It consists of pieces of hardened steel bar with usually two spiral grooves, or flutes, ending in two angled cutting edges. The flutes assist in removing the cuttings.

Twist drills range in size from a fraction of a mm to over 10 cm. The shank, that is the end opposite to the cutting end, is either straight to suit a drill 'chuck' or has a taper, known as a 'Morse taper', to suit the spindle of a drilling machine.

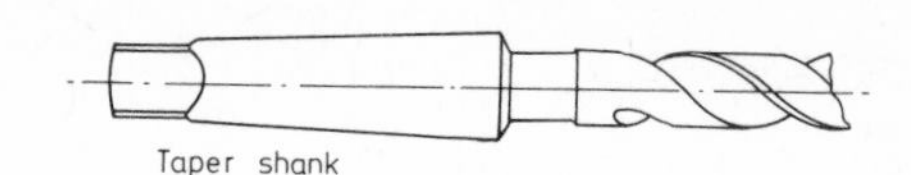

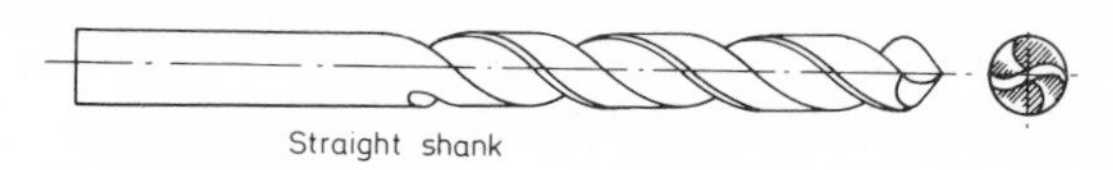

Figure 3.12 *Twist drills*

HAND DRILL

A hand drill is a tool with a chuck which takes twist drills. The drill is rotated by turning a geared handle. The name is also applied to hand-held electrically powered drills.

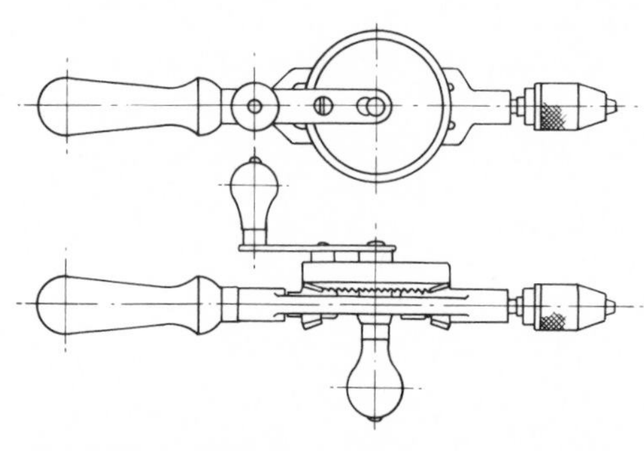

Figure 3.13 *Hand drill*

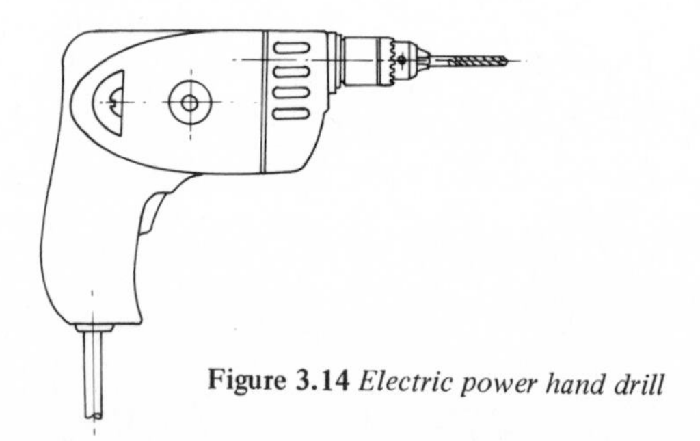

Figure 3.14 *Electric power hand drill*

MASONRY DRILL

A twist drill with hardened inserts on the cutting edges suitable for drilling bricks, concrete, etc.

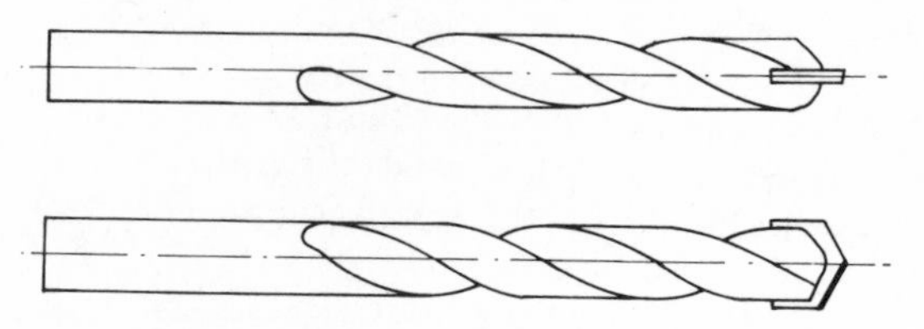

Figure 3.15 *Masonry drill*

COUNTERSINKING TOOL

A rotating cutting tool with a conical end having cutting teeth used for countersinking drilled holes.

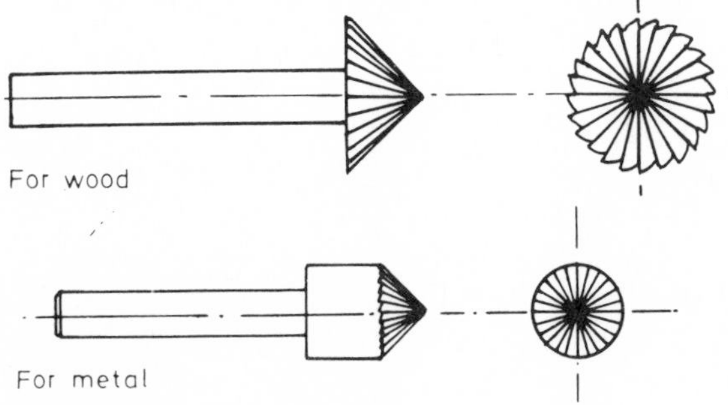

Figure 3.16 *Countersinking tools*

REAMER

A cylindrical cutting tool similar in appearance to a drill but with a flat end and either straight or helical cutting edges on the cylindrical surface. Hand reamers have a long lead (tapered section) to align the reamer with the hole.

Figure 3.17 *Reamer*

TAPER REAMER

This is a small reamer with the cutting length tapered to produce holes for taper pins.

Figure 3.18 *Taper reamer*

TAP

A tap is a tool used to produce an internal screw thread in a drilled or bored hole. It is essentially a screw with three or four longitudinal grooves providing cutting edges which, when hardened, will cut a mating thread inside a hole. The shank has a square end which will fit either a machine spindle or a hand-tapping wrench.

A set of taps consists of three taps with the same thread but with different tapers at the end. The first has a long taper for starting the thread, the second a shorter taper for finishing through holes, and the third tap is a plug tap for taking the thread to the bottom of a blind hole. The hole must be initially drilled to the tapping size, that is to a diameter slightly smaller than the diameter at the bottom of the threads.

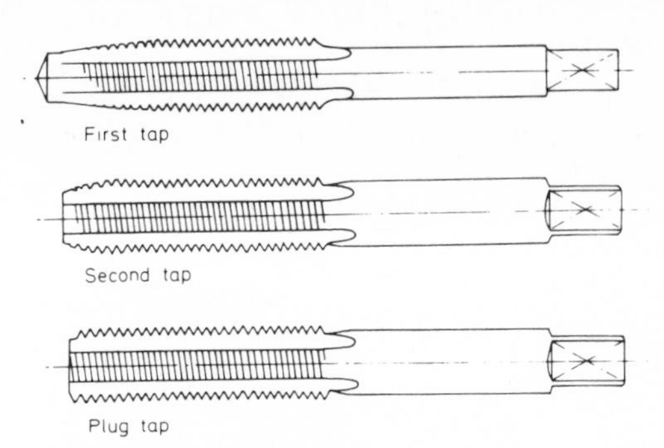

Figure 3.19 *Set of screw taps*

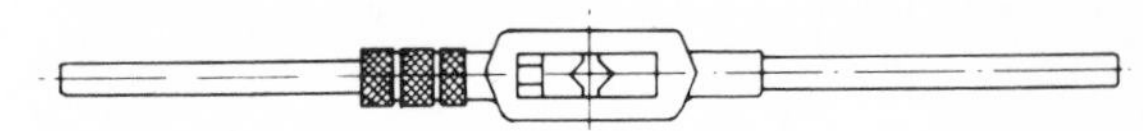

Figure 3.20 *Tap wrench*

TAP WRENCH

A tap wrench which is used for manual tapping, comprises a bar with a central adjustable hole (to suit the square on a tap shank) and handles.

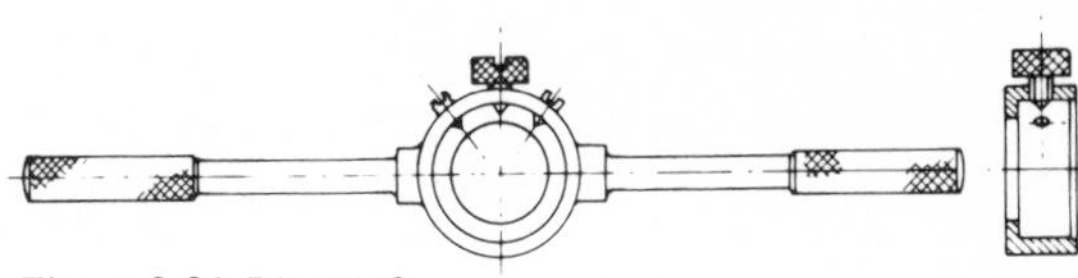

Figure 3.21 *Die stock*

DIE

A die is used to cut an external screw thread on a cylindrical surface. It consists of a hardened, circular steel nut with an internal thread which is relieved by three or four longitudinal grooves to produce cutting edges. The die is split so that the diameter of the hole can be reduced by means of two screws and increased by means of a third pointed screw. The die is held in a circular recess in a 'stock' fitted with handles for manual operation.

The first cut is made with the die opened slightly, and second or third cuts are made with it progressively closed until the correct depth of thread is obtained.

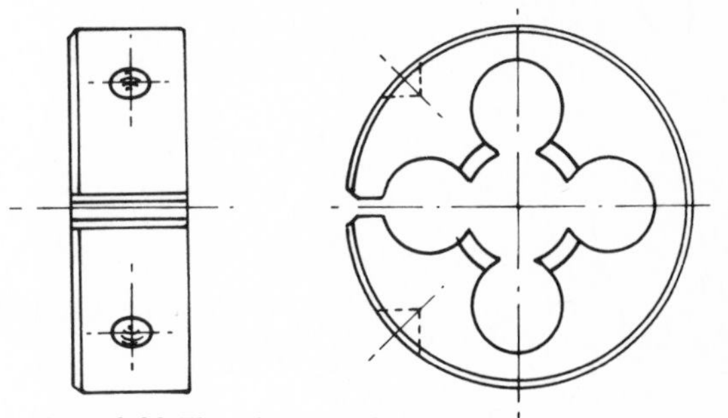

Figure 3.22 *Thread-cutting die*

HAMMERS

A hammer is a hand tool with a heavy steel head on the end of a hand-held shank usually made of wood but sometimes made of steel tube with a handgrip.

Hammers are available in many sizes and weights from 100 gm to 10 Kg, and with many shapes of head, and they are used to give blows of varying force.

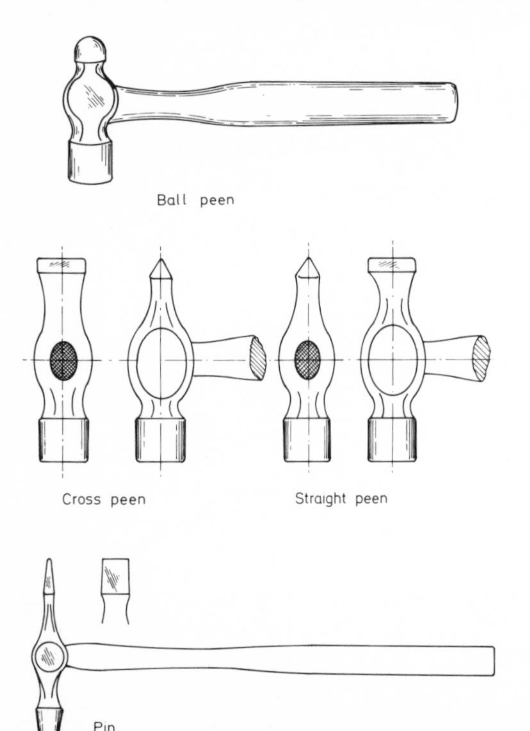

Figure 3.23 *Hammers*

Ball peen hammer This is the most common type of hammer which has a ball-shaped end on the head opposite to the striking face. It is used for all kinds of engineering work, the ball end being useful for sheet metal forming, and it is made in weights from 100 gm to 1.5 Kg.

Cross peen and straight peen hammers These have blunt, chisel-shaped ends on the head opposite the face.

Pin hammer A name often applied to the smallest hammers, and these may be ball peen or cross peen.

Sledge hammer (maul) This is a heavy, double-faced hammer weighing up to 15 Kg which is swung using both hands.

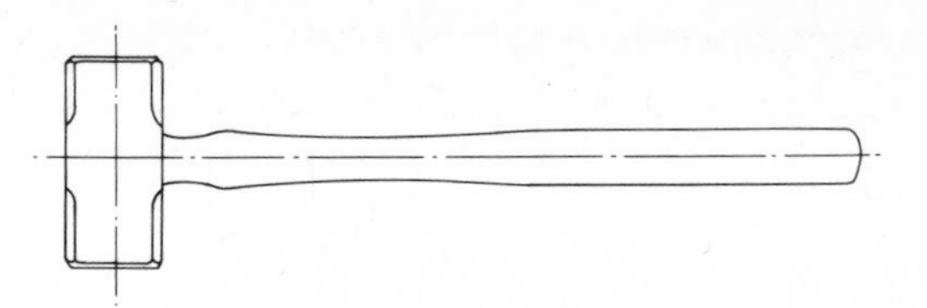

Figure 3.24 *Sledge hammer (maul)*

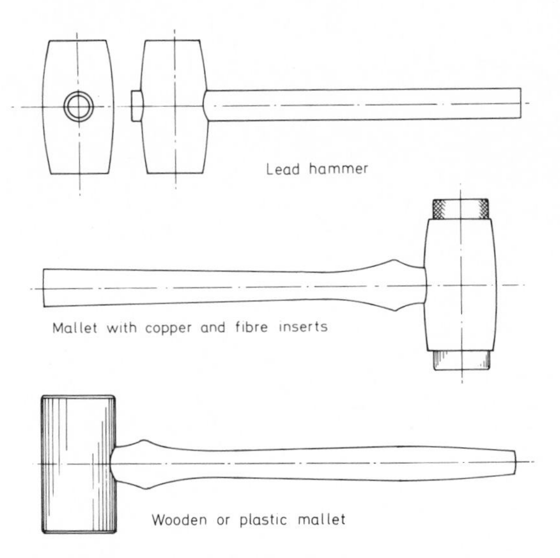

Figure 3.25 *Soft hammers (mallets)*

Soft hammers (mallets) To avoid damage to machined surfaces soft hammers, or mallets, are used, the main types being: lead hammer, with iron handle; mallet, with copper and fibre inserts in an iron head; mallets with heads of boxwood, plastic or hide.

RULES

Engineers' rules are made from hardened and tempered steel marked off with high accuracy. They are made from strips 10–30 mm wide and in lengths from 10 cm (4 ins). Folding pocket rules are available with an extended length of 60cm (24 ins.).

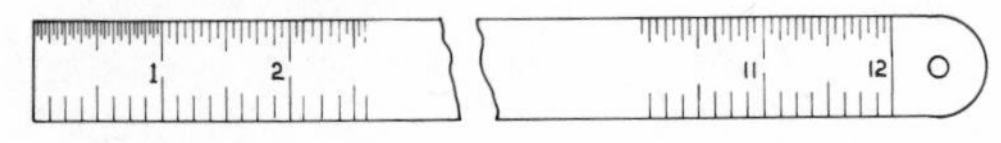

Figure 3.26 *Engineers' rule – 12 in. (300mm)*

Extending spring rules are used where great accuracy is unnecessary.

In engineering, rules are used for marking-off, setting callipers and dividers, etc.

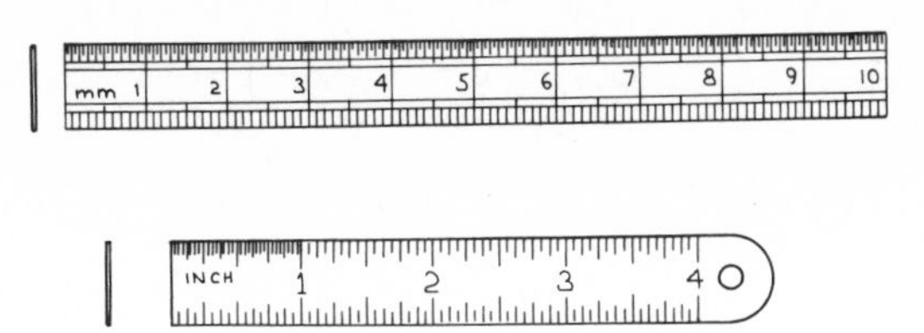

Figure 3.27 *Small engineers' rule – 4-6 in. (100-150mm)*

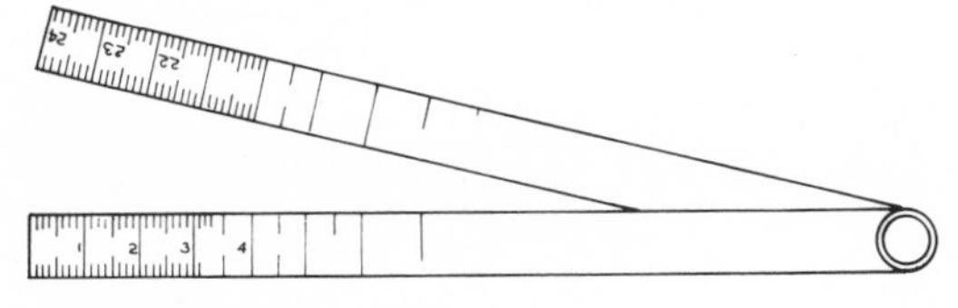

Figure 3.28 *Folding rule*

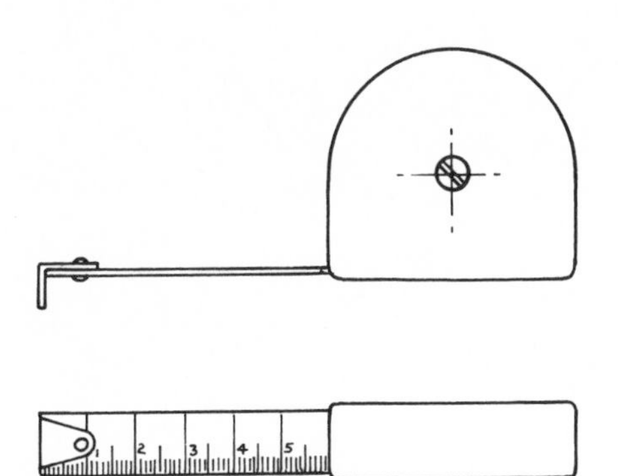

Figure 3.29 *Spring tape rule*

THICKNESS GAUGE (FEELER GAUGE)

Thickness, or feeler, gauges are thin blades of spring steel of exact thickness used for measuring small gaps (or clearances) between parts. They are usually made in sets of various thicknesses pinned together at one end.

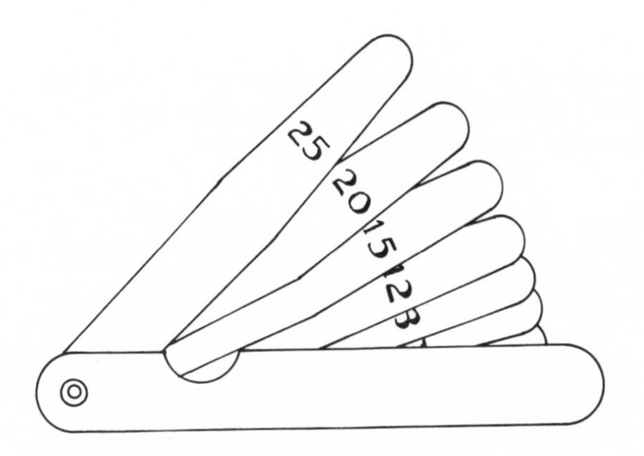

Figure 3.30 *Thickness gauge (feeler gauge)*

THREAD GAUGE (SCREW PITCH GAUGE)

The thread gauge has several blades, each with a number of teeth of different standard pitch and form, and mounted at either end of a holder. These blades are used when machining threads so that the thread form and pitch may be checked.

Another type of gauge is used for setting thread-cutting tools.

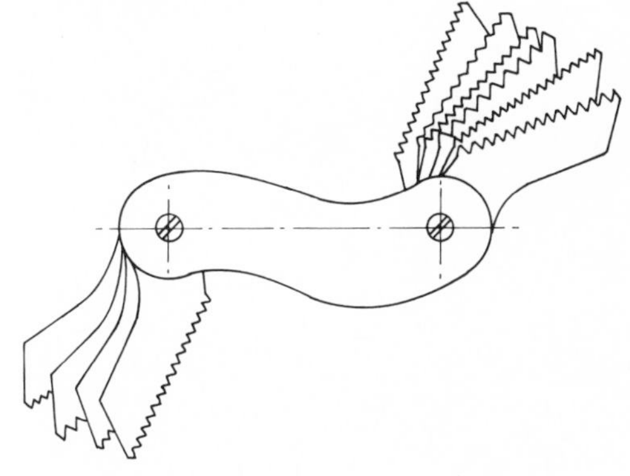

Figure 3.31 *Thread gauge (screw pitch gauge)*

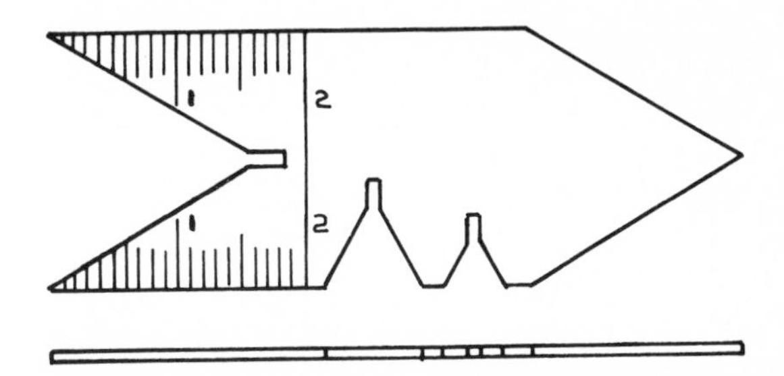

Figure 3.32 *Screw-cutting tool setting gauge*

SCRIBER

A scriber is a thin steel rod with a pointed end or ends, one of which may be bent at right angles to allow access to holes. Some scribers may have a knurled handle in the middle.

The scriber is used for marking-off, and it produces a fine scratched (or scribed) line on a machined face.

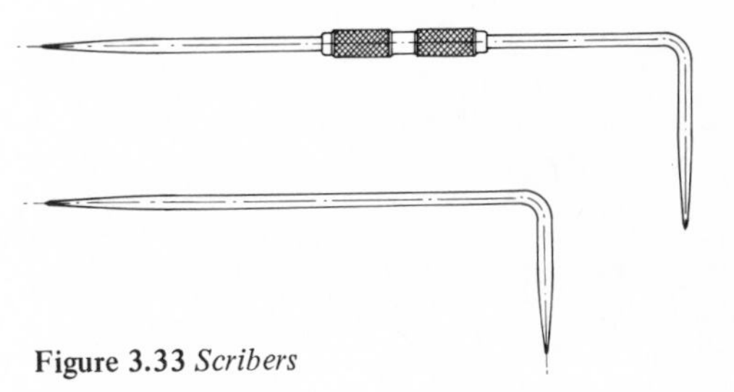

Figure 3.33 *Scribers*

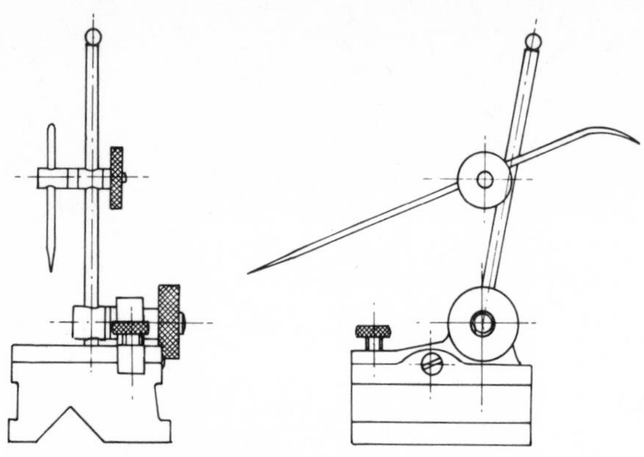

Figure 3.34 *Surface gauge with scriber*

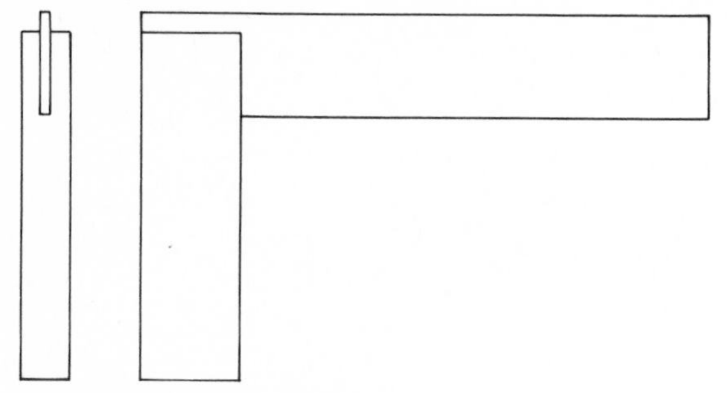

Figure 3.35 *Square (try square)*

SQUARE (TRY SQUARE)

This is made from two rectangular pieces of steel joined at right angles, and is used to check internal and external right angle corners, especially when hand-fitting.

SURFACE GAUGE

A surface gauge has three main parts, a base, a post and a scriber.

The base is ground flat and has a machined V groove for use on round work. The post can be tilted by means of a screw and carries either a scriber for marking-off, or a dial gauge.

COMBINATION SET

This consists of a steel rule with a slot (or keyway) along its length, to which one of three heads may be attached, namely, a square, a centre finder and a protractor.

DIVIDERS

Dividers consist of a pair of adjustable hinged points used for measuring and transferring sizes and also for scribing circles and radii when marking-off.

The hinge may be of the 'firm joint' type or with a spring, as shown.

OUTSIDE CALLIPERS (CALLIPERS)

An adjustable pair of curved and hinged legs used for measuring the thickness of parts and diameters of shafts, etc. The callipers may have a 'firm joint', as shown, or be of the 'spring joint' type.

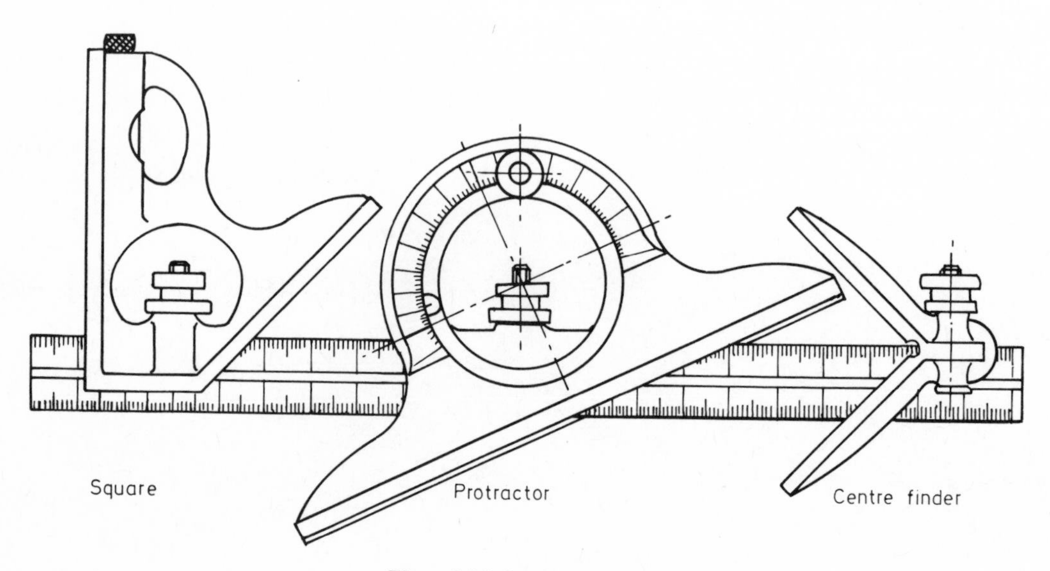

Figure 3.36 *Combination set*

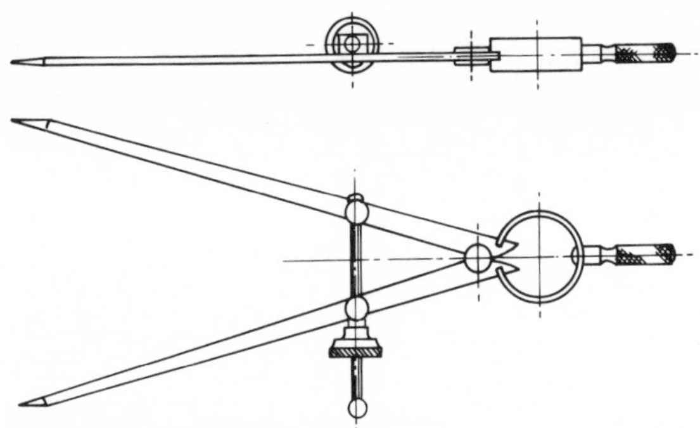

Figure 3.37 *Spring dividers*

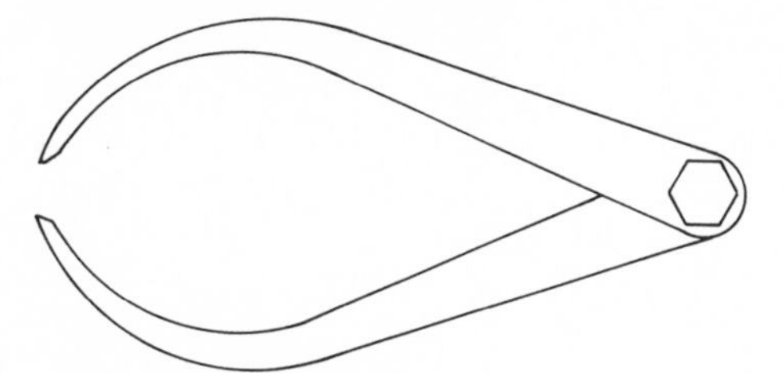

Figure 3.38 *Outside callipers*

INSIDE CALLIPERS

The hinged legs are bent outwards so that inside measurements such as the bore of a pipe may be measured.

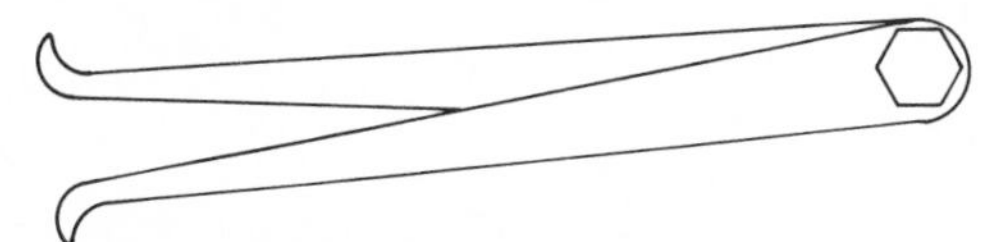

Figure 3.39 *Inside callipers*

JENNY CALLIPERS

Also known as *hermaphrodite callipers* or *odd legs*, these have one leg curved inwards and one straight leg which sometimes has a replaceable point. They are used for measuring the distance from a point to an outside surface.

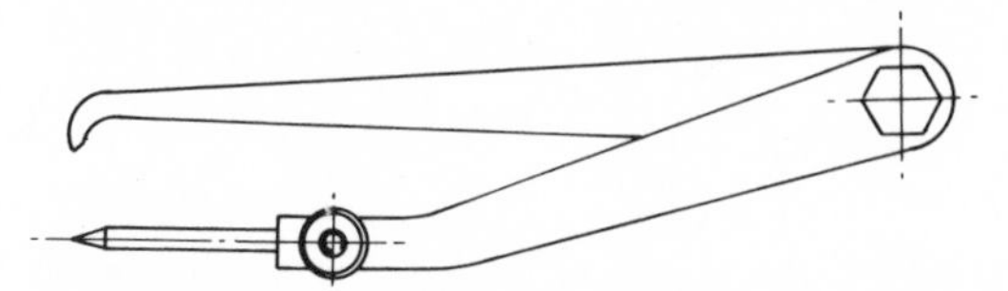

Figure 3.40 *Jenny (hermaphrodite, odd leg) callipers*

GEAR-TOOTH CALLIPERS

A gear-tooth calliper has an 'inside' leg and an 'outside' leg. It can be used for measuring the distance from an inside edge to an outside edge.

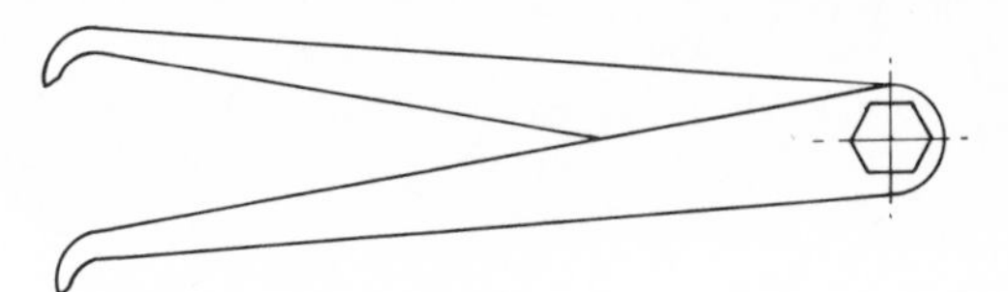

Figure 3.41 *Gear-tooth callipers*

MICROMETERS

Micrometers are instruments used for the accurate measurement of internal and external dimensions of objects, particularly those of cylindrical shape. The measurement is based upon the advance of an internally-threaded thimble rotated on a precision screw.

Micrometers are made in a very large range of types and sizes, the most common being the *outside micrometer* measuring up to 25mm in 0.01mm intervals (1 in. in 0.001 in. intervals). It has a fixed graduated barrel screwed to take the graduated thimble which is knurled to give a good finger grip and which has a movable anvil attached to it. The barrel is attached to a semi-circular frame at the opposite end of which is mounted a fixed anvil.

The object to be measured is placed between the anvils and the thimble is rotated until the object is nipped by them. The size is then read from the graduations on thimble and barrel.

Large outside micrometers are supplied with extensions for the fixed anvil.

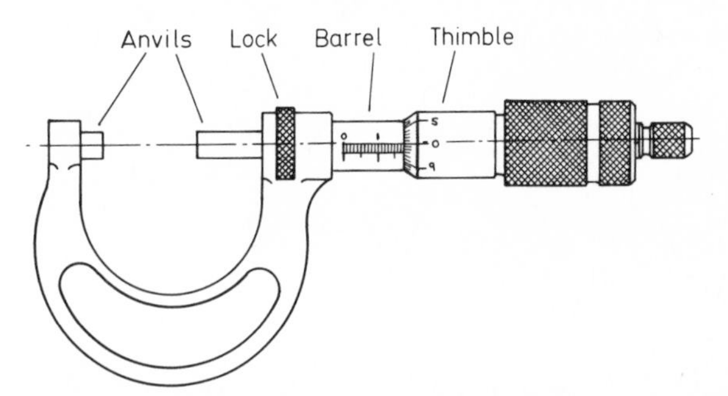

Figure 3.42 *Outside micrometer (1 in. – 25mm)*

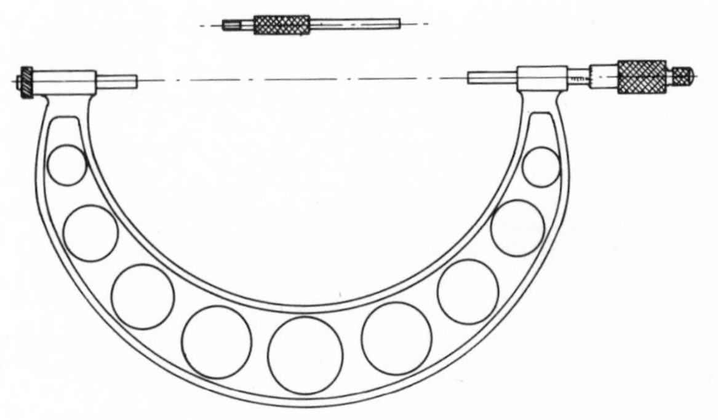

Figure 3.43 *Large outside micrometer with extension rod*

An *inside micrometer* has the fixed anvil projecting from the end of the thimble opposite to the moving anvil, and extension rods may be used to extend the range.

The barrel and thimble assembly, called a *micrometer head*, can be obtained separately and can be attached to any precision measuring instrument.

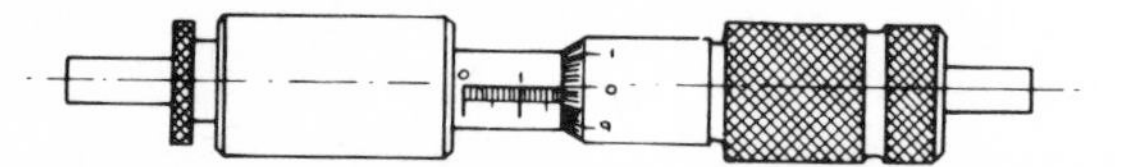

Figure 3.44 *Inside micrometer*

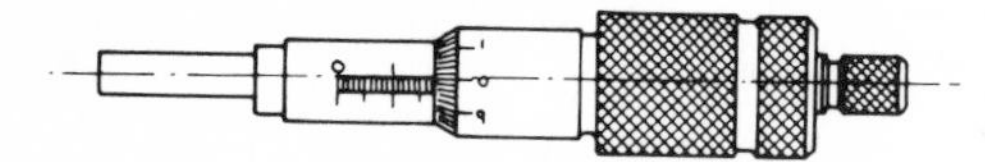

Figure 3.45 *Micrometer head*

VERNIER CALLIPER GAUGE

This instrument, used for internal and external measurement, has a long flat scale to which a fixed jaw is attached at one end, and a sliding jaw with a cursor running along the scale. A scale on the cursor is read in conjunction with the fixed scale.

Outside measurements are made between the jaws and inside measurements over projections on the jaws.

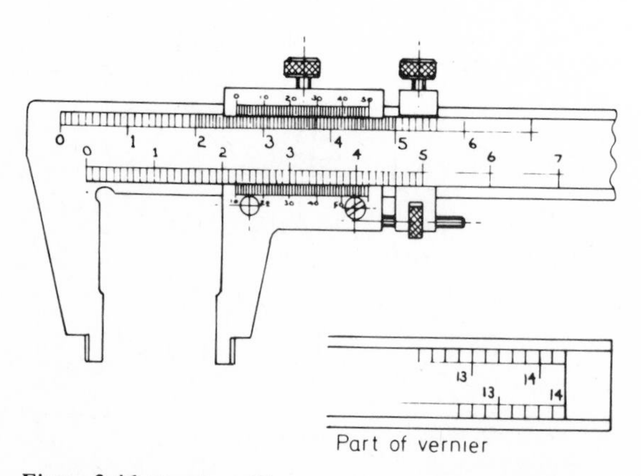

Figure 3.46 *Vernier calliper gauge*

DIAL GAUGE

The movement of a plunger is magnified and displayed on a dial on which intervals of 0.002 mm (0.0001 in.) are possible. The dial has a fixing lug by which it can be attached to a surface gauge post or a magnetic base test set. When a bell-crank lever is attached, the combination is referred to as a *Dial Test Indicator-lever operated.*

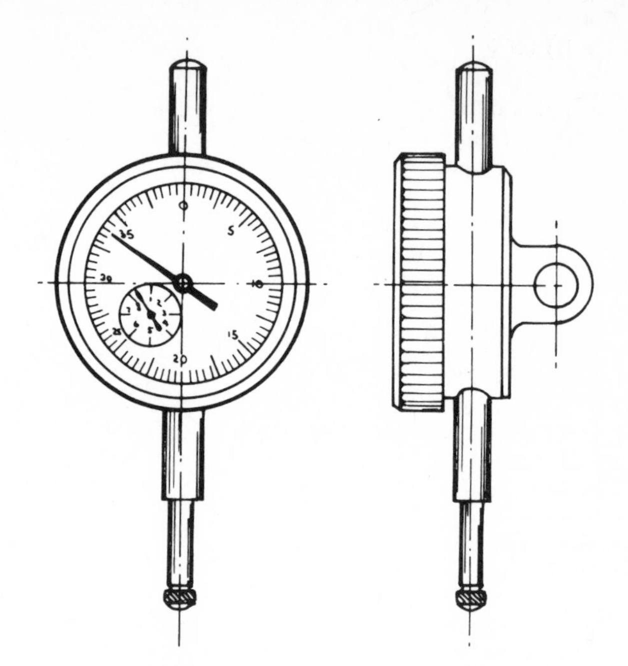

Figure 3.47 *Dial gauge*

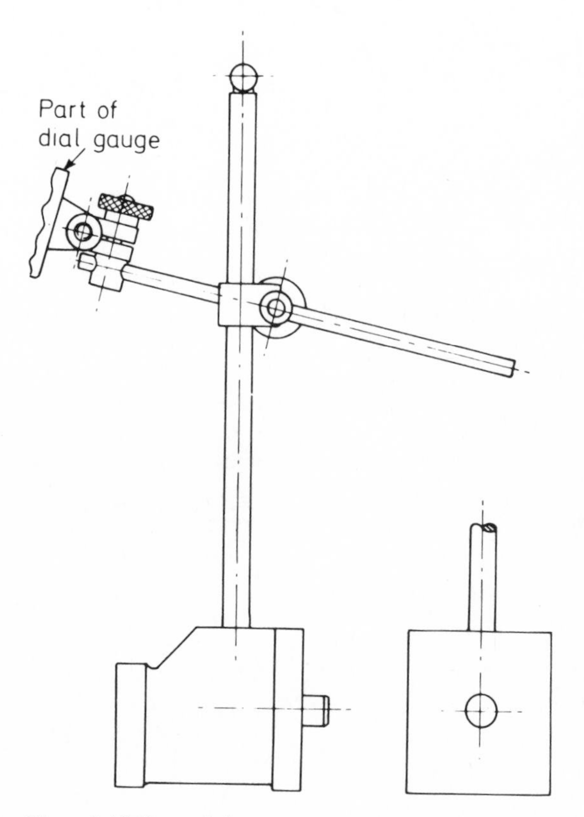

Figure 3.48 *Magnetic base test set*

V BLOCK

V blocks are used for holding cylindrical objects while they are being machined or marked off. They have a ground base and sides with a ground V in the top. Sometimes the sides have grooves to take a clamp for holding the object rigidly onto the block.

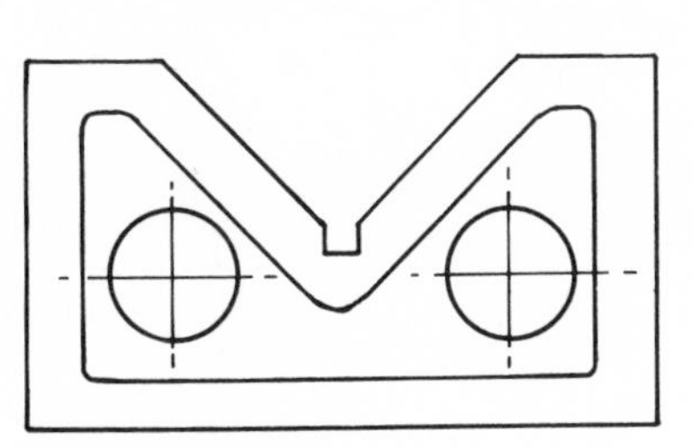

Figure 3.49 *V block*

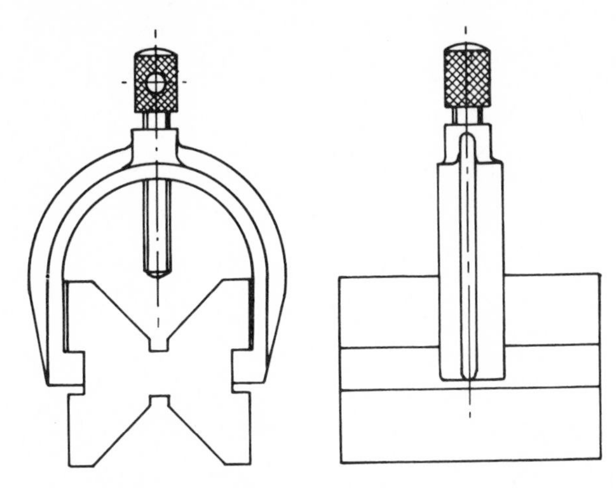

Figure 3.50 *V block with clamp*

SURFACE PLATE

A heavy plate of cast iron or steel with a flat surface of high accuracy used for marking off and gauging. A larger version is called a *surface table*.

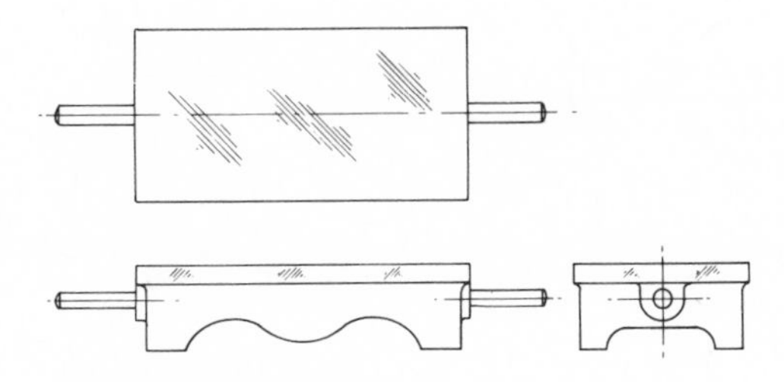

Figure 3.51 *Surface plate*

CLAMPS

Various types of clamp are used for temporarily holding down during machining, bolting, riveting etc. The range includes the *C clamp*, the *toolmakers' clamp* and the *strap clamp*.

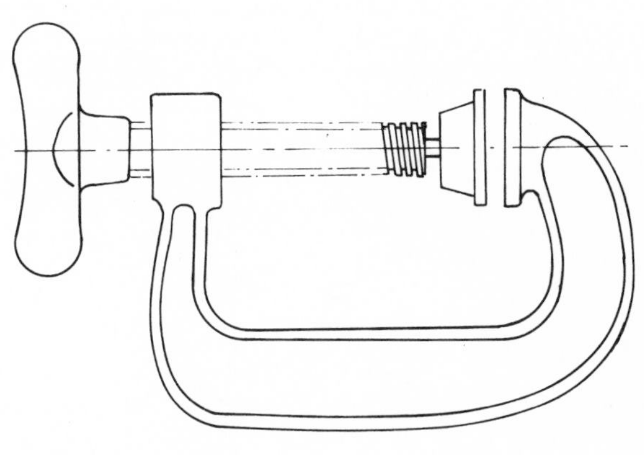

Figure 3.52 *C clamp*

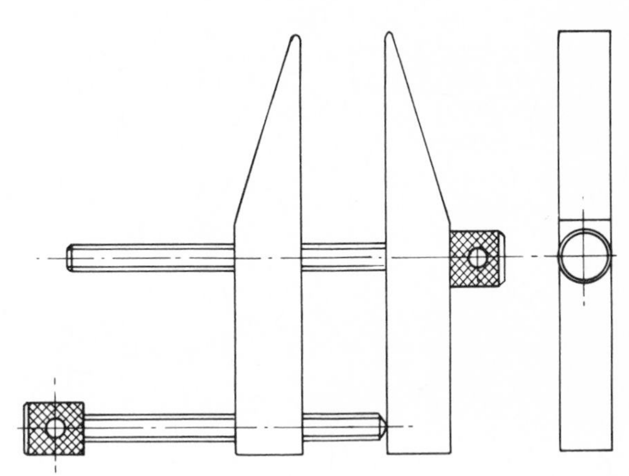

Figure 3.53 *Toolmakers' clamp*

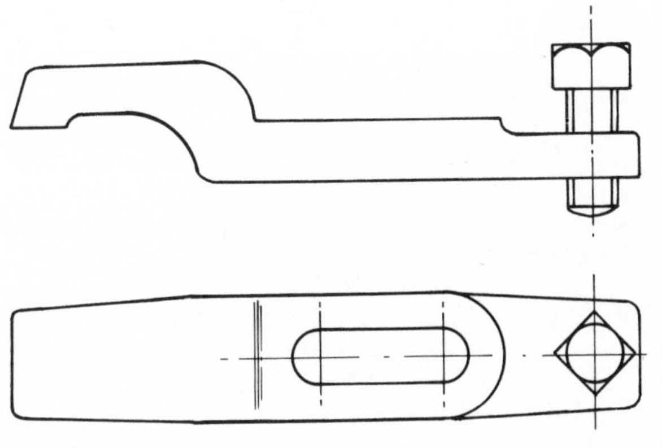

Figure 3.54 *Strap clamp*

VICE (VISE)

A vice is a bench or machine-mounted clamping device for holding work while manual or machine operations are being carried out. It comprises two jaws which are brought together by a hand-operated screw to clamp the work. The jaws are made of hardened steel and are serrated to improve their grip on the work. To avoid accidental marking of soft metals, 'grips' of lead, copper, aluminium or fibre may be fitted. The *bench vice* is used for general fitting, and the *machine vice*, which is often able to tilt and swivel, is mounted on the table of a machine, e.g. a drilling machine. *Pipe vices* are used for holding pipes while they are being cut or screwed.

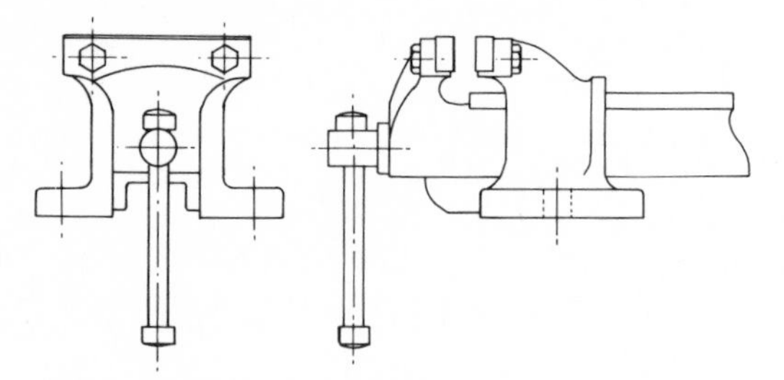

Figure 3.55 *Engineers' vice*

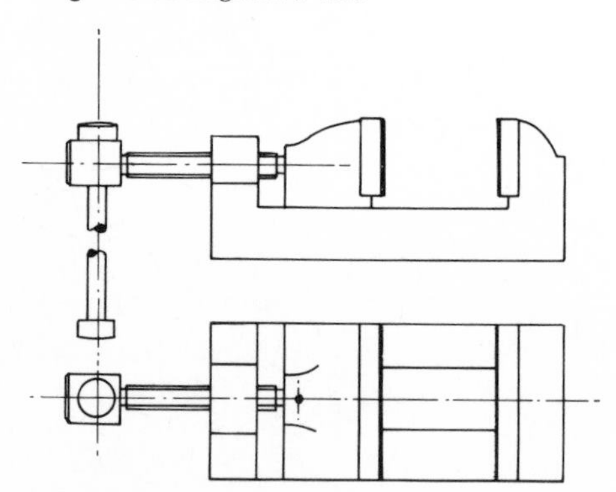

Figure 3.56 *Machine vice*

PLIERS

Pliers are hand tools used for gripping small components, bending, wire cutting, etc. Two handles with a common pivot have jaws with serrations (pipe grips), and usually have blades for side cutting and notches for wire cutting. For electrical uses the handles are insulated.

Long-nose pliers (needlenose pliers) These are useful for holding small work and bending loops in wire.

Round-nose pliers These are used for bending loops in wire and narrow strip and have no serrations.

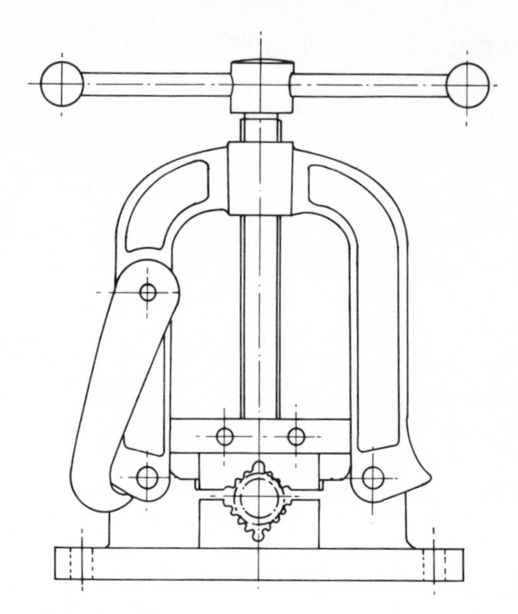

Figure 3.57 *Pipe vice*

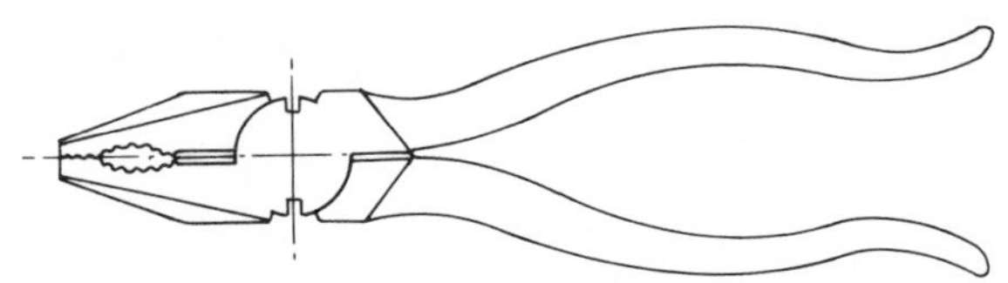

Figure 3.58 *Pliers*

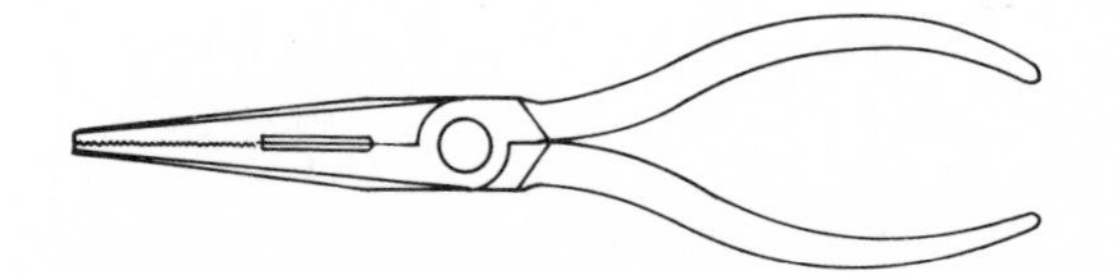

Figure 3.59 *Long-nose (needlenose) pliers*

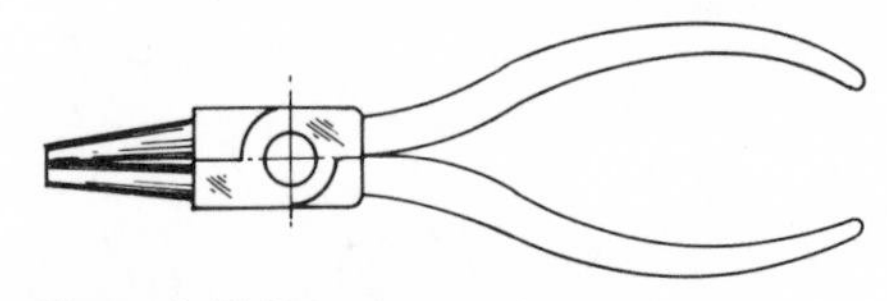

Figure 3.60 *Round-nose pliers*

WIRE CUTTERS

Wire cutters have blades suitable for cutting copper and small gauge iron wire.

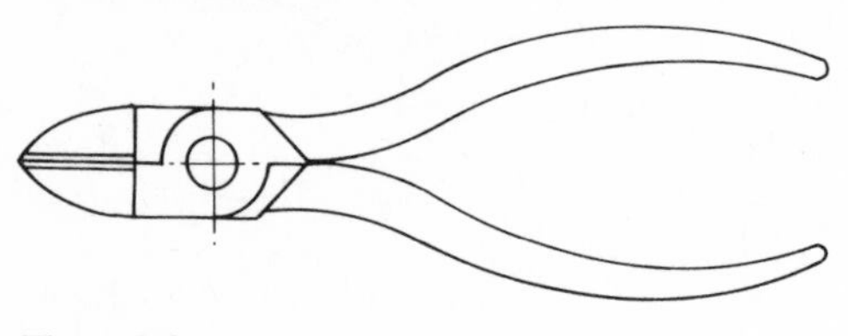

Figure 3.61 *Wire cutters*

SHEARS (SNIPS, TINSNIPS)

Hand tools of the scissor type for cutting thin sheet metal, jointing, etc.

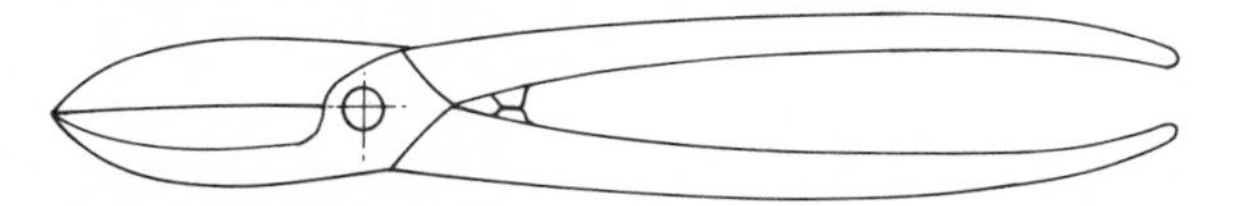

Figure 3.62 *Shears (snips)*

SCREWDRIVERS

These are tools used for hand-driving screws. They consist of a usually round bar of carbon tool steel heat-treated to give hardness and toughness with a handle at one end and the other end formed to suit the recess in the screw. This may be a slot, hexagonal hole or cross recess.

Screwdrivers are made in sizes ranging from extremely small jewellers' and instrument-makers' types to large ones over 40cm in length.

Ratchet screwdrivers can be adjusted to be rigid in both directions of rotation or to slip in either direction.

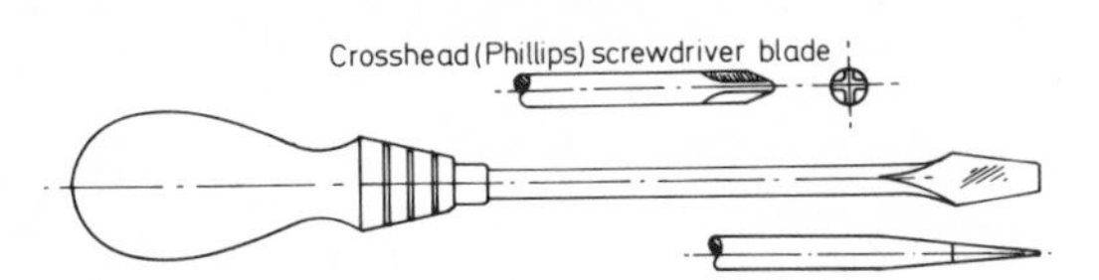

Figure 3.63 *Wooden-handled screwdriver*

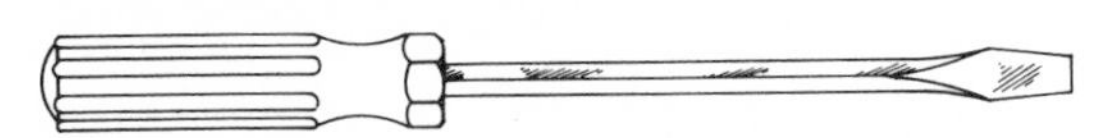

Figure 3.64 *Heavy screwdriver with plastic handle*

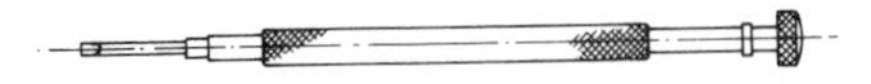

Figure 3.65 *Instrument makers' screwdriver*

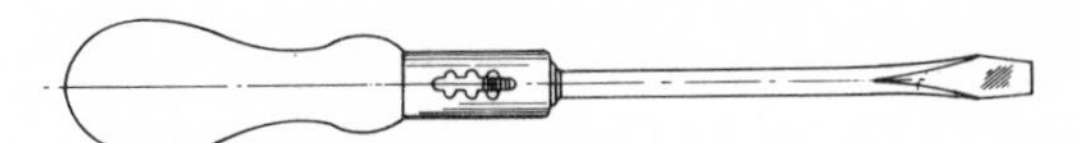

Figure 3.66 *Ratchet screwdriver*

SPANNERS (WRENCHES)

A spanner, or *wrench*, is a device employing leverage and it is used for tightening or releasing nuts, bolts, and other screwed fasteners. Most spanners are hand-operated but power-driven spanners are available.

Open-ended spanner One or both ends of this spanner has open parallel jaws which, in the double-ended type, are usually of different sizes. These jaws fit the flats on nuts and bolt heads. They are obtainable singly or in sets of different sizes.

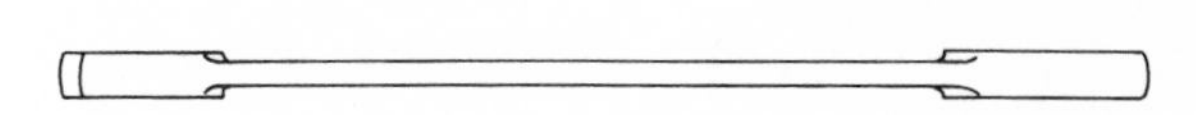

Figure 3.67 *Open-ended (open-jaws) spanner (wrench)*

Ring spanner (box wrench) The ends of this spanner are in the form of rings with twelve internal corners to suit hexagon nuts and bolts. The hexagon size is different at each end and sets of up to twelve spanners are available. The spanners may be flat or have the ends offset.

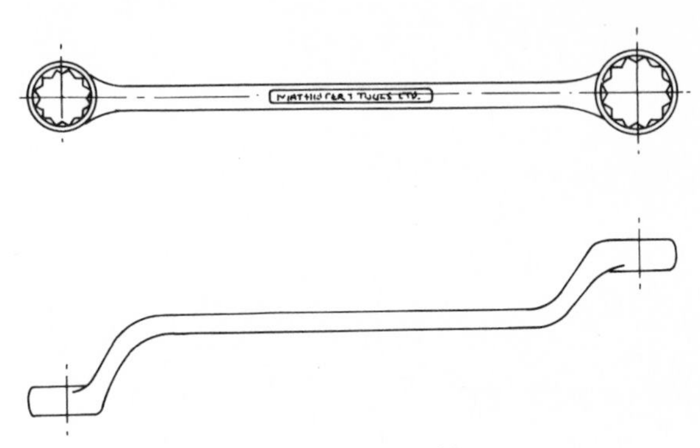

Figure 3.68 *Ring spanner (box wrench)*

Tubular box spanner Tubular spanners are made of tough alloy steel circular tube formed at the ends into different sizes either of hexagon or square. Holes are drilled through the tube to take a *tommy bar* which provides the required leverage.

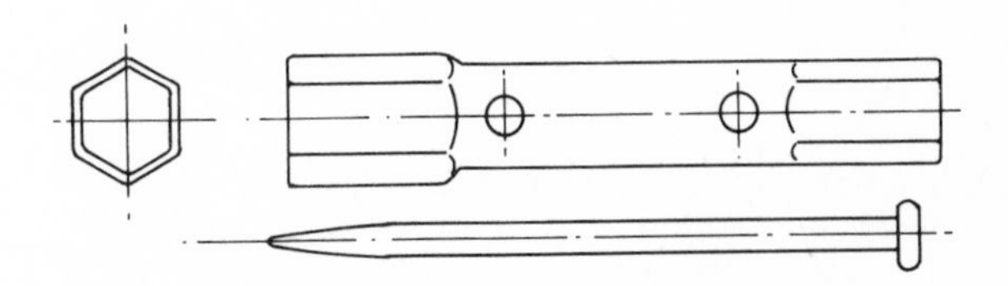

Figure 3.69 *Tubular box spanner (socket wrench) and tommy bar*

Socket spanners (socket wrenches) These are short circular tubes of alloy steel with twelve internal corners at one end to suit hexagonal nuts, etc. and a square socket at the other end to suit various attachments. Sets of sockets contain up to 24 different sizes.

The following attachments are available: bar handle, ratchet handle, brace, extensions, universal joint.

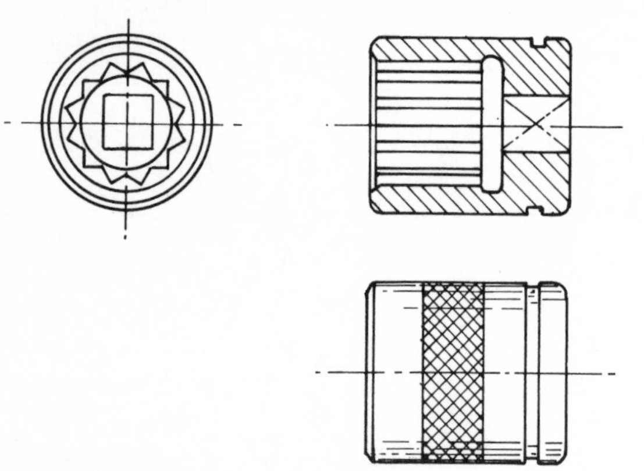

Figure 3.70 *Socket for socket spanner (wrench)*

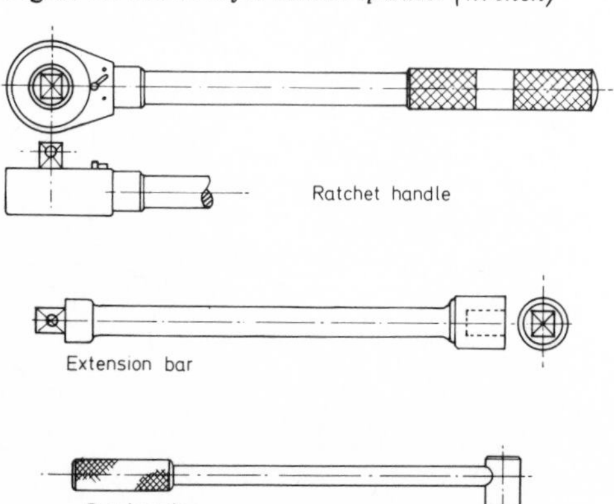

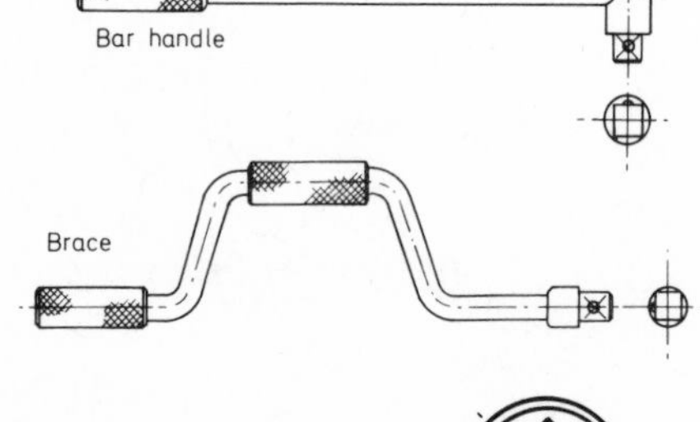

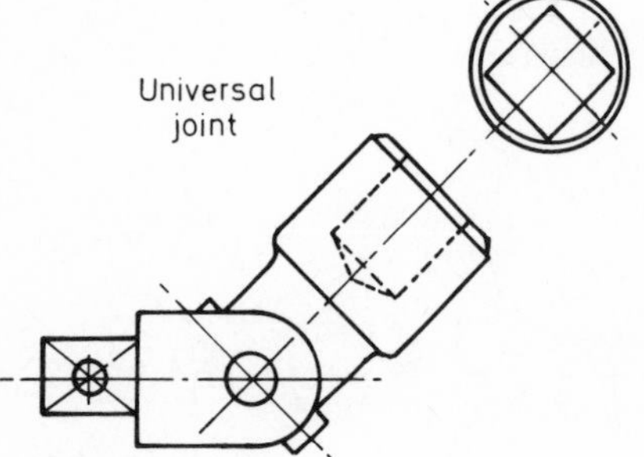

Figure 3.71 *Attachments for socket spanners (wrenches)*

Adjustable spanner (wrench) An open-jawed spanner with one jaw adjustable so that the gap in the jaws can be altered to suit different sizes of nuts and bolts.

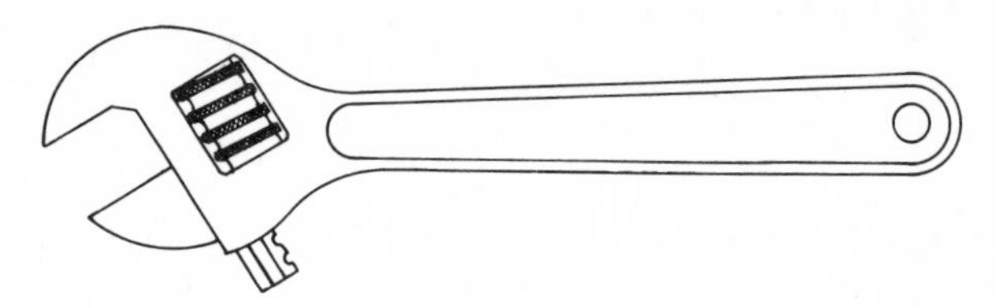

Figure 3.72 *Adjustable spanner (wrench)*

Face spanner (wrench) At the end of the handle a flat C-shaped section has a circular pin at each end of the C which engage with holes in a ring nut.

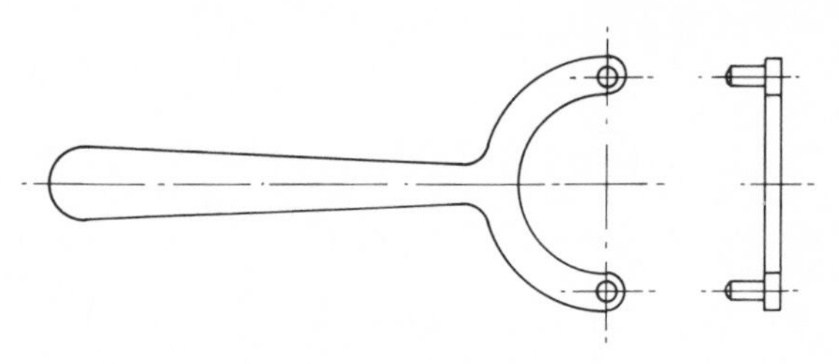

Figure 3.73 *Face spanner (wrench)*

C spanner (wrench) The end of this spanner is curved into the form of a C with a square peg at the end which engages with a notch in the circumference of a ring nut.

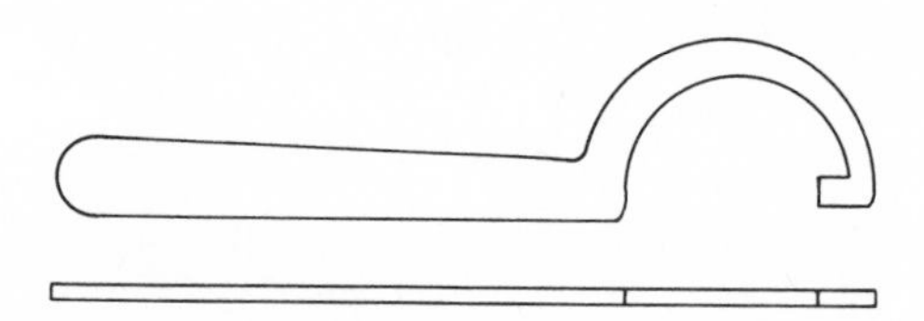

Figure 3.74 *C spanner (wrench)*

Hexagon socket wrench (Allen key) A piece of hexagon bar with the end bent at right angles, used in conjunction with hexagon socket screws.

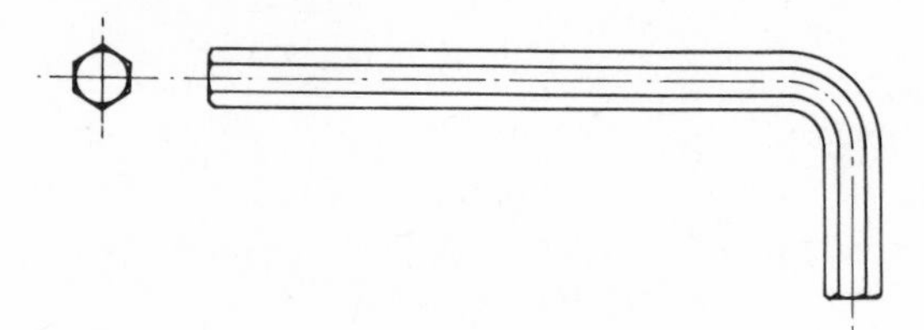

Figure 3.75 *Hexagon socket wrench (Allen key)*

Torque spanner A torque spanner is used to tighten nuts to a predetermined torque to avoid overstraining the threads. There are two types, one has a dial which indicates the torque and another which can be set to slip at the required torque.

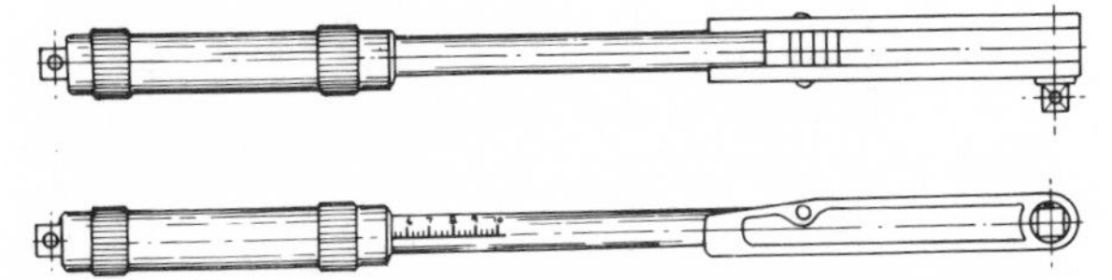

Figure 3.76 *Torque spanner (wrench) for use with sockets*

Pipe wrench (Stillson wrench) A type of adjustable spanner designed to grip pipes and other circular objects.

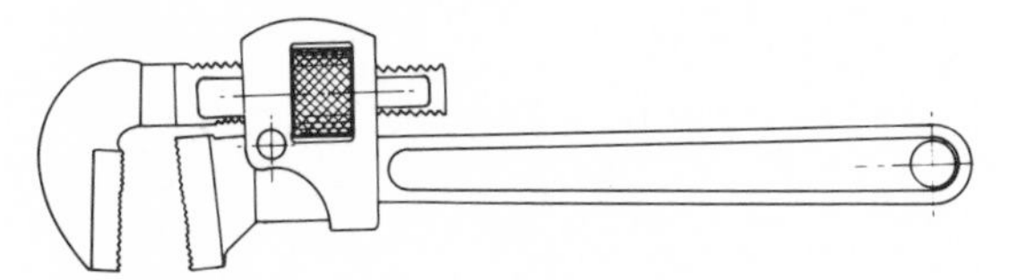

Figure 3.77 *Pipe wrench (Stillson wrench)*

3.2 MACHINE TOOLS

The term 'machine tool' applies to any power-driven, non-portable machine designed to shape usually metal parts. It includes milling machines, shapers, lathes, drilling machines, borers, gear cutters, etc.

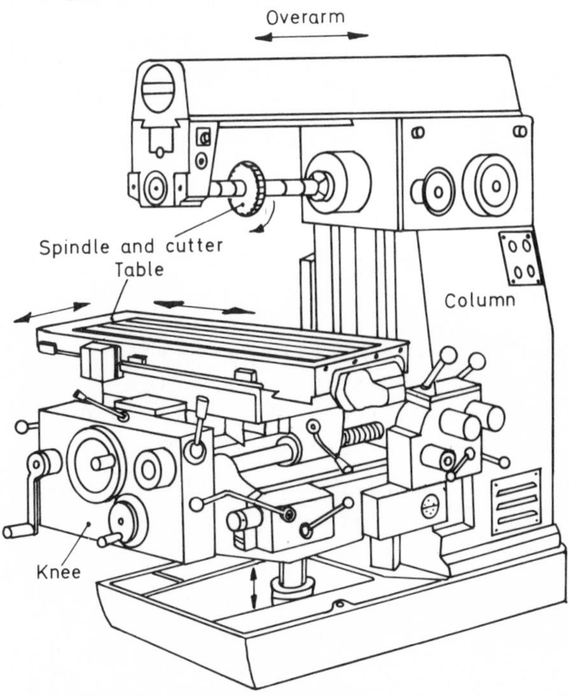

Figure 3.78 *Horizontal milling machine*

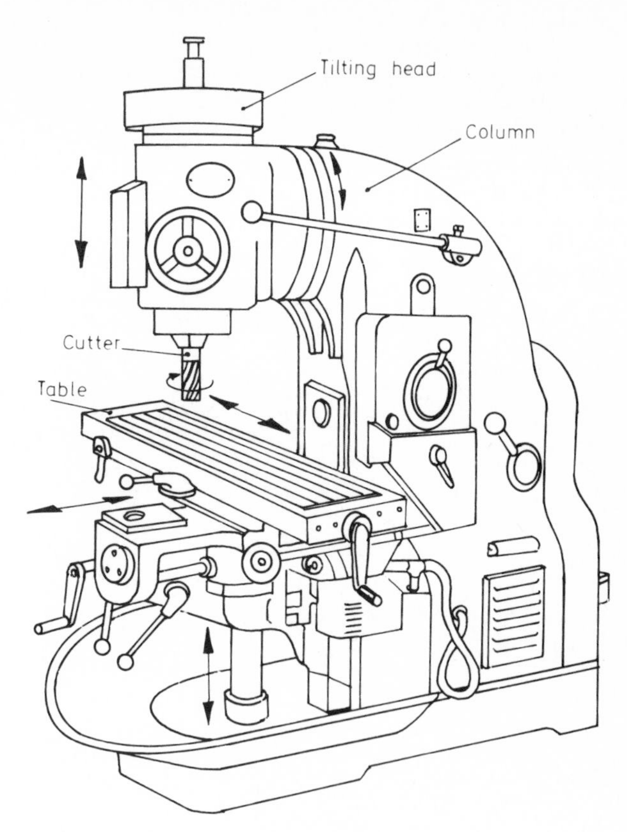

Figure 3.79 *Vertical milling machine*

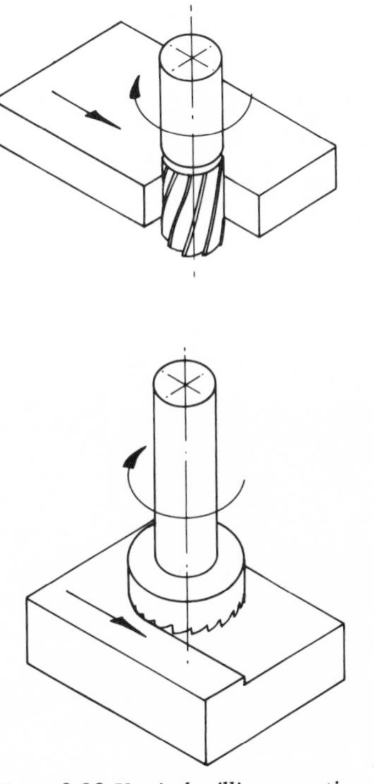

Figure 3.80 *Vertical milling operations*

MILLING MACHINE

A milling machine produces mainly flat surfaces by means of a rotating cutter. The work is mounted on a table which can be driven in three directions, and the milling cutter is driven at various speeds by an electric motor mounted on a column.

The two most common types of milling machine are the horizontal machine which has a spindle with a horizontal axis, and the vertical spindle machine which may have a tilting head to incline the spindle axis to the vertical.

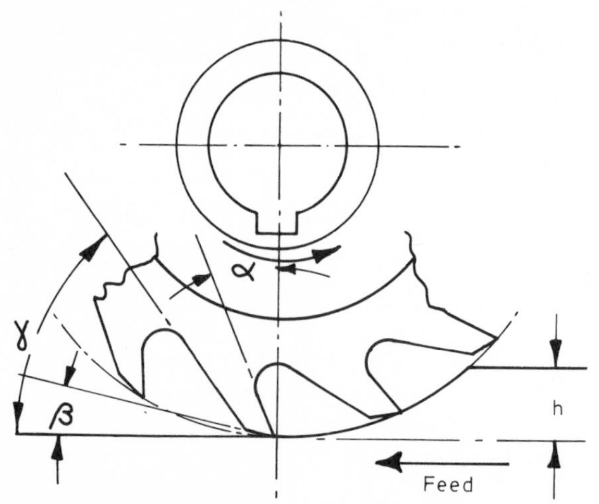

Figure 3.81 *Milling cutter nomenclature: α-rake; β-primary clearance; γ-secondary clearance; h-depth of cut*

MILLING CUTTERS

Milling cutters have cutting teeth around the circumference and/or on the end of a disk or cylinder. The teeth may be parallel to the axis of rotation, or helical, and may be contoured. Several cutters may be 'ganged' together to produce complicated profiles.

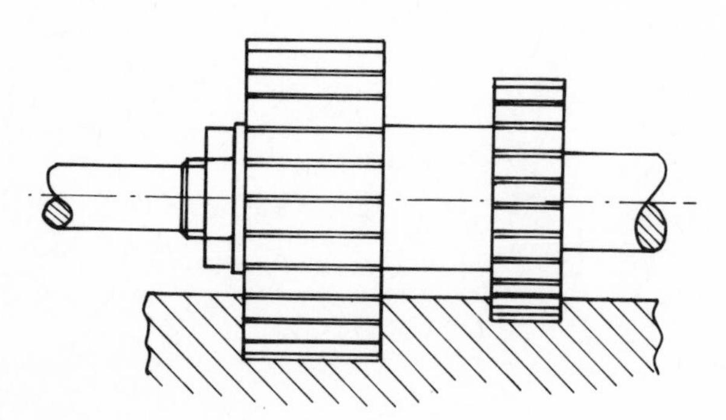

Figure 3.82 *Ganged milling cutters*

Slot milling cutter A disk with teeth on the rim which cut on the periphery only. It is used for machining slots or as a slitting saw, and is mounted on a shaft or *arbor* in a horizontal milling machine.

Figure 3.83 shows the conventional 'up-cutting' action, but if the feed is reversed a 'down-cutting' action is obtained, as shown in Figure 3.83a. This tends to drive the work in the feed direction, and a backlash eliminator in the table drive is required.

Side and face milling cutter This has cutting edges on the sides of the disk so that it can be used for side cutting as well as edge cutting.

Contour milling cutter These have special profiles such as concave or convex circular arcs, and they are used for producing internal and external radii, etc.

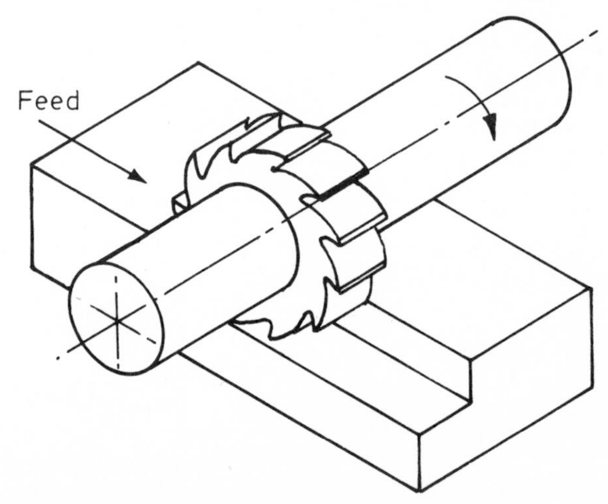

Figure 3.83 *Horizontal milling – up cut*

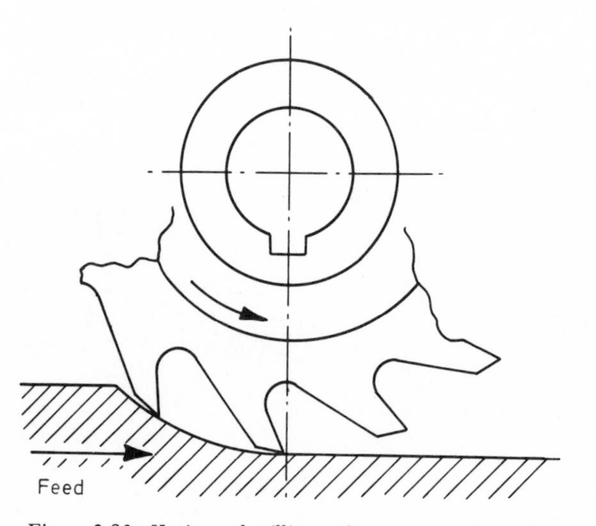

Figure 3.83a *Horizontal milling – down cut*

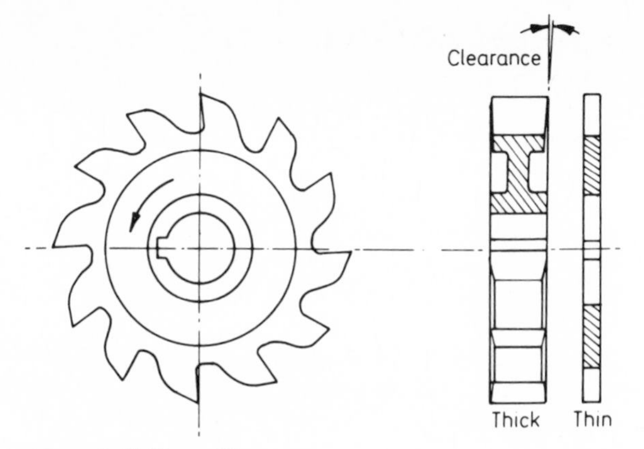

Figure 3.84 *Slot milling cutter*

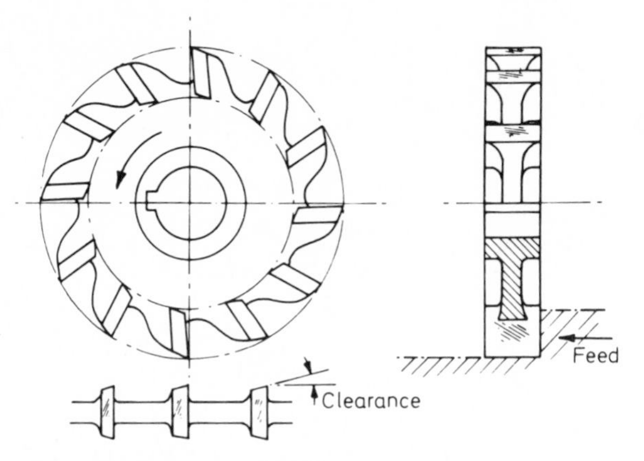

Figure 3.85 *Side and face milling cutter*

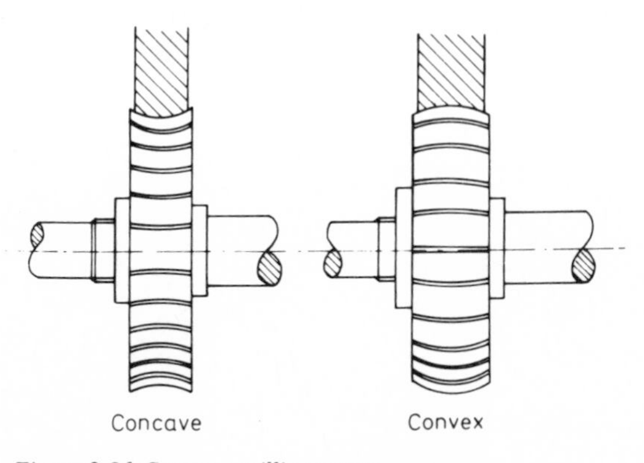

Figure 3.86 *Contour milling cutter*

Slab or rolling milling cutter A large cylindrical cutter used for machining horizontal surfaces. Usually it is mounted on a horizontal arbor, and to prevent vibration helical teeth are preferred.

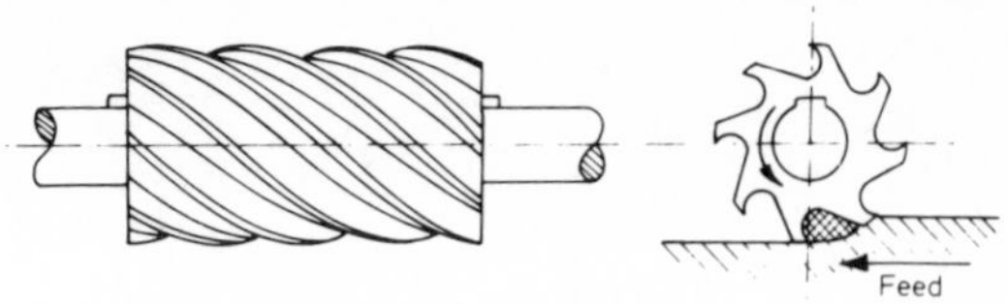

Figure 3.87 *Slab or rolling milling cutter*

End milling cutter Small end mills are made from solid bar with straight shanks to suit a collet. Larger cutters with separate shanks tapered to suit the machine spindle nose are known as *shell end mills*.

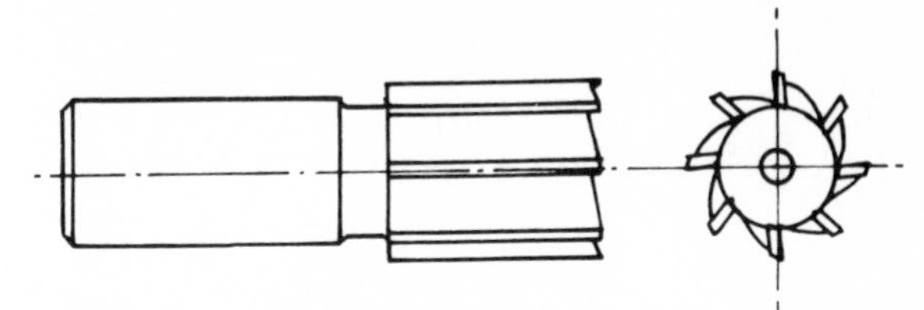

Figure 3.88 *End milling cutter*

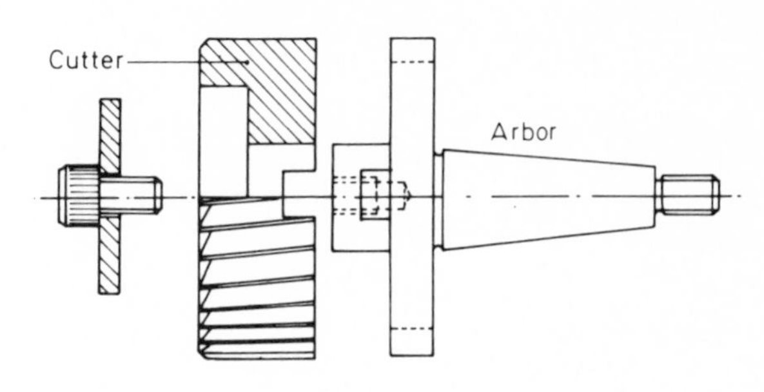

Figure 3.89 *Shell endmilling cutter*

Angular tooth milling cutters The teeth are on a conical surface so that angled surfaces may be machined. Typical angles are 45° and 60° to the horizontal. One type is known as a *dovetail cutter*.

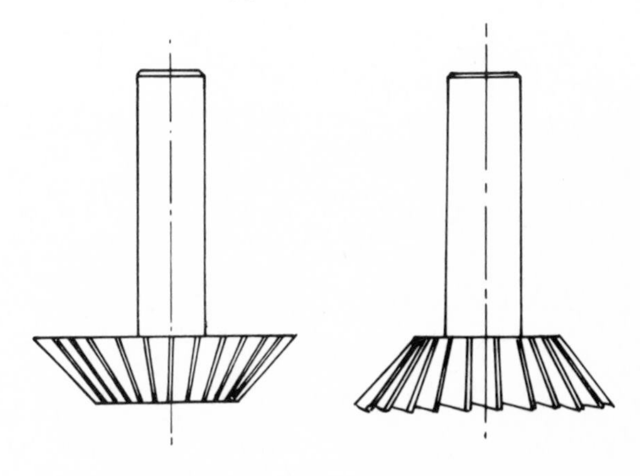

Figure 3.90 *Angular tooth milling cutter*

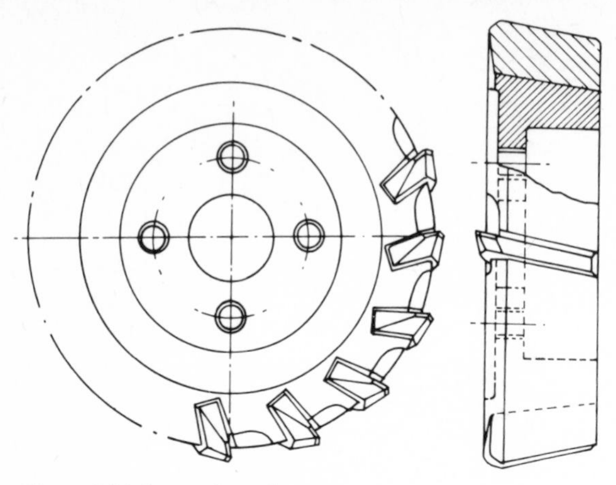

Figure 3.91 *Inserted tooth cutter*

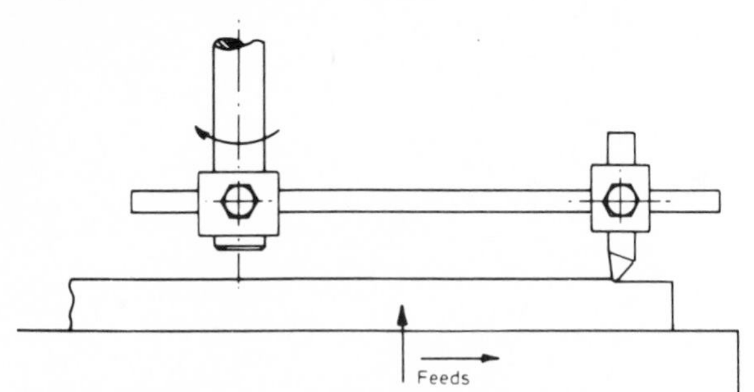

Figure 3.92 *Milling large surface with fly cutter*

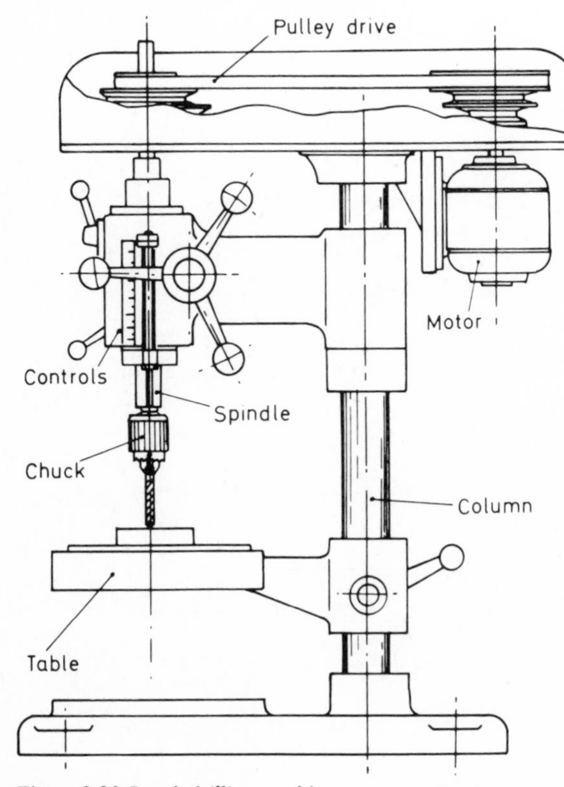

Figure 3.93 *Bench drilling machine*

Inserted tooth milling cutter Large, end or peripheral milling cutters are made which have separate teeth inserted into the disk which can be replaced when worn. Alternatively, the teeth can be re-sharpened.

Fly cutter To machine large surfaces a single-point cutter mounted on a disk or bar may be used. The bar-mounted cutter can be set at any radius and several cutters may be used to reduce the load.

DRILLING MACHINES (DRILL PRESSES)

These are machines which provide rotation at various speeds for drills to produce holes in a wide variety of materials. They vary in size from small bench-mounted machines to very large radial-arm floor-mounted machines.

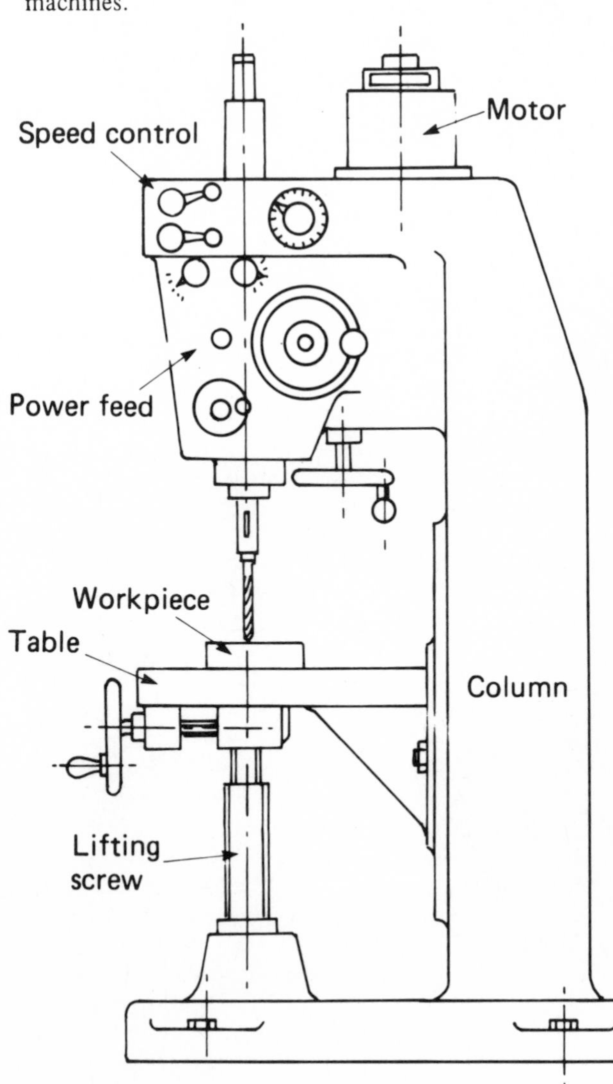

Figure 3.94 *Vertical box column drilling machine*

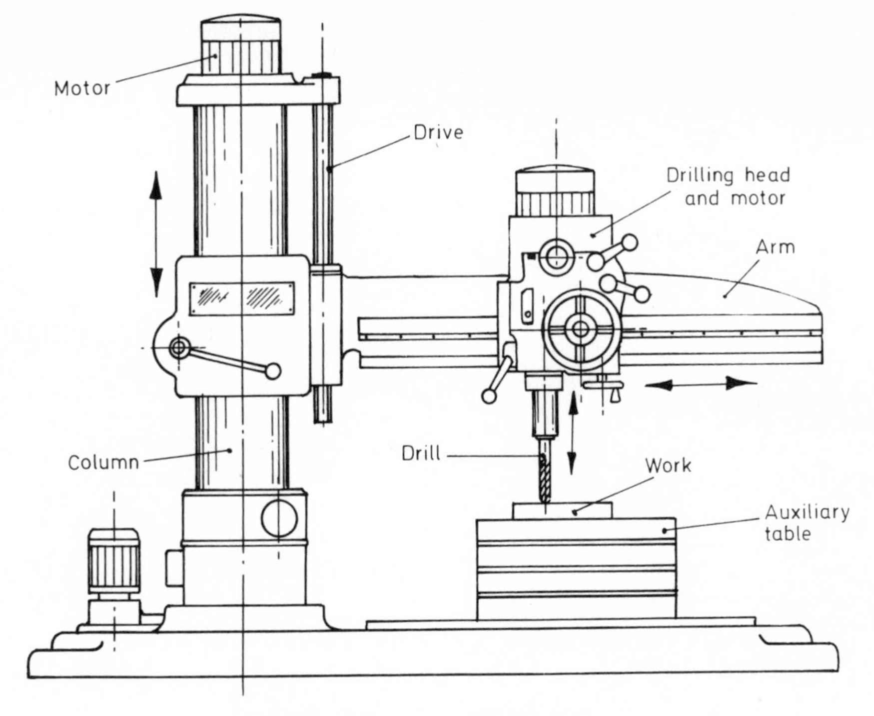

Figure 3.95 *Radial-arm drilling machine*

Radial-arm drilling machine The drilling head with the motor, speed change gearbox and drill spindle is mounted on a horizontal slide on the arm. The arm can be raised or lowered by an auxiliary motor and swung horizontally on a vertical post. Work is attached to the bedplate or to an auxiliary table. This machine is suitable for drilling heavy casting, forgings and weldments.

Bench drilling machine In this machine the vertical spindle is driven by an electric motor through a set of stepped V pulleys to give several speeds. The drill is either held in a chuck or has a taper shank which fits directly into the spindle. There is a table which can be adjusted vertically or swung horizontally on a post, and an adjustable stop controls the depth of hole. The work is clamped to the table or held in a machine vice bolted to the table.

Bench drilling machines for light work with drill sizes of up to about 10mm diameter and speeds of up to 9 000 rev/min are often referred to as *sensitive drilling machines*. Heavier duty machines take drills of up to 25mm diameter.

Vertical box column drilling machines This is a floor-mounted machine with a heavy cast column carrying a head with a vertical spindle. A multi-speed gearbox fitted to the drive gives a wide range of speeds and there is a power feed. Work is mounted on a table which can be raised or lowered by a screw.

DRILL CHUCK

Straight shank drills are held in a chuck with jaws operated by a key, but taper shank drills fit directly into the machine spindles via taper adaptors. Drills of up to 20 mm (¾ in.) may be accommodated.

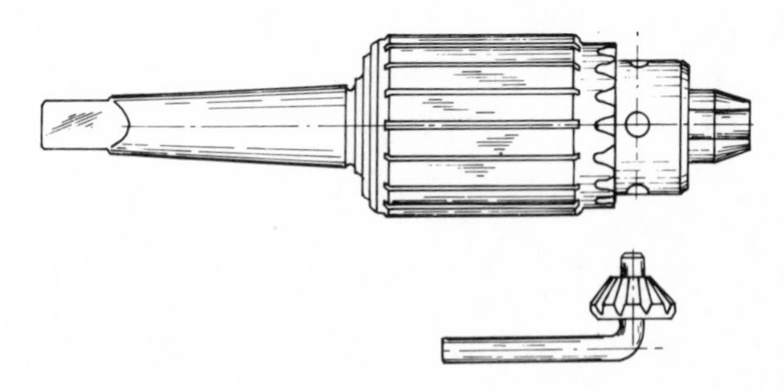

Figure 3.96 *Chuck and key*

DRILLING MACHINE OPERATIONS

In addition to drilling through and blind holes other operations are possible as follows:

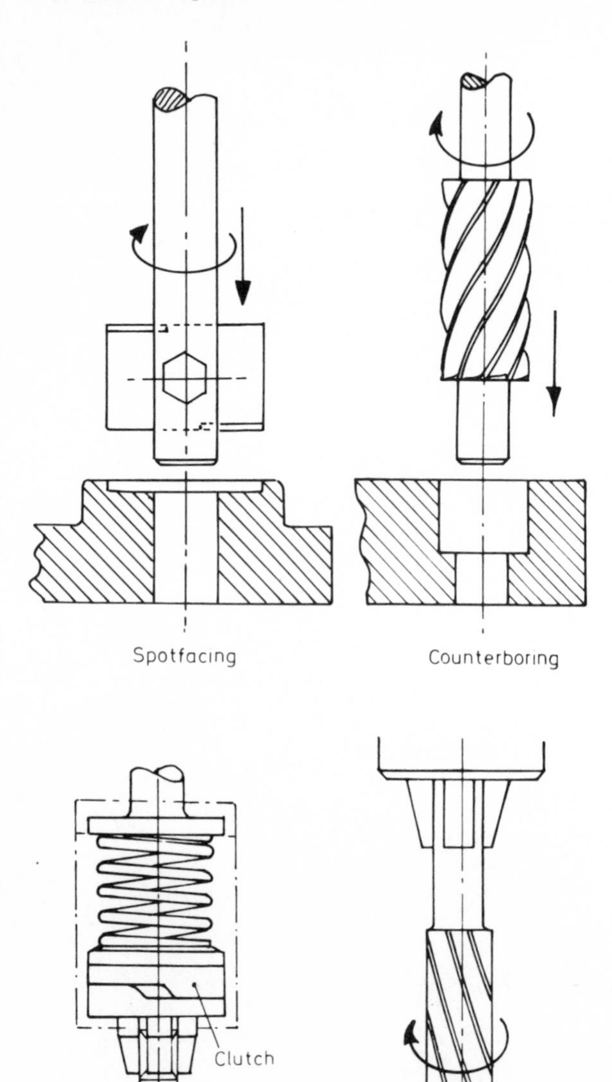

Figure 3.97 *Drilling machine operations*

Spotfacing A blade-type cutter attached to a bar is used to cut a face at the entrance to a hole in a rough casting etc.

Counterboring Enlarges the drilled hole to take the head of a socket screw, etc. A special tool, similar to an end mill but with a pilot, is used.

Tapping May be done on the machine using a tap holder with a spring-loaded clutch which slips when the tap reaches the bottom of the hole until the direction of rotation is reversed.

Reaming May be done using a low speed and plenty of cutting fluid.

SHAPING MACHINE (SHAPER)

A shaping machine, or shaper, is used to produce flat surfaces by means of a single-point reciprocating tool. The surfaces may be vertical, horizontal or angled.

The machine consists of a reciprocating arm driven by a variable-speed, quick-return mechanism, with a tool head which has a vertical feed and a table with feed in two horizontal directions. The 'head' is mounted in a vertical slide and carries the 'clapper box' which in its turn carries the 'tool post'. The clapper box is designed to tilt on the return stroke to avoid rubbing of the tool.

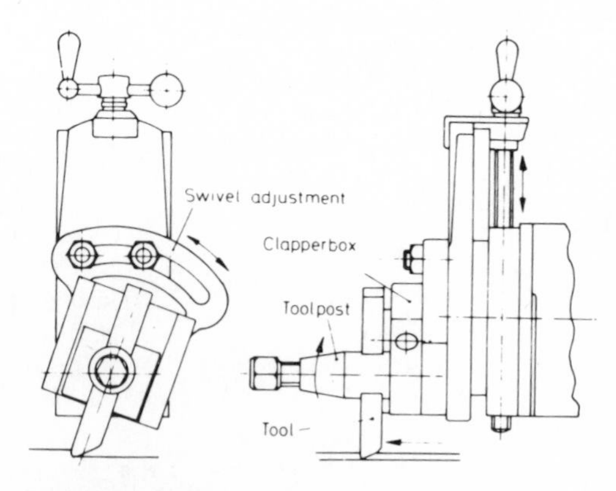

Figure 3.98 *Shaping machine tool head*

Two typical tools are the 'straight' tool and the 'swan-necked' tool. The swan-necked tool has the cutting edge behind the clapper box pivot. Bending the tool tends to lift the cutting edge and prevent 'digging-in'.

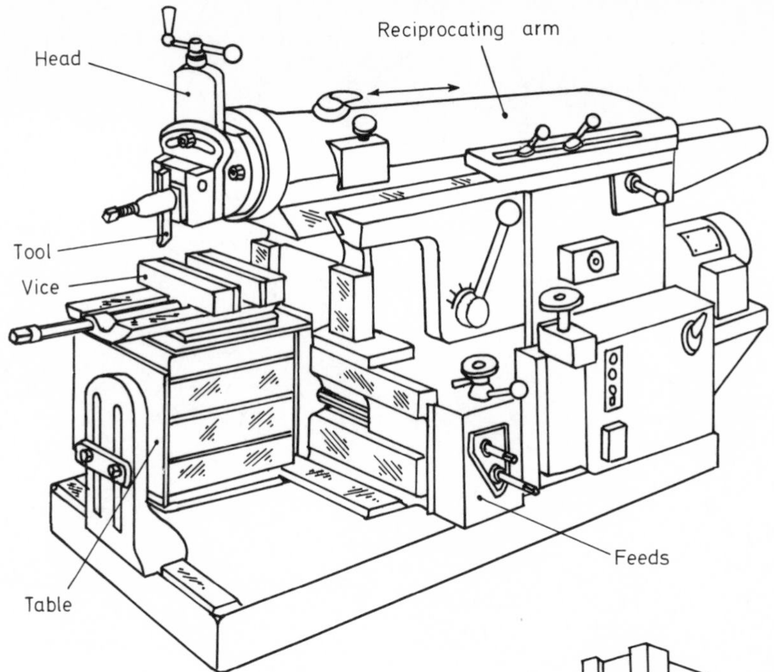

Figure 3.99 *Shaping machine (shaper)*

VERTICAL SHAPER (SLOTTER)

Vertical shapers, or slotters, are used for internal cutting and planing at angles. The table has a rotary feed to give curved machined surfaces.

These machines are used for cutting keyways in gears, pulleys, etc.

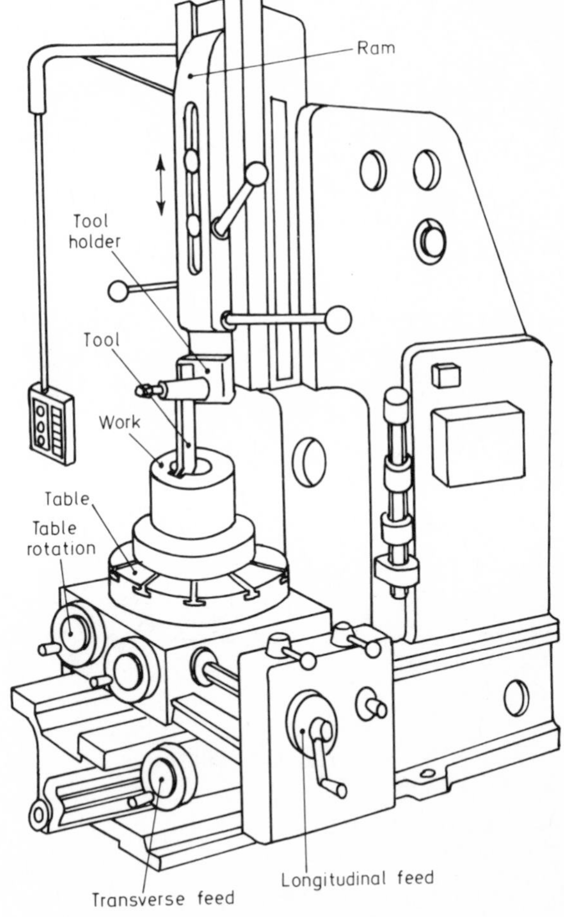

Figure 3.101 *Vertical shaper (slotter)*

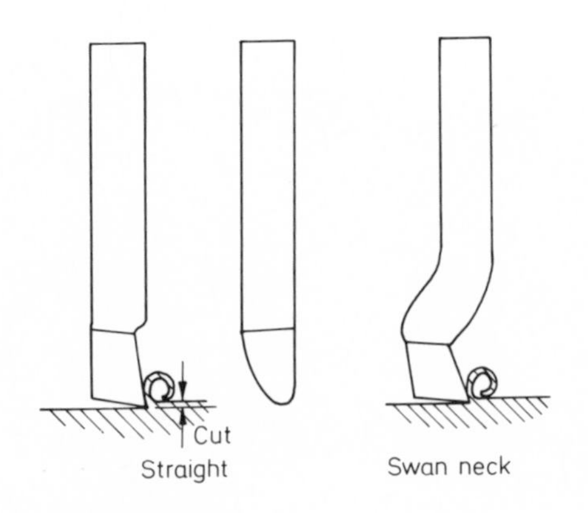

Figure 3.100 *Shaper tools*

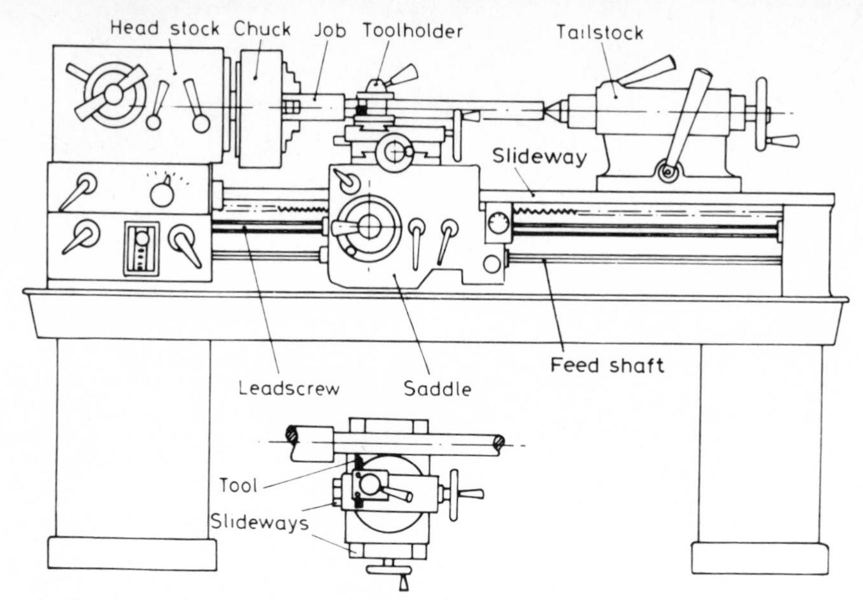

Figure 3.102 *Centre lathe (engine lathe)*

CENTRE LATHE (ENGINE LATHE)

The centre lathe is a machine tool used to produce flat, cylindrical and conical surfaces with a single point tool and the work rotating. It consists of a bed, headstock, tailstock and saddle with a leadscrew.

Bed A casting resting on the floor and carrying the other parts of the lathe. Running along the length of the bed is a slideway on which the tailstock is fixed and on which the saddle moves.

Headstock A box mounted at one end of the bed and containing a spindle driven by speed change gears and an electric motor. The end of the spindle takes a chuck or faceplate to hold the workpiece.

Tailstock This is mounted at the opposite end of the bed to the headstock. It holds a conical 'centre' which can support the end of the workpiece, or a drill chuck when required. The tailstock can be moved along the bed on a slideway and locked in the desired position.

Saddle This carries the toolholder and the slides and turntable which control the tool position. It is traversed along the bed either manually or by a *feed shaft* (lay shaft). When carrying out screw-cutting it is driven by a *lead screw* geared to the motor.

LATHE OPERATIONS

The most common operation performed on the lathe is that of 'turning' cylindrical surfaces. Others are parting-off, boring, facing, drilling and screwcutting.

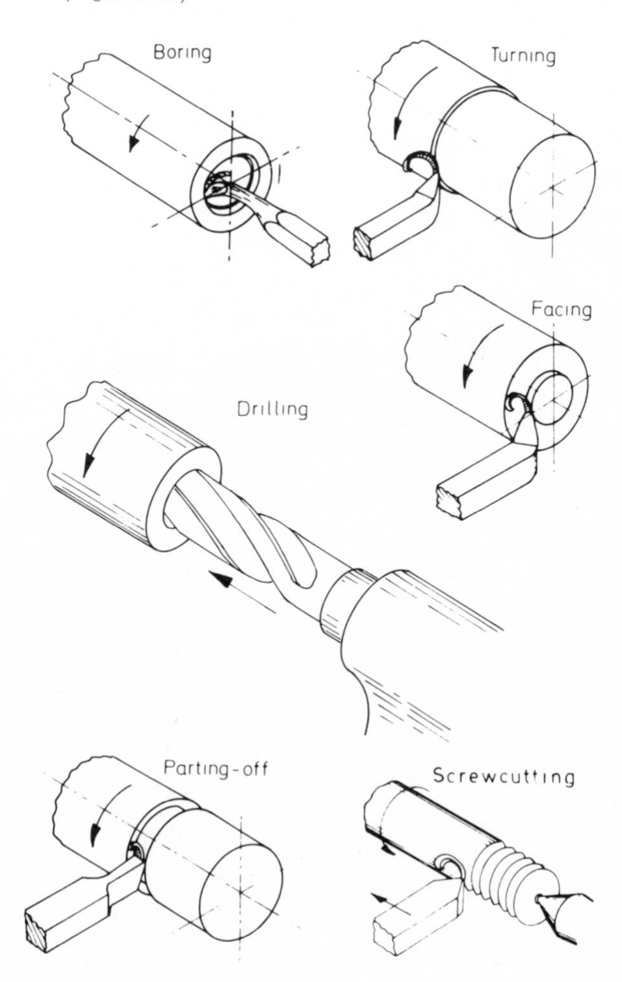

Figure 3.103 *Lathe operations*

LATHE TOOLS

There are numerous types of lathe tool designed to suit specific operations. The principle ones are: bar-turning, turning and facing, parting-off, facing, boring and screw-cutting.

Some tools are made from one piece of tool steel, others have high-speed steel tips welded to carbon steel shanks and some have tungsten carbide tips brazed on to a steel shank. A tool-holder with interchangeable tips can also be used.

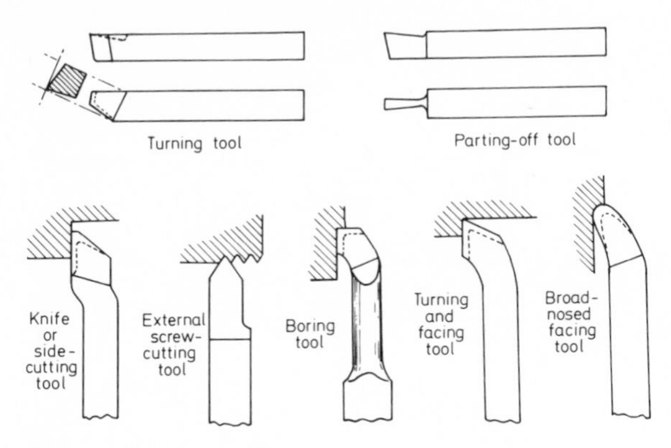

Figure 3.104 *Lathe tools*

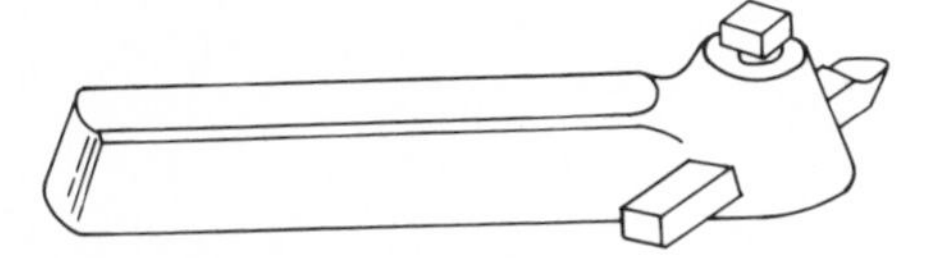

Figure 3.105 *Lathe tool holder*

LATHE CHUCKS

The chuck is a device for holding the workpiece in a lathe, and the three main types are: *three-jaw self-centring, four-jaw independent, collet.*

Self-centring three-jaw chuck This has a cylindrical body with jaws in three radial slots driven by a scroll plate in the body. As the scroll plate is rotated by means of a bevel gear operated by a hand key, the jaws move in the slots simultaneously.

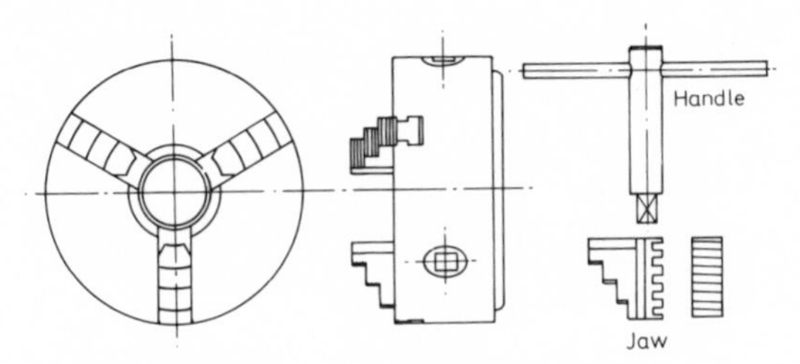

Figure 3.106 *Self-centring three-jaw chuck*

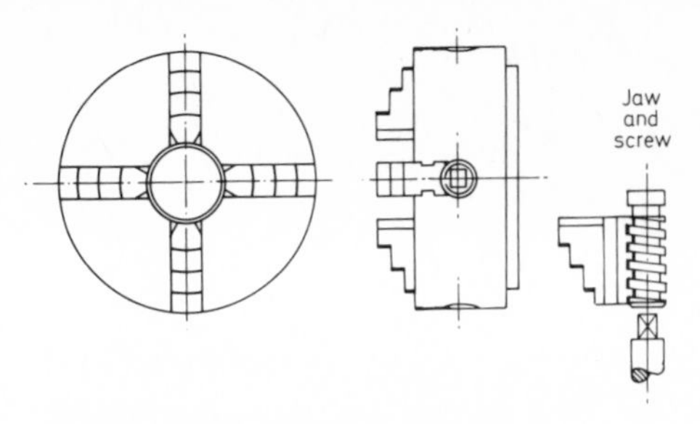

Figure 3.107 *Independent four-jaw chuck*

Independent four-jaw chuck Each of the four jaws is moved radially by a square thread on a key-operated screw which engages with a mating thread on the back of the jaw.

Collet chuck (collet) Collets are used to hold standard sizes of round, square and hexagonal stock bar. The bar is held in a tapered sleeve tightened by means of a screwed collar.

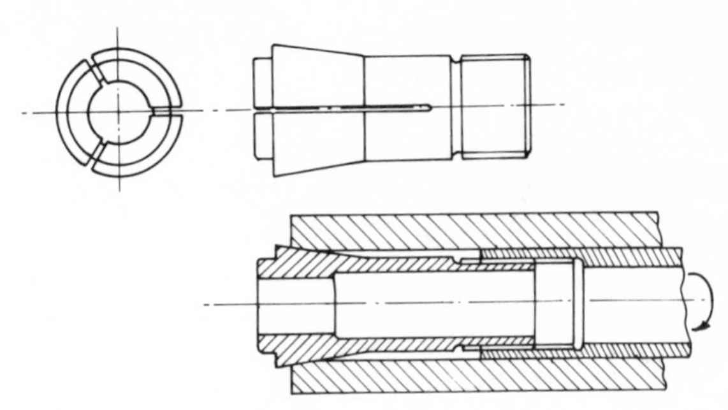

Figure 3.108 *Spring collet*

FACE PLATE

A face plate is used instead of a chuck for objects of irregular shape such as castings. It is a flat circular plate screwed to the spindle and pierced with slots to which the workpiece is clamped. It is often necessary to use a balance weight to prevent vibration.

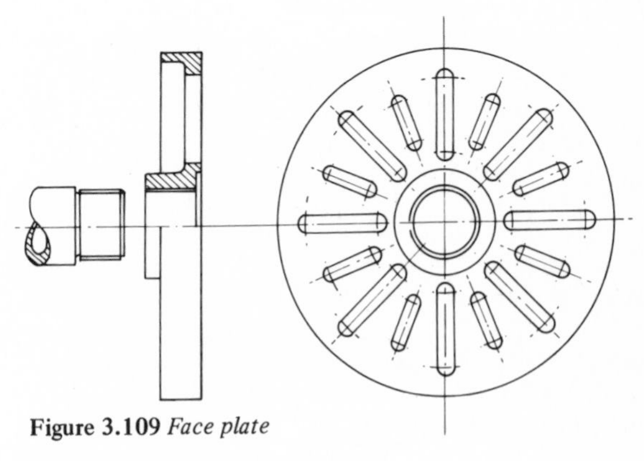

Figure 3.109 *Face plate*

TURNING BETWEEN CENTRES

Objects such as shafts are often mounted between centres instead of in a chuck. 'Centre holes' are drilled in the ends of the shaft by a centre drill, and conical centres in the spindle nose and tailstock are fitted into them. A driving pin on a 'catch plate' locked to the spindle nose engages with a driving dog clamped to the workpiece.

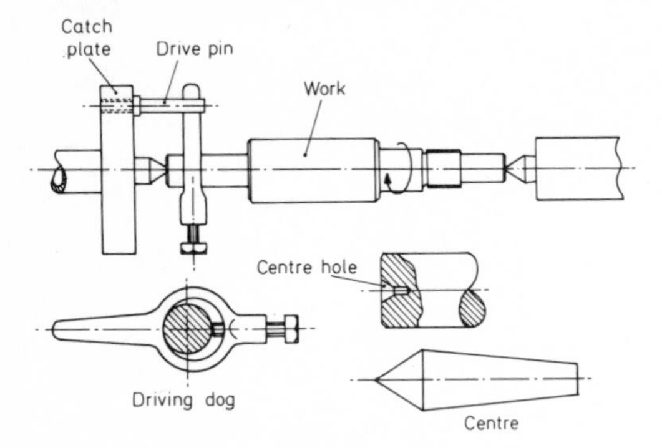

Figure 3.110 *Turning between centres*

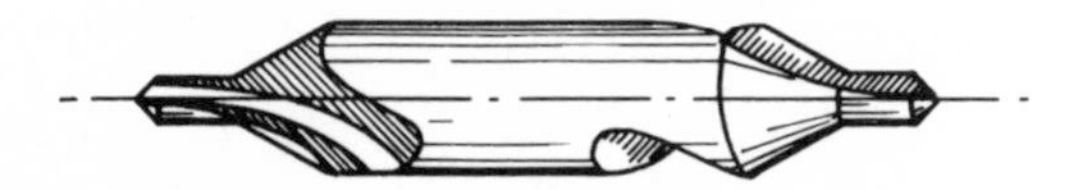

Figure 3.111 *Centre drill*

GRINDING MACHINES

Grinding machines are used to produce flat, cylindrical and other surfaces by means of high-speed rotating abrasive wheels. Grinding is often a means of giving a more accurate finish to a part already machined but it is also a machining process in its own right.

Surface grinding machine This is used to produce a highly-finished flat surface. The work is held on a horizontal reciprocating table by clamps or by a magnetic chuck. A grinding wheel rotates on a horizontal axis at right angles to the table motion. This table is movable along the wheel axis and the wheel can be moved vertically to give the required cut.

The magnetic chuck is a flat steel plate with permanent magnets embedded in it, and it is particularly useful for holding down thin plate.

Cylindrical grinding machine A machine similar in layout to a centre lathe but with the tool replaced by a seperately-driven grinding wheel. Cylindrical surfaces are produced by traversing the wheel along the axis, and complex profiles may be produced by specially-shaped grinding wheels.

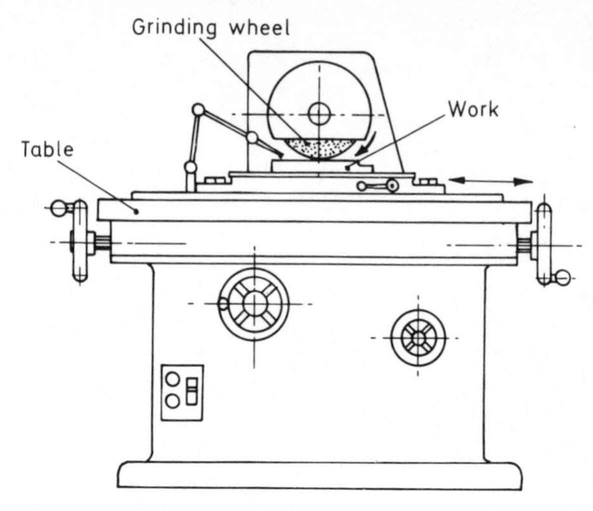

Figure 3.112 *Surface grinding machine*

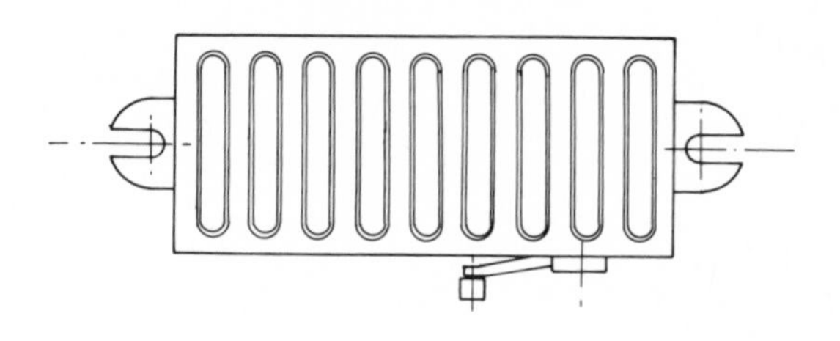

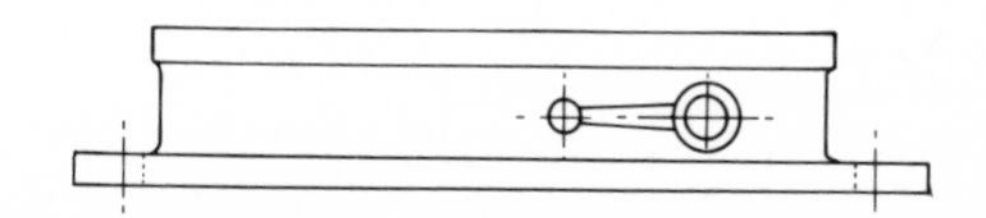

Figure 3.113 *Magnetic chuck for surface grinding machine*

GRINDING WHEELS

Grinding wheels are made in a vast number of materials, shapes and sizes. Typical materials are bonded abrasive powders such as aluminium oxide (Al_2O_3), silicon carbide (Si C), or diamond. Some typical shapes are shown.

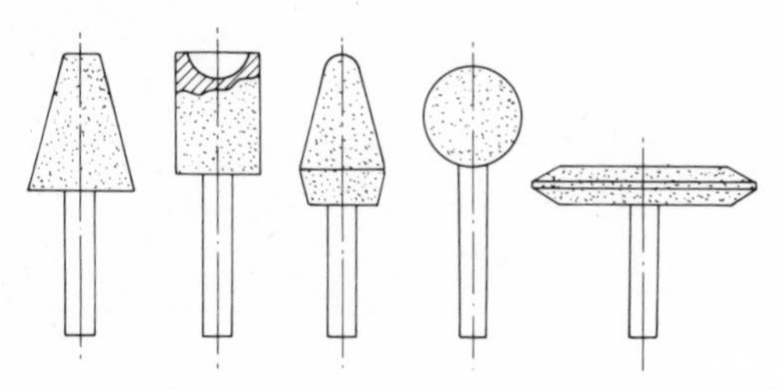

Figure 3.114 *Contour grinding wheels*

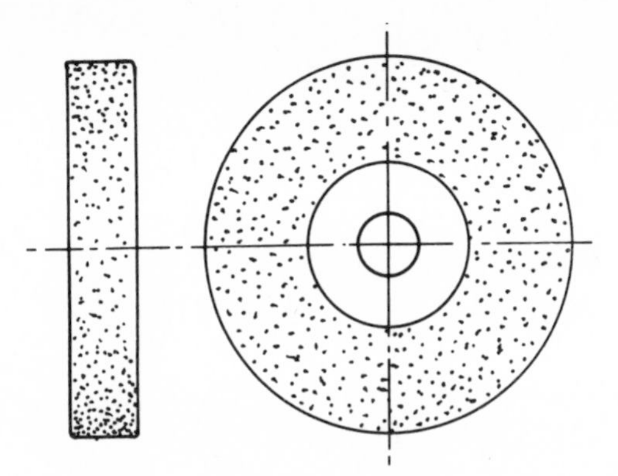

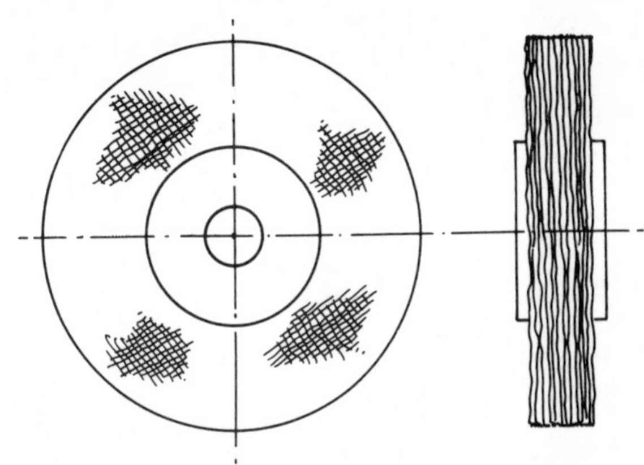

Figure 3.117 *Polishing (buffing) mop*

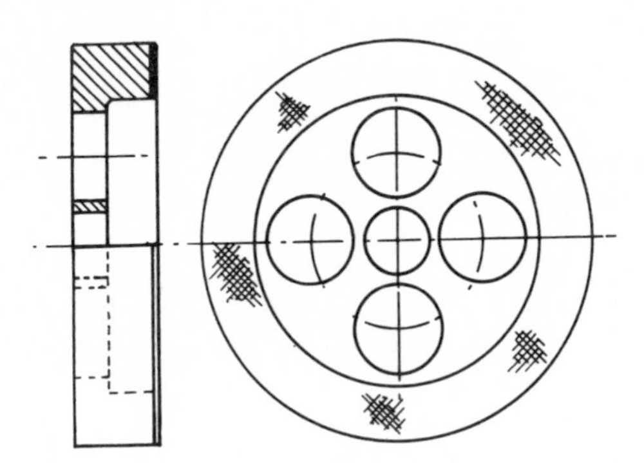

Figure 3.115 *Grinding wheels*

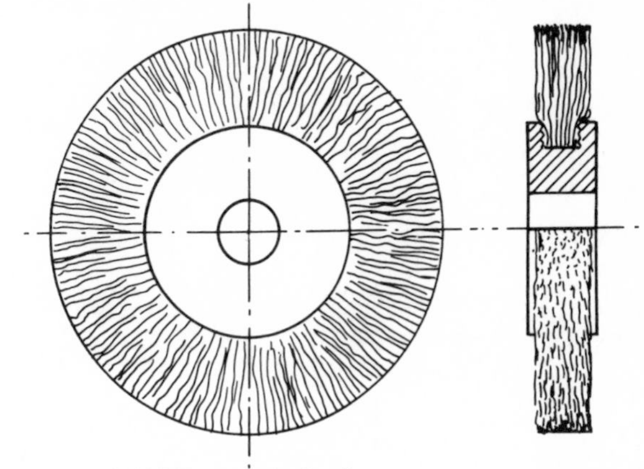

Figure 3.118 *Rotary wire brush*

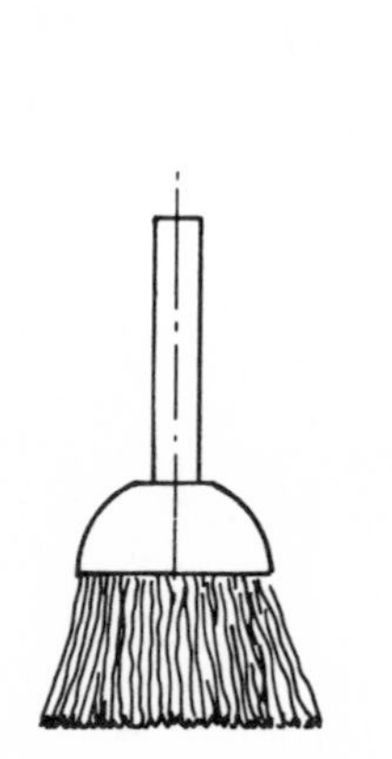

Figure 3.116 *Rotary wire brush*

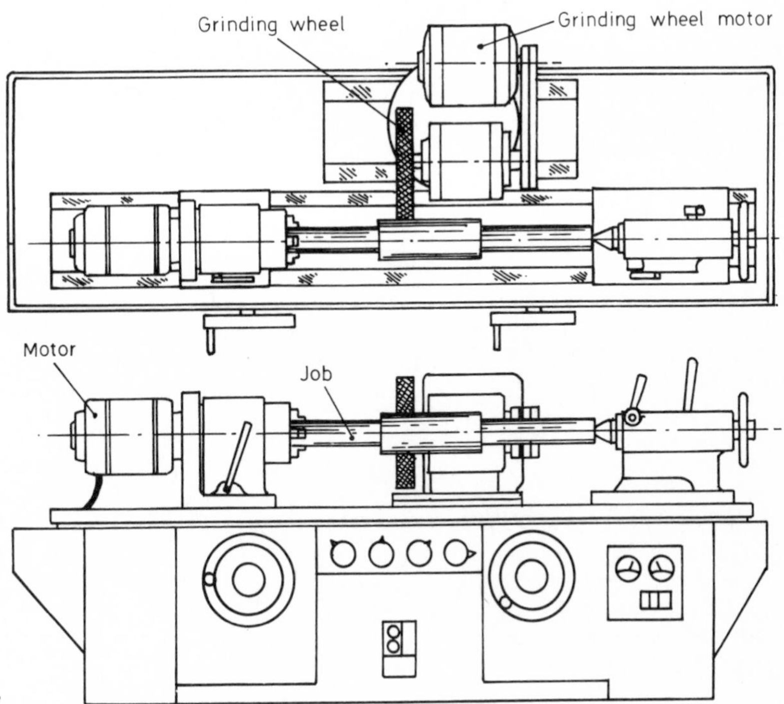

Figure 3.119 *Cylindrical grinding machine*

BENCH AND PEDESTAL GRINDERS

These machines are used for manual grinding operations such as sharpening tools for lathes, shapers, etc., and for sharpening chisels, screwdrivers and other hand tools.

The wheels are mounted on the shafts at both ends of an electric motor. Wire brush wheels and buffing mops may be fitted.

These machines and the hand-held grinder are generally referred to as 'off-hand' grinders as opposed to 'precision' grinders.

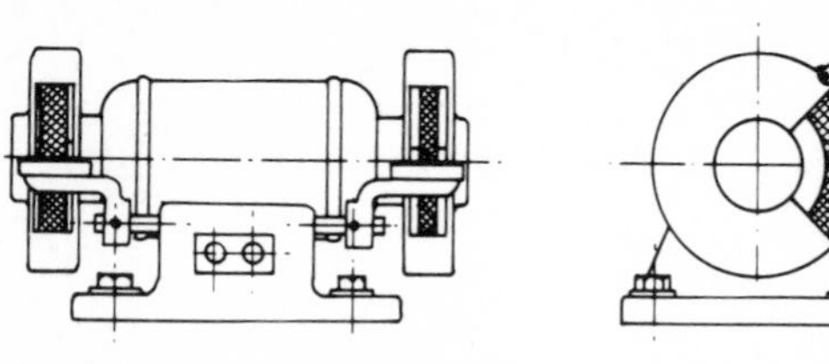

Figure 3.120 *Bench grinder*

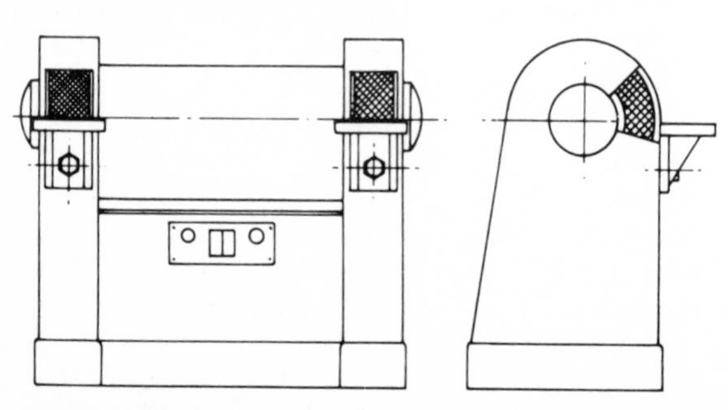

Figure 3.121 *Heavy duty pedestal grinder*

BORING MACHINES

To make large diameter holes boring is used as an alternative to drilling.

In a boring machine the work is mounted on a stationary table and the boring bar rotates on a vertical spindle. In a *boring mill* the work is usually very large and it rotates while the boring bar remains fixed.

Horizontal boring machines These are used for very large work and they also have drilling and milling facilities.

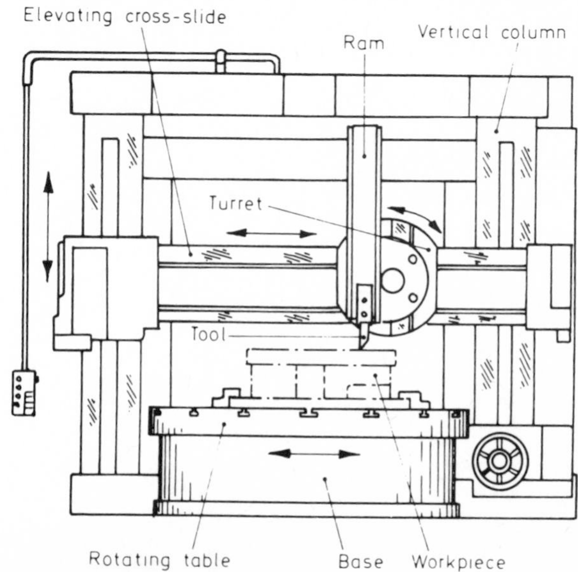

Figure 3.122 *Vertical boring mill*

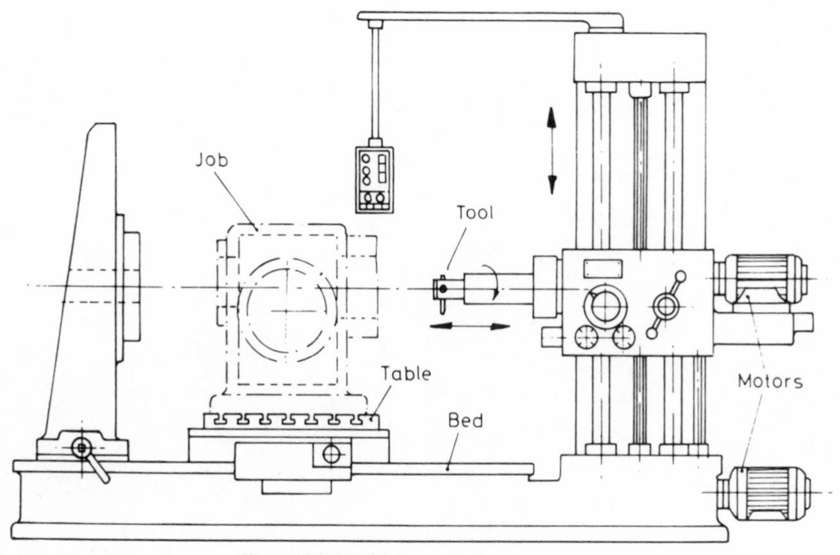

Figure 3.123 *Horizontal boring machine*

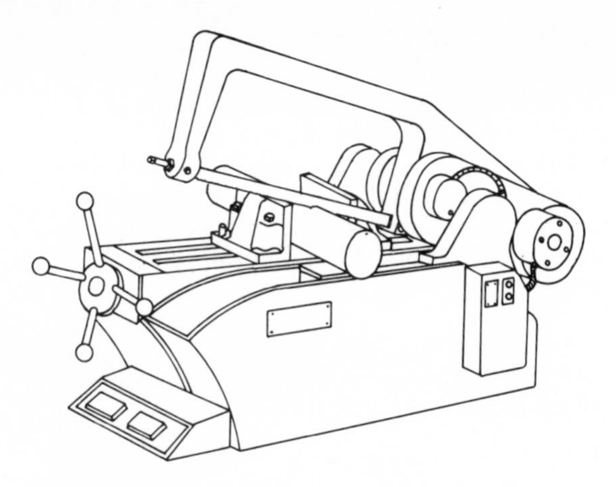

Figure 3.124 *Reciprocating power hacksaw*

POWER SAWS

There are two main types of power say, the *reciprocating power hacksaw* and the *bandsaw*.

The reciprocating saw has a blade and action similar to that of a hand hacksaw. The work, usually heavy bar, is clamped in a vice with the feed being controlled by a *dashpot* which dampens vibrations of the saw.

The light duty bandsaw has a continuous flexible blade driven vertically past the work which is moved by hand on a horizontal table. This saw is suitable for cutting wood, plastics and thin sheet, usually of soft metals.

The reciprocating power saw is being replaced by heavy duty bandsaws capable of cutting very thick, tough metal. The work is clamped on a table which may be tilted and is fitted with a feed mechanism.

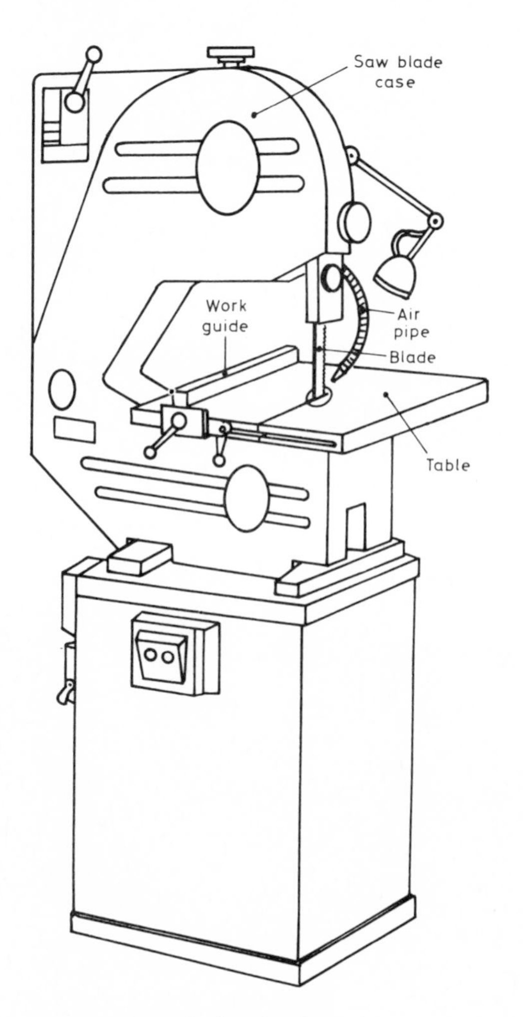

Figure 3.125 *Light duty bandsaw*

3.3 SOFT-SOLDERING, BRAZING AND WELDING EQUIPMENT

SOFT-SOLDERING

Soldering is the hot bonding of metal parts by adhesion using a thin film of low melting point alloy known as solder. Small joints are made by applying heat with a soldering iron while large joints are made by 'sweating' the parts together in a gas flame.

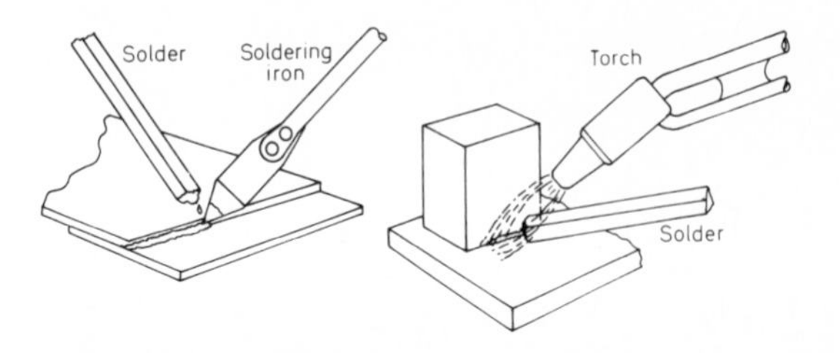

Figure 3.126 *Soft soldering*

SOLDERING IRONS

For heavy engineering work soldering irons have heavy copper 'bits' mounted on an iron shank with a wooden handle. Bits may be of either the 'straight' or the 'hatchet' type, and both may be heated by a gas flame or have an internal electric heating element. Electric irons are made in small sizes for electronic work. The bit is heated to the required temperature and before use the working edge is coated with solder, or 'tinned'.

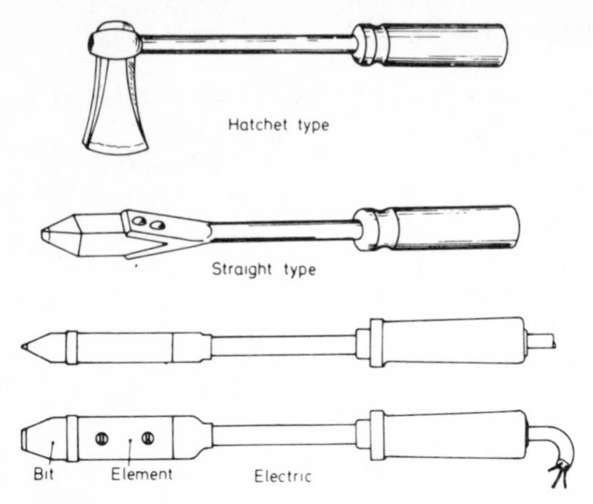

Figure 3.127 *Soldering irons*

SOFT SOLDER

Soft solder is a mixture of tin and lead which melts at the relatively low temperature of 183°C. The proportion is approximately two parts of tin to one part of lead. It is available in bar form for general engineering work and also in the form of wire with a resin flux core.

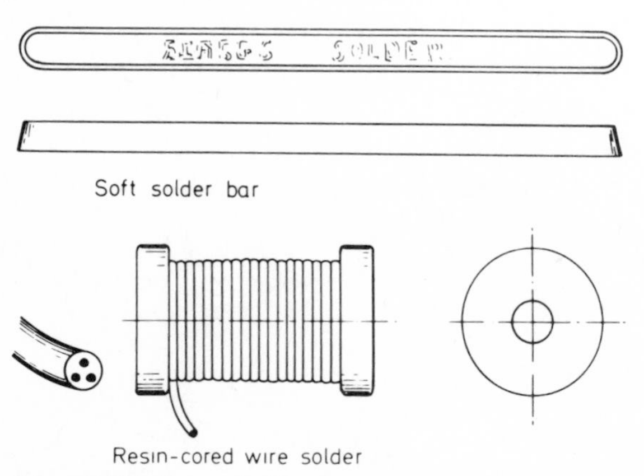

Figure 3.128 *Types of solder*

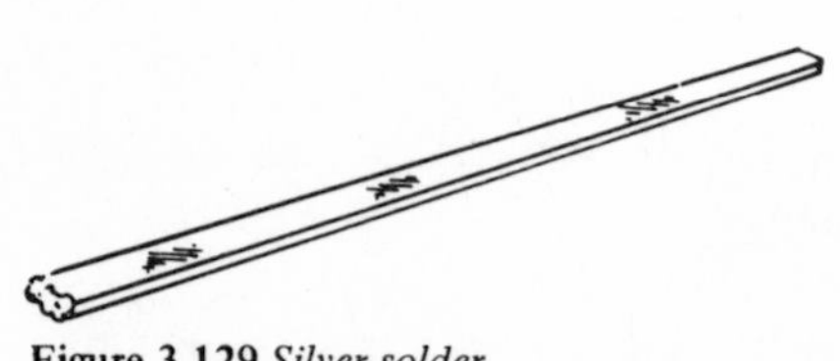

Figure 3.129 *Silver solder*

SILVER SOLDERING

Silver solder is an alloy of silver, copper and zinc with a melting point of about 700°C, that is, lower than that required for brazing. It may be used for joining brass and copper. The solder is supplied in a strip form.

FLUX

Flux is a substance which, when heated, provides a liquid or gaseous shield which excludes oxygen and prevents oxidisation of the surface of the metal being soldered. It may be an active flux such as zinc-chloride (killed spirit) or a passive flux such as resin.

Figure 3.130 *Soft solder fluxes*

BRAZING (HARD SOLDERING)

In brazing, the joining metal is brass consisting of varying proportions of copper and zinc known as 'spelter'. The brazing temperature of about 900°C is much higher than that for soft soldering. Spelter is supplied in the form of round rod of small diameter or in granular form mixed with flux.

Borax is generally used as brazing flux in the form of a powder which is mixed to a paste with water. The heat of brazing melts the borax to form a protective slag.

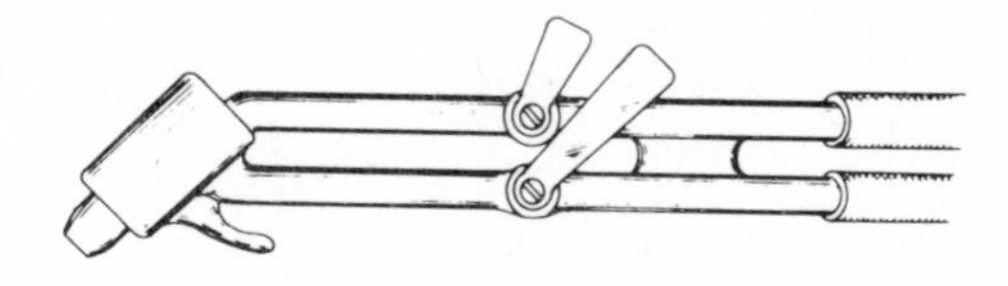

Figure 3.131 *Gas-air brazing torch*

BRAZING TORCH

A special torch is required for brazing. The usual type is supplied with mains gas and air from a blower, and it is fitted with adjustable gas and air taps for controlling the flow and mixture of gases.

BRAZING HEARTH

Brazing is best carried out in a hearth designed for the purpose. The hearth is made from steel lined with fire brick and has an electrically-driven air blower mounted on it.

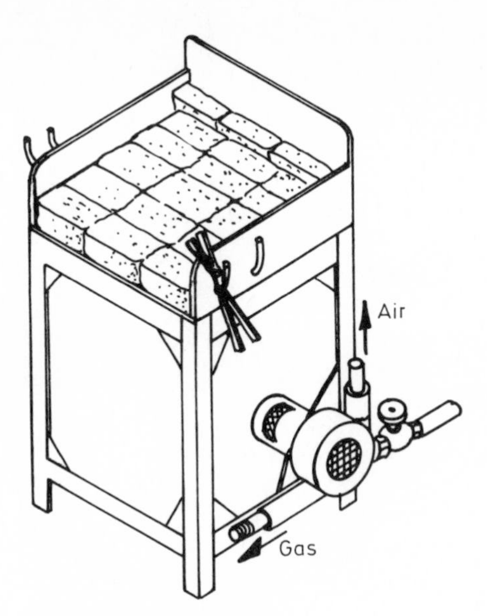

Figure 3.132 *Brazing hearth*

WELDING

Welding is a process for joining metals, plastics, etc. by heating them locally until they can be joined by fusion or forging. The main methods of fusion welding are: electric arc, gas torch, friction and resistance welding.

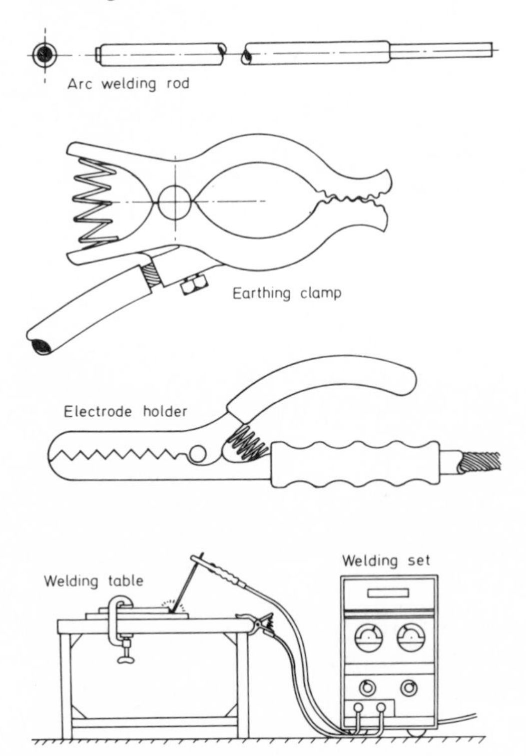

Figure 3.133 *Arc welding equipment*

ARC WELDING

In this process the heat of fusion is generated by an electric arc struck between two electrodes, one of which is the workpiece and the other a welding rod. The welding rod is made of a material similar to that of the parts being welded and is coated with a solid flux which melts when heated. It is used to 'fill' the welded joint.

Power is obtained from an a.c. or d.c. *welding set* providing a regulated low voltage, high current supply to an *electrode holder* and an *earthing clamp*. The work is done on a special *welding table* made of steel on which the work is clamped and to which the earthing clamp is attached to complete the electric circuit.

TYPES OF WELD

Most welds in machine elements are fillet welds although butt welds are used a great deal for pressure vessels. These and other types of weld commonly used are described in the following:

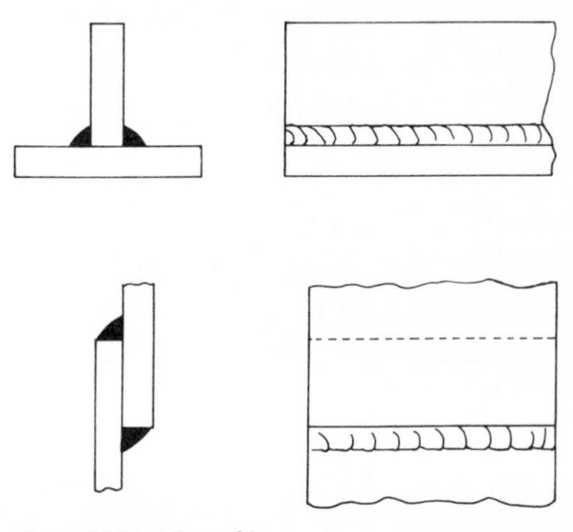

Figure 3.134 *Fillet welds*

Fillet weld A weld joining two plates at right angles, or overlapping plates. The weld is formed in the corner and is of approximately triangular shape.

Intermittent weld In the interests of economy and to reduce distortion, fillet welds are often intermittent.

Butt weld A weld joining two plates end to end to form a continuous plate. The plates are usually prepared by chamfering and the weld may be on one side or both sides of the plates (*see* Flash weld).

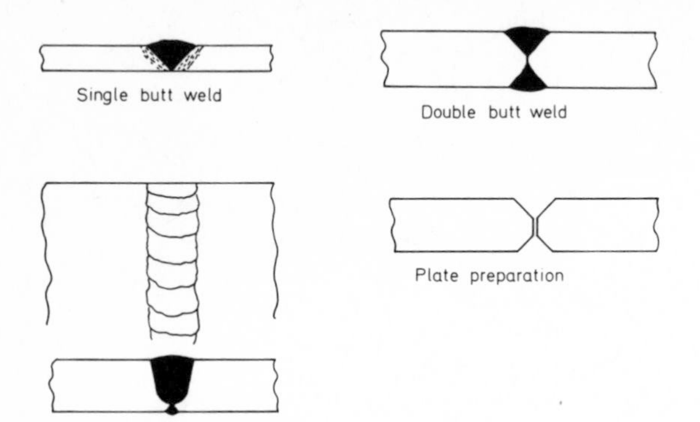

Figure 3.135 *Butt welds*

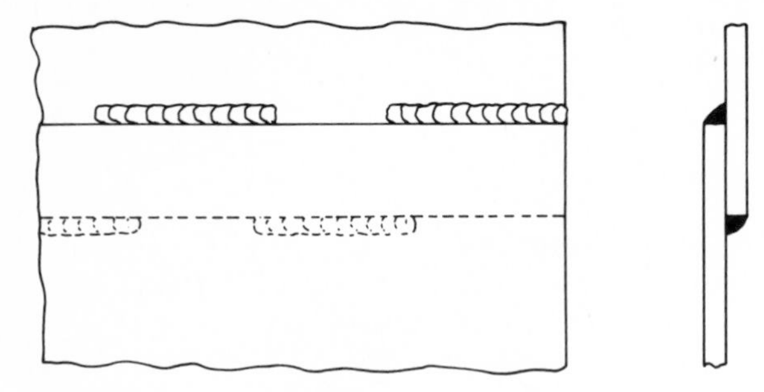

Figure 3.136 *Intermittent weld*

Plug weld A method of joining plates in which a series of holes in one plate are filled with weld to join it to the other plate to give a result similar to riveting.

Slot weld A similar method to plug welding using slots instead of holes.

Tack weld A short intermittent weld used to hold parts together temporarily before further welding.

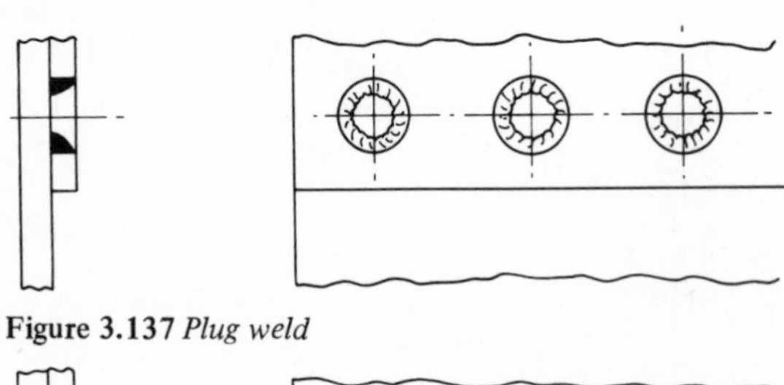

Figure 3.137 *Plug weld*

Figure 3.138 *Slot weld*

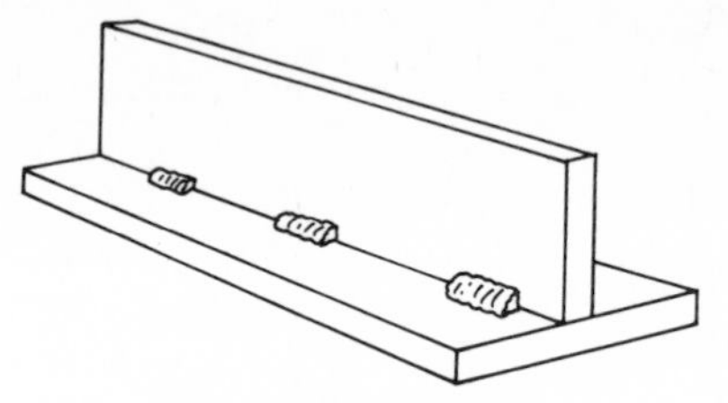

Figure 3.139 *Tack weld*

RESISTANCE WELDING

Welding is produced by fusion due to the heavy current flowing between two metal objects when they are held in close contact by electrodes. The current depends upon the nature of the surface and the contact pressure. This method is used for joining sheet metal and for attaching studs, rods and bosses etc. to plates.

Spot weld A type of resistance weld where thin plates are joined by local spots of fusion. It is used extensively for lightly-loaded light metal parts.

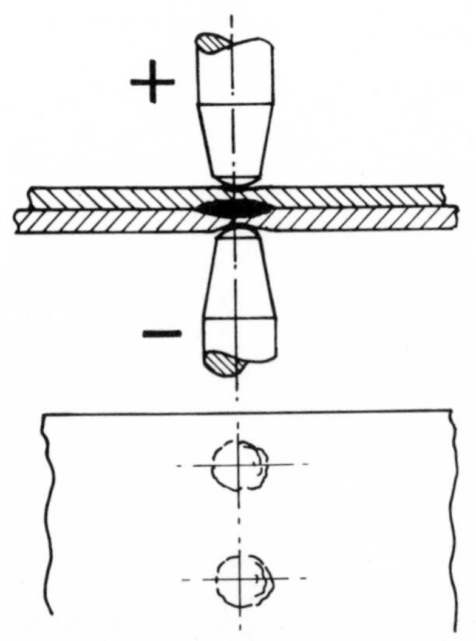

Figure 3.140 *Spot welding*

Resistance seam weld A continuous process in which two overlapping plates are joined by fusion due to the current flowing between two rotating wheels.

Flash weld A method of butt welding bars by resistance welding. The ends of the bars are connected to an electrical supply and brought together under pressure to complete the circuit. The arc produced causes fusion and the power is cut off to allow the joint to solidify.

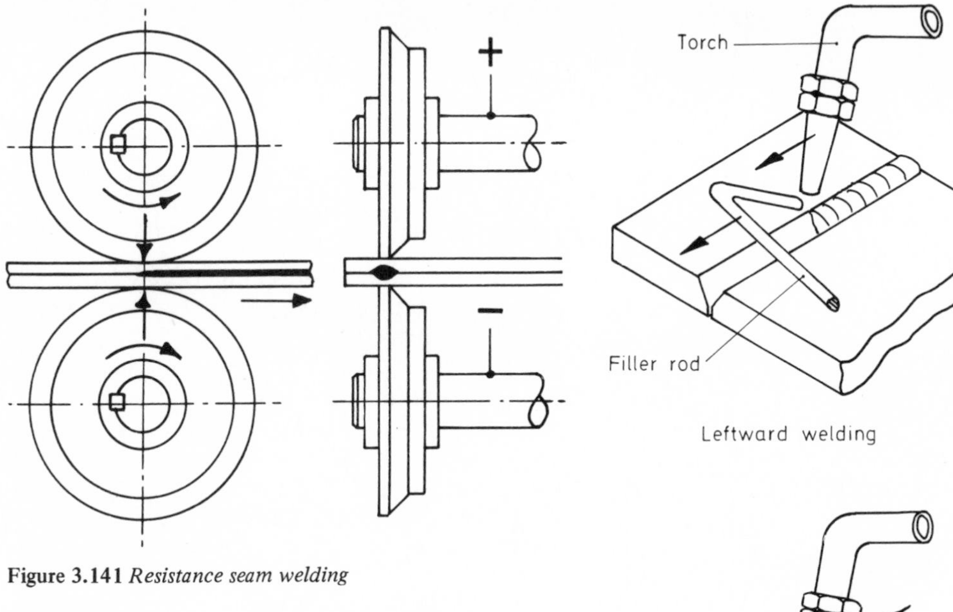

Figure 3.141 *Resistance seam welding*

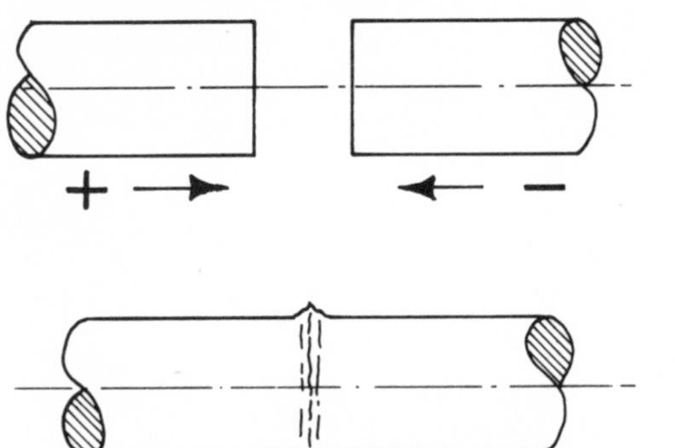

Figure 3.142 *Flash welding*

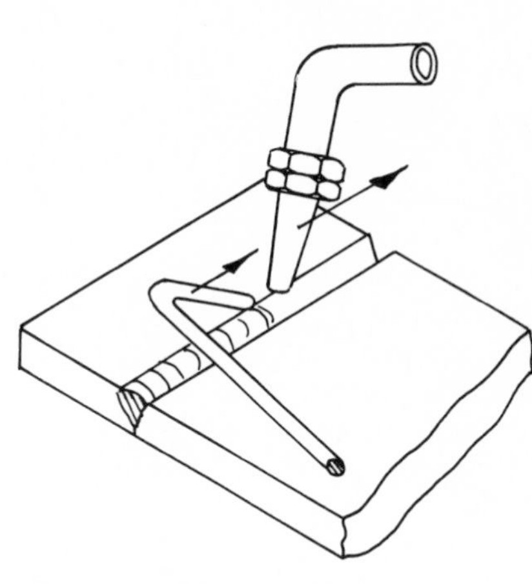

Figure 3.143 *Gas welding*

GAS WELDING

Gas welding is suitable for most sheet metals up to a thickness of a few mm.

The heat of fusion is obtained by burning pure oxygen with gases such as acetylene, butane, propane or hydrogen in a specially designed torch. A filler rod is fed by hand.

Welding may be carried out to the left or right, these methods being known respectively as 'leftward welding' and 'rightward welding'. The former is used for metal thickness of up to 3mm and the latter for over 3mm, but gas welding is not often used for plate over 3mm.

Gas welding equipment The welding torch, fitted with gas and air control valves and interchangeable nozzles, is connected to gas cylinders by flexible hoses leading from regulators on the bottles.

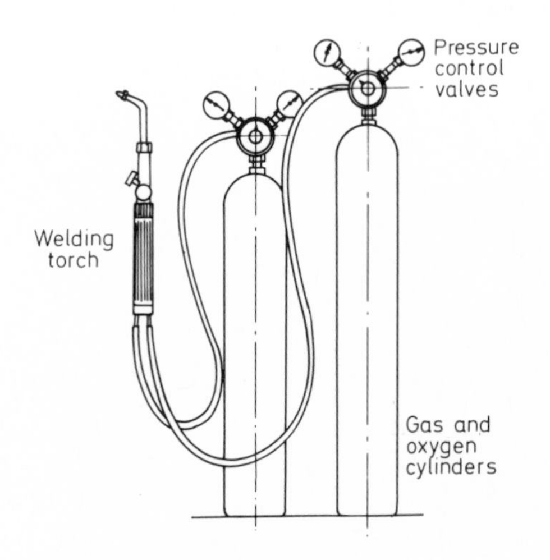

Figure 3.144 *Gas welding equipment*

FLAME CUTTING

Flame cutting is a method of producing shaped flat parts cut from steel plate, especially of large thickness. The torch may be hand-held or mounted in a welding machine in which a template of the required shape is followed by the cutting flame.

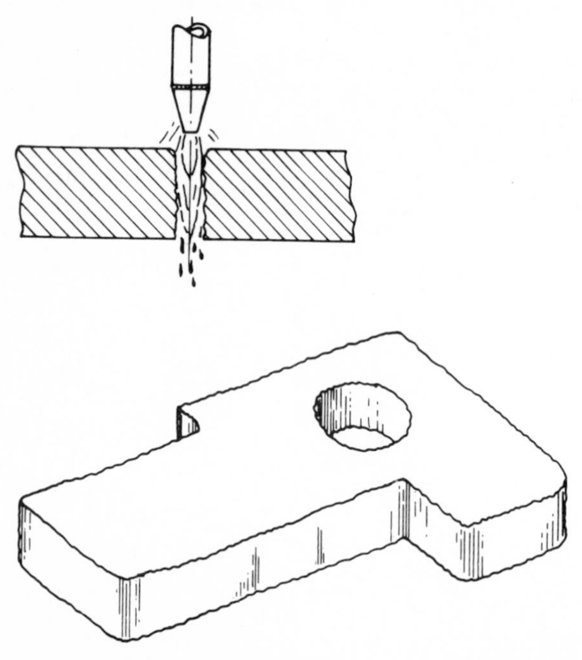

Figure 3.145 *Flame cutting*

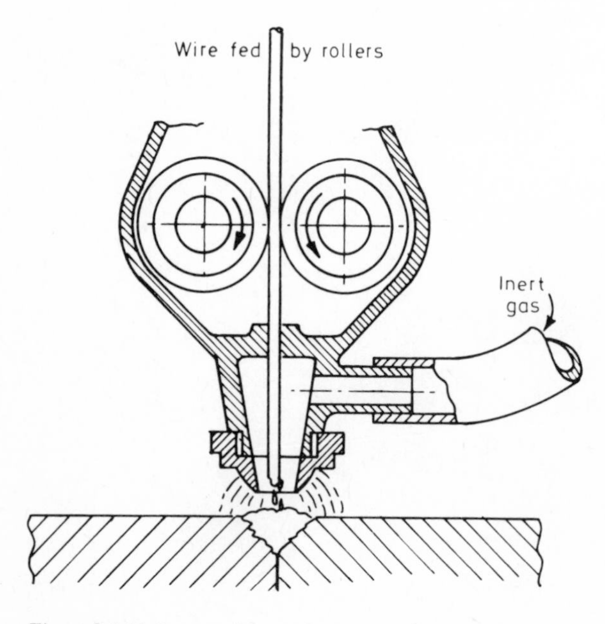

Figure 3.146 *Gas metal arc welding*

GAS SHIELDED METAL ARC WELDING

In this process, also called Metal Inert Gas (MIG), an inert gas such as argon is used as a flux for arc welding. The electrode is a continuously-fed consumeable wire.

FRICTION WELDING

Parts may be welded by the heat generated by mechanical friction. One of the parts is rotated in a chuck and the other part, which does not rotate, is brought into contact with it under pressure. When the resulting friction has produced sufficient heat to fuse the contacting surfaces, the non-rotating part is freed and allowed to rotate. On cooling, the parts are joined. This method is useful for joining dissimilar metals which are otherwise difficult to weld.

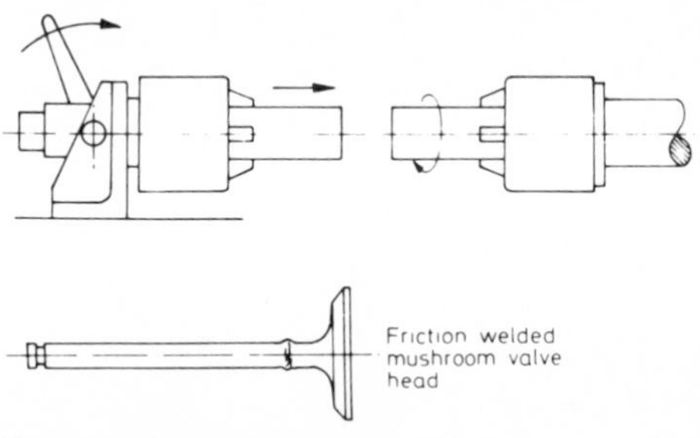

Figure 3.147 *Friction welding*

3.4 METAL-FORMING EQUIPMENT

CASTINGS

A casting is produced by pouring molten metal, or any other material, into a suitably shaped mould and allowing it to solidify. The term 'casting' also refers to the actual process.

Most castings are *sand castings* which are made in a mould using a special moulding sand. The mould is made in a *moulding box* divided horizontally into halves which are located with dowels and bolted together during casting. A wooden replica, or *pattern*, of the part to be cast is embedded in the sand to produce a cavity. Any holes required in the casting are produced by inserting *cores* into the mould. These cores are previously made in a *core box* out of baked sand. The molten metal is poured into the mould through runners until it fills the cavities and appears in risers. When the metal has set the sand is removed, the sticks of metal in the runners and risers are removed, and the casting is cleaned by chipping, grinding and sandblasting.

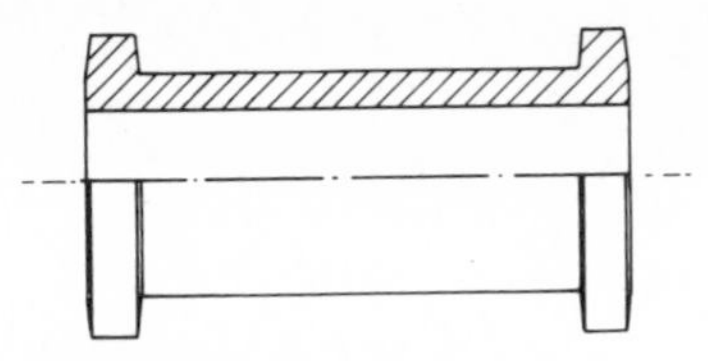

Figure 3.148 *Required casting*

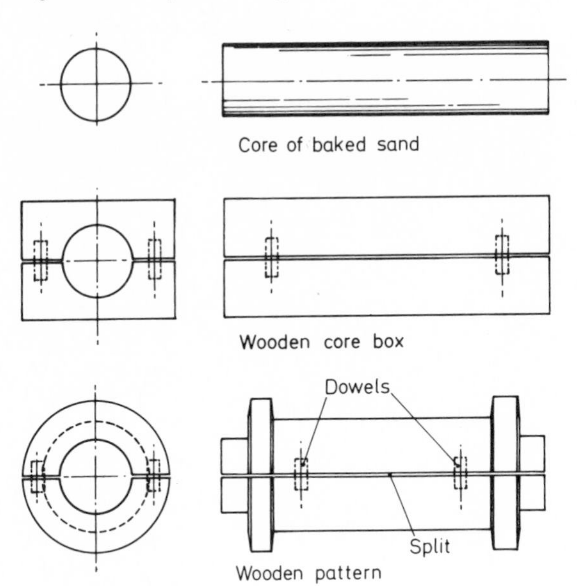

Figure 3.149 *Casting*

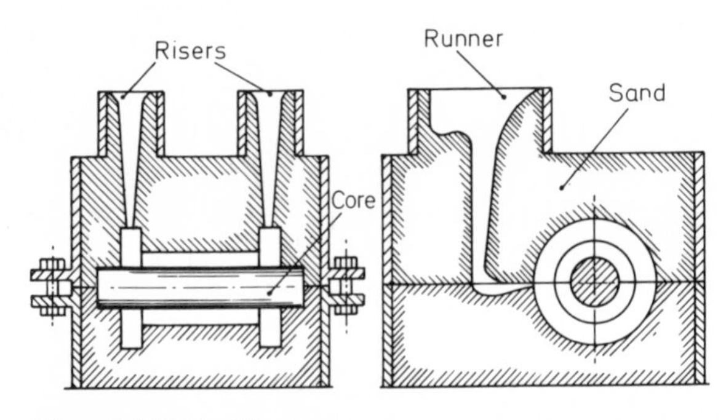

Figure 3.150 *Moulding box*

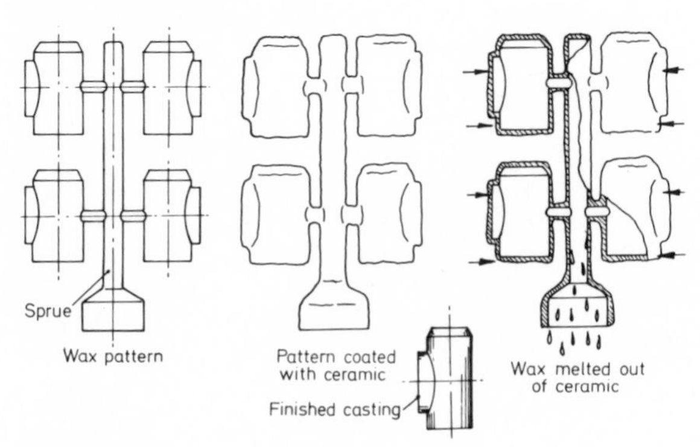

Figure 3.151 *Investment casting*

Investment casting (lost wax casting) A permanent metal mould is made and from it wax patterns are produced. These are coated with several layers of ceramic slurry, each layer being allowed to harden. The coated patterns are baked and the wax melts and runs away leaving a cavity which is filled to give a precision casting.

Die casting The mould is made of steel in several parts dowelled together. Molten metal is fed into the mould under gravity or pressure and when solid it is ejected by pins.

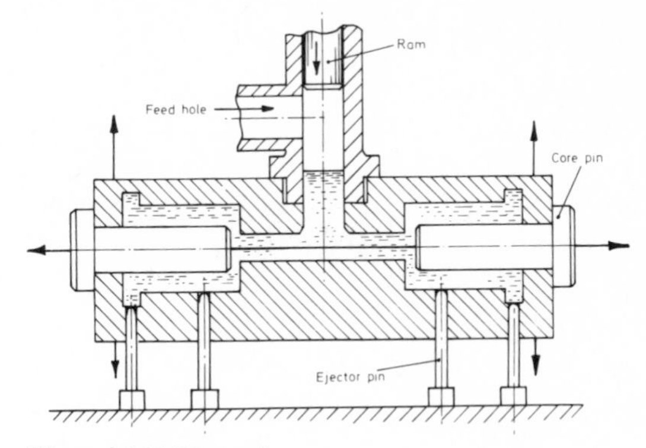

Figure 3.152 *Die casting*

Centrifugal casting Cylindrical and circular components, such as piston rings, cylinder liner pipes, gear wheels and locomotive wheels, may be cast in a rotating mould in which centrifugal pressure in the molten metal produces a fine-grain high-quality casting. Molten metal is poured into the mould while it is rotating and allowed to solidify before rotation ceases.

Wheel-shaped objects are cast with the axis vertical whereas pipes are cast with a horizontal axis.

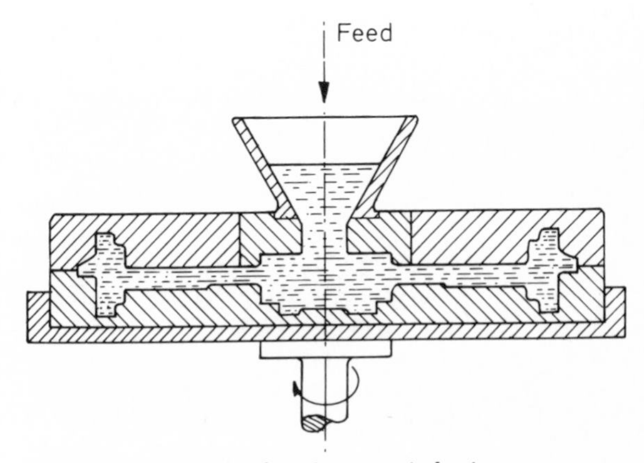

Figure 3.153 *Centrifugal casting – vertical axis*

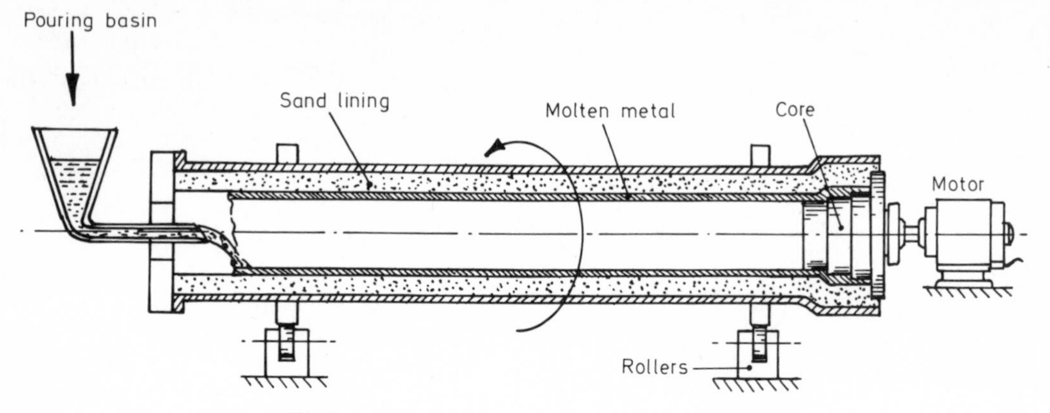

Figure 3.154 *Centrifugal casting of pipe – horizontal axis*

FORGING

Forging is the forming of metal parts by hammering, pressing or bending to the required shape, usually while the metal is at red heat.

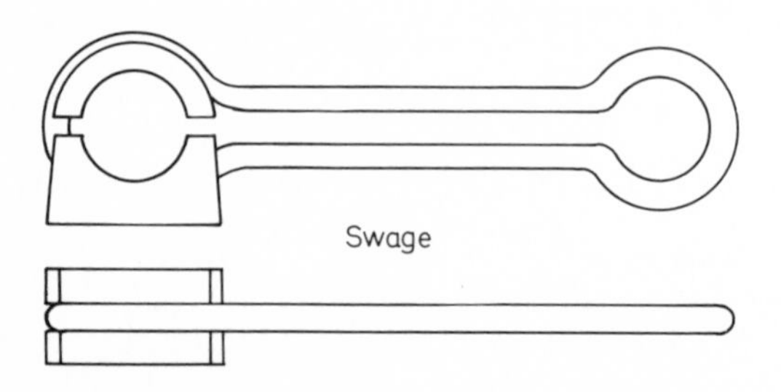

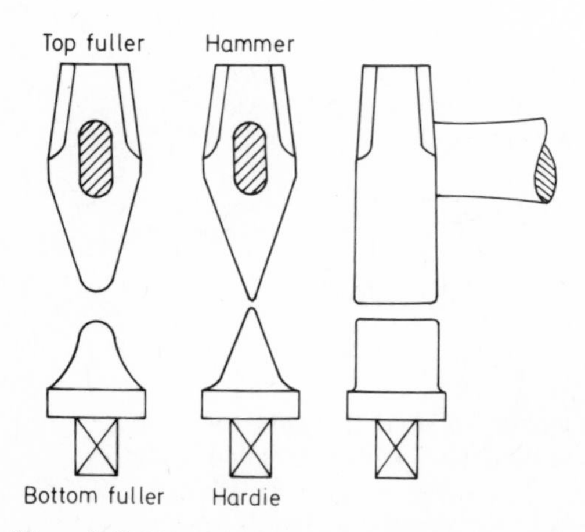

Figure 3.155 *Hand forging tools*

Hand forging This is the process used by a blacksmith where parts are formed on an *anvil* using special hammers, chisels and swages. The anvil has a hardened top face used for cutting on and a soft 'beak' for bending bars. In the top face is a square hole called a 'Hardie hole' used for holding various tools.

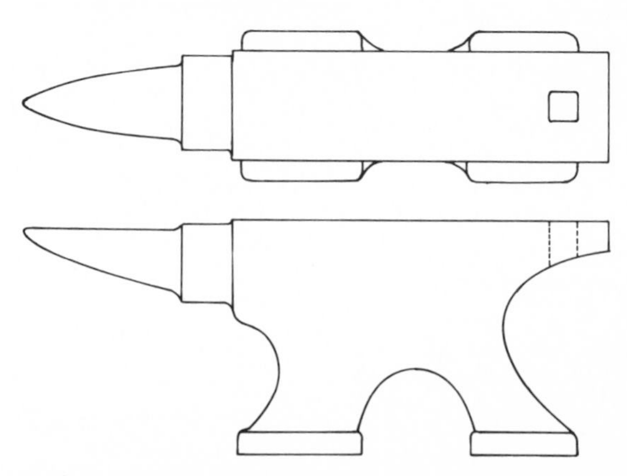

Figure 3.156 *Anvil*

Drop forging machine This is a machine used for forging in which pneumatic or hydraulic pressure is used to provide the force. Hot metal blanks are compressed between hard steel dies one of which is attached to the powered hammer and the other to the machine table.

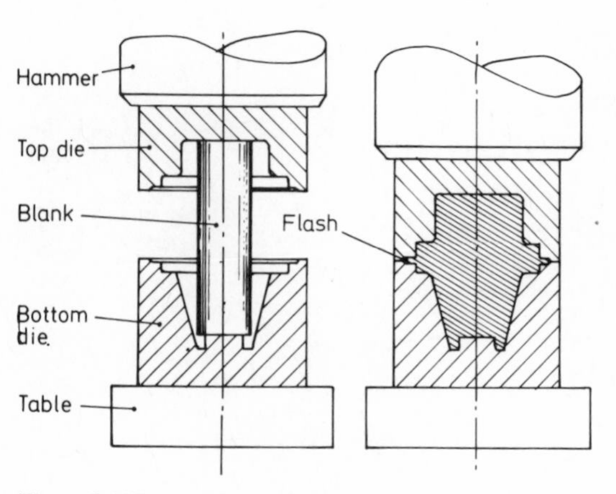

Figure 3.157 *Drop forging machine*

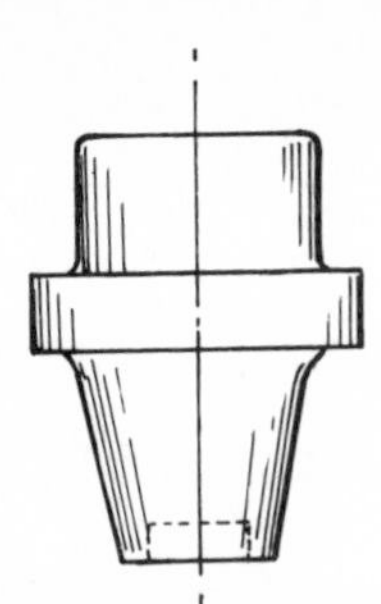

Figure 3.158 *Forging with flash removed*

ROLLING MILL

Red-hot ingots of steel, or other metals, are passed through successive pairs of rollers specially shaped to produce flat sheet, I, T, channel, angle or any other section bar. Final cold rolling is sometimes carried out to give a better finish.

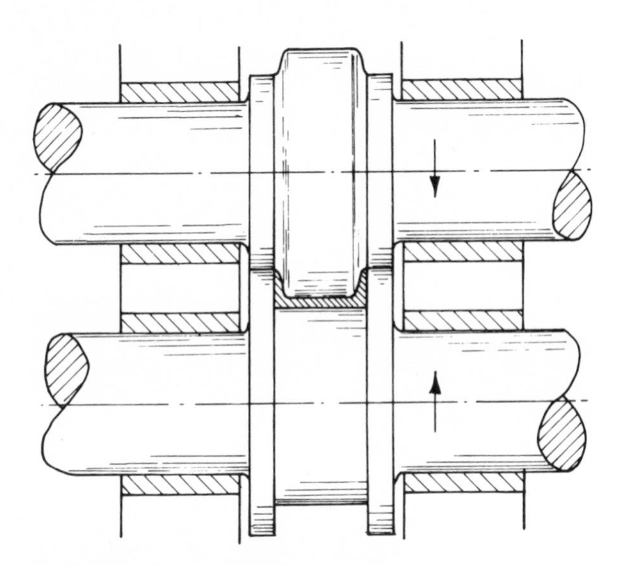

Figure 3.159 *Rolling mill (rolling channel)*

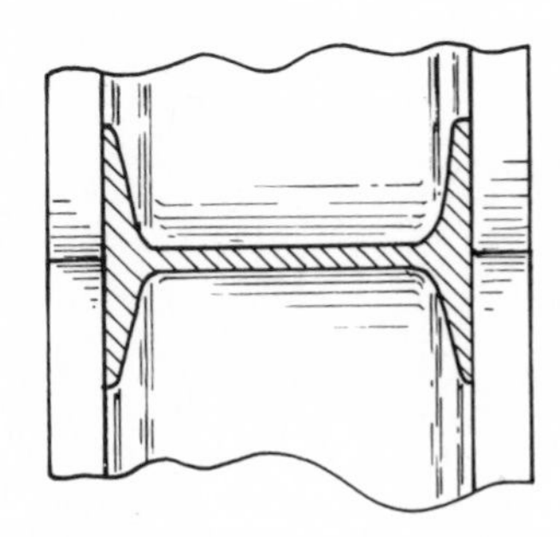

Figure 3.160 *Rolls for I section*

EXTRUSION

When metal is sufficiently soft, either at normal temperatures or when heated, it can be forced under pressure to flow through a die like toothpaste from a tube to form bars of any desired cross-section.

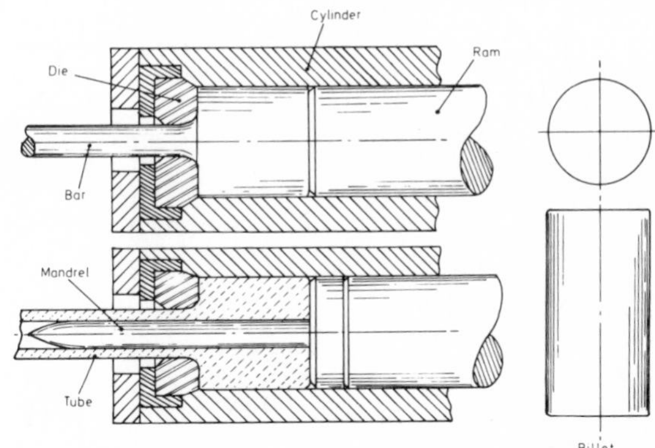

Figure 3.161 *Hot extrusion*

Figure 3.162 *Hot extruded sections*

Hot extrusion A piece of metal bar, or *billet*, is heated to the desired temperature and fed into a cylinder. It is then forced by a ram through a *die* of the correct shape to produce long lengths of bar which can be cut to the required length. Hollow sections can be made using a mandrel placed in the orifice.

Cold extrusion Soft metals such as copper, zinc and aluminium can be extruded when cold, and sometimes it is necessary to carry out the process in several stages.

Impact extrusion A metal which is plastic when cold may be formed by the impact of a high velocity punch to form a tube. A 'slug' of metal is given a single blow which 'splashes' it up the sides of the punch. This process is used for the manufacture of toothpaste tubes, battery cases, ignition coil cans, etc.

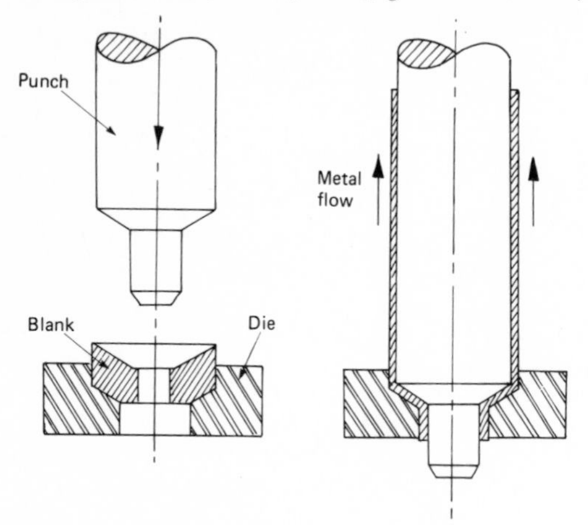

Figure 3.163 *Impact extrusion*

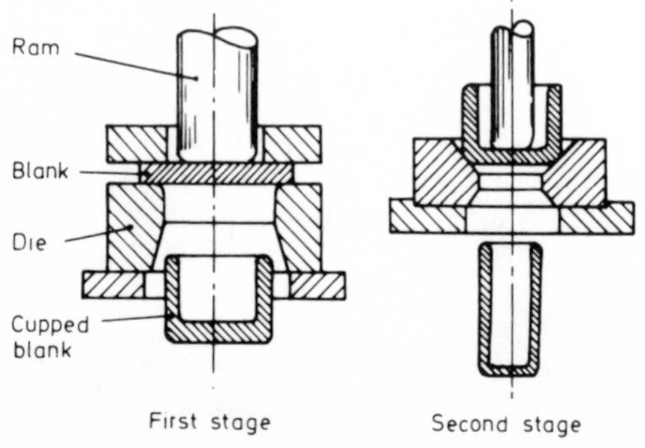

Figure 3.164 *Deep drawing*

DEEP DRAWING

Deep drawing is the forming of sheet or plate into box- and cup-shaped articles by pressing it with a shaped punch into a die. It involves considerable plastic deformation of the material. The process is used for cartridge cases, washing machine tubs and many electrical fittings.

PRESS

A press is used for a wide range of processes such as punching, piercing, blanking, notching, bending, drawing, folding, flanging, etc. It may be operated by means of a crank connected to a heavy flywheel or by hydraulic power.

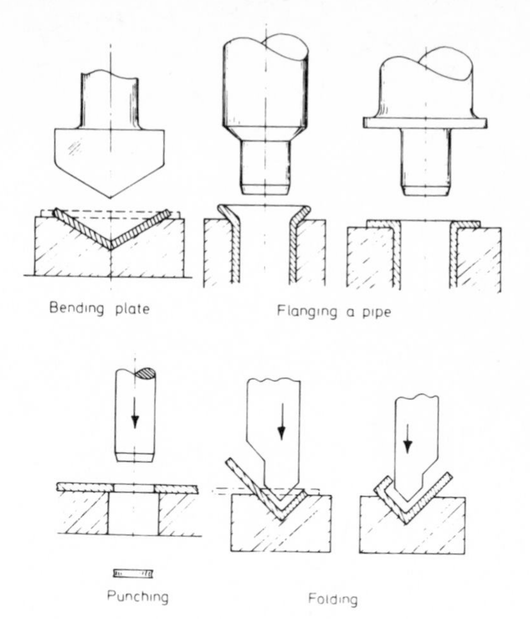

Figure 3.165 *Press work*

SHEARING MACHINE

A shearing machine consists of a fixed blade and a manually- or power-operated moving blade used for cutting sheet metal.

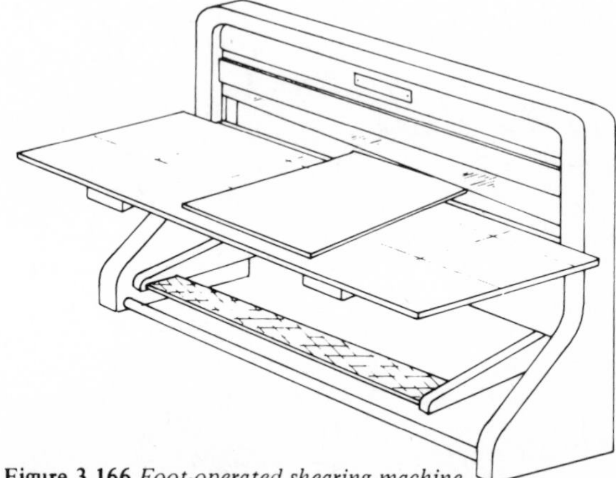

Figure 3.166 *Foot-operated shearing machine*

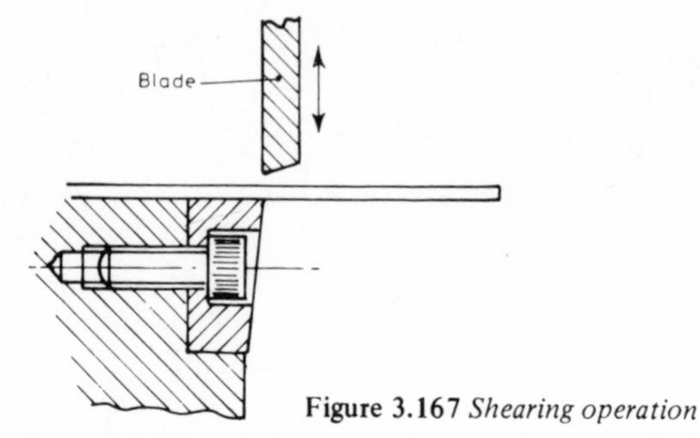

Figure 3.167 *Shearing operation*

WIRE DRAWING

A method for producing small diameter wire by drawing it while cold through successively smaller dies. Because of work hardening, the yield strength of the material of the wire increases at each drawing.

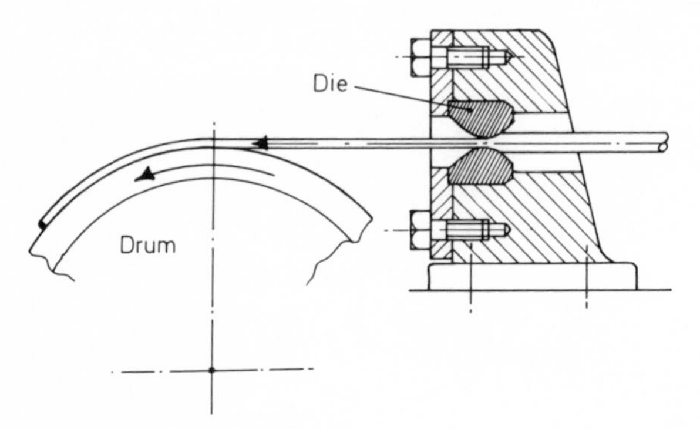

Figure 3.168 *Wire drawing*

SPINNING

Spinning is the forming of items out of sheet metal by rotating a thin metal disk at high speed, usually in a lathe, and pressing it into a cup or cone shape over a former using either a forming tool or a roller.

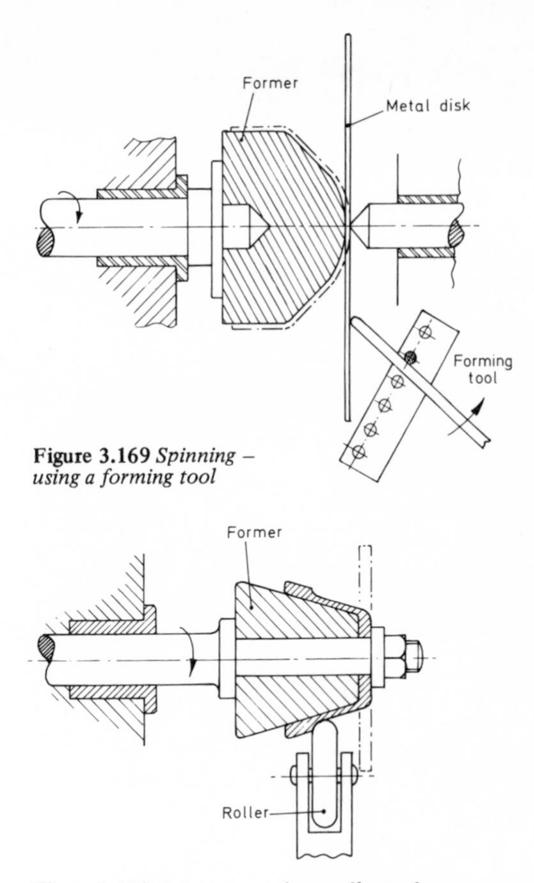

Figure 3.169 *Spinning – using a forming tool*

Figure 3.170 *Spinning – using a roller to form*

4. Engineering Materials

4.1 METALS

CAST IRON

Cast iron contains a considerable amount of carbon (2.4–4.5%) and is too brittle for 'working'. It is, however, very fluid when molten and is suitable for intricate castings.

Though quite strong in compression it is weak in tension and shear, but the strength can be increased considerably by the addition of alloying materials such as nickel, chromium and copper. These alloy cast irons can be used for gears, camshafts and crankshafts and are cheaper than steel.

SPHEROIDAL GRAPHITE (SG) IRON

In this iron (also called Nodular Iron) the graphite is in the form of small spheres resulting in increased ductility. The mechanical properties approach those of steel combined with good castability.

MALLEABLE CAST IRON

This is tougher and more shock-resistant than cast iron and is suitable for automobile parts, such as levers and pipe fittings.

There are three main types, *white heat* with superior castability, *black heat* with superior machineability, and *pearlitic* superior to the other two but difficult to produce.

STEEL

Steel is essentially an alloy of iron and iron carbide with small amounts of other elements in controlled quantities. A wide range of steels is available with properties varying considerably depending upon the alloying elements and subsequent heat treatment.

Carbon steel The amount of carbon determines the strength of steel. The main types are: dead mild (or low carbon), mild, medium carbon and high carbon.

Dead mild (low carbon) The carbon content is 0.07–0.15%. It is used for pipes, wire, nails, boiler plates, chains, etc., and it is worked when hot but does not machine easily.

Mild The most widely used of engineering materials whose carbon content of 0.15–0.25% allows it to be easily worked, machined and welded. Typical applications are ships' plates, forgings, nuts and bolts, gears and shafts.

Medium carbon A type which can be heat-treated to give greater strength, medium carbon steel is also easily machined. Its uses are machine parts, forgings, castings, springs and drop hammer dies.

High carbon This type contains 0.5–1.5% carbon which gives it great strength when heat-treated. At the lower carbon content it is used for screwdrivers, hammers, spanners, chisels, forging and pressing dies, while the highest carbon content is used for drills, lathe tools, hacksaws, ball bearings, taps and dies.

Alloy steels The addition of alloying elements to steel makes it more responsive to heat treatment, and this results in increased hardness, strength and toughness and greater resistance to corrosion. The main alloying elements are nickel, chromium, manganese, molybdenum, vanadium, tungsten, silicon and cobalt.

Nickel-chrome Nickel-chromium steels are among the most important alloy steels used in engineering. Heat treatment gives a wide range of properties with good resistance to shock and good ductility. They are used for high-tensile bolts, hardened gears, machine tools, etc.

Stainless A corrosion-resistant steel with about 12% chromium and other elements, used for turbine blades, and in sheet form for chemical and food containers.

Silver A bright-drawn high-carbon steel in the form of circular rod, containing manganese and chromium.

Tool High carbon steel to which manganese, tungsten and chromium have been added. When hardened it is used for dies, and to a limited extent for machine tools having been largely replaced by tungsten carbide inserts or brazed tips.

TUNGSTEN CARBIDE

An extremely hard material used for machine tool tips.

COPPER

A reddish, ductile metal of low strength but which is a very good conductor of heat and electricity. It is used for making pipes, electricity cables, gaskets and washers for fluid sealing, and is extensively alloyed with zinc, tin, aluminium, etc.

Copper nickel alloys There is a wide range of these alloys with amounts of nickel varying from 2–70%. Alloys with 40–45% nickel are used for resistance wire, e.g. Constantan, and they have a high resistivity and small resistance/temperature coefficient. Alloys containing about 70% nickel are known as *monel metal*. These are as strong as steel and have excellent resistance to corrosion by sea water, salt solutions and organic acids. They are suitable for steam turbine blades and condenser tubes.

Beryllium copper If 2% beryllium is added to copper the result is a very hard alloy as strong as tool steel. It is used for springs, bellows, bourdon tubes in pressure gauges and for non-sparking tools.

BRASS

This is the most widely used alloy of copper. It consists of 30–50% zinc and the remainder copper, to which a small amount of lead may be added to improve machinability. Brasses with a low zinc content are used for cold working in the production of condenser tubes, cartridge cases, gas and electric light fittings. Brasses with 39–46% zinc are easily hard worked and are used for extruded sections, pump parts, hydraulic fittings, nuts, bolts and screws.

BRONZE

'Bronze' refers to a copper-tin alloy which is used for electrical parts, hydraulic components, bearings and gears.

Gunmetal This is a bronze with 2% zinc added to improve the fluidity when casting and increase hardness. It is used extensively for castings, particularly those of a complicated form.

Lead bronze The addition of lead improves machinability in bronzes and improves the wear resistance of bronze bearings.

Phosphor bronze Phosphor bronze contains from 0.1–1.0% phosphorus. It is used for heavy-duty bearings, gears and non-ferrous springs, and is hard with good resistance to wear and corrosion.

Manganese bronze This is a bronze to which ferro-manganese has been added. It is used for very high strength castings.

ALUMINIUM

A light, ductile metal which is a good conductor of heat and electricity. It is used for electrical conductors and parts of switchgear, kitchen utensils, wrapping foil, window frames and as a base for many alloys.

Aluminium is extremely soft and ductile but is difficult to cast. Its properties can be greatly improved by adding small amounts of copper, silicon, manganese, magnesium, iron, zinc, nickel, bismuth and titanium. Aluminium alloys are classed as ***wrought*** and ***casting*** and may be ***heat-treatable*** or ***non-heat-treatable***.

Silicon lowers the melting point and improves castability. Copper, magnesium, manganese, zinc, titanium and nickel increase the strength. Lead and bismuth increase machinability.

Duralumin This most important of aluminium alloys contains copper, manganese, magnesium and silicon. It is as strong as mild steel with a third of the weight and is used for forgings, stampings, bar, sheet and rivets.

Aluminium-copper-zinc alloys These have a low melting point and are easily cast. They are cheap and are used for gearboxes and crankcases.

Y alloy This is an aluminium alloy containing 4% copper, 2% nickel and 1.5% magnesium. It is used extensively for castings such as cylinder heads and pistons for IC engines.

MAGNESIUM ALLOYS

Magnesium is only two thirds the weight of aluminium, and its alloys are useful for producing lightweight forgings and castings.

NIMONIC ALLOYS

An important range of alloys composed mainly of nickel and chromium with small amounts of titanium and carbon. They are very strong up to temperatures of 900°C and are therefore suitable for gas-turbine and jet-engine applications.

ZINC

Zinc is used as a protective coating for sheet metal, wire, nails, etc. It is also used in alloys with aluminium, copper and magnesium. Zinc alloys are used for die castings.

CHROMIUM

Chromium is used in electroplating to provide a surface with a high polish and high corrosion-resistance. It is alloyed with steel to give extremely high strengths.

CADMIUM

A fairly expensive metal used for plating and in certain types of battery.

TITANIUM

An expensive metal used in the production of aircraft parts alloyed with aluminium, vanadium, manganese, tin, etc. It has high strength, low weight, good heat- and corrosion-resistance.

LEAD

Lead is a heavy, soft, ductile metal with little mechanical strength. Because of its good resistance to corrosion it is used for roofing, cable sheathing and lining chemical apparatus. It is used extensively in nuclear work for radiation shielding and is alloyed with other metals for bearing metals and solders.

WHITE METAL (BABBITT METAL)

The name given to a range of tin-based alloys containing copper and antimony and sometimes lead. The antimony is important in ensuring low friction in bearings. These alloys are expensive and used only in high performance applications.

FUSIBLE ALLOYS (LOW MELTING POINT ALLOYS)

Alloys of bismuth, lead and tin have very low melting points and are used for solders and fusible plugs.

4.2 PLASTICS AND OTHER NON-METALLIC MATERIALS

PLASTICS

The term 'plastics' covers a wide range of man-made materials which can be moulded to the required shape by the application of heat and pressure.

There are two main types of plastic, *thermoplastic* and *thermosetting*. Thermoplastic materials become soft and pliable when heated and can be moulded into the required shape. They can be reheated and remoulded repeatedly. Thermosetting plastics suffer a chemical change when subjected to heat and pressure and they cannot be softened by reheating.

PVC (POLYVINYL CHLORIDE)

Rigid PVC is a thermoplastic material used for pipes and ducts, plasticised PVC is used for cable covering, mouldings, fabric and flexible sheet. It is flame- and water-resistant.

PERSPEX (ACRYLIC RESIN)

Perspex, a thermoplastic material, is one of the most common acrylic resins. It can be made very clear or coloured and has good optical properties. It is available in sheet, bars, tubes, etc.

POLYSTYRENE

A thermoplastic which can be moulded into complicated shapes with fine detail. It is an excellent electrical insulator but is not weather resistant.

POLYTHENE (POLYETHYLENE)

A thermoplastic polymer with good electrical properties, especially at high radio frequencies, which is suitable for use as weatherproof sheeting.

POLYPROPYLENE

This is similar to polythene but has greater heat resistance.

CELLULOSE PLASTICS

These include celluloid used for drawing office equipment, Cellophane used in film form for packaging, and rayon used for clothing, cements, petrol pipes and photographic film.

NYLON

A plastic used in fibre form for fabrics and also moulded into parts requiring light weight, low friction and flexibility. It has good self-lubricating properties when used for bearings.

EXPANDED PLASTICS

Polythene, polystyrene, polyurethane and PVC can be foamed by the introduction of gas bubbles during manufacture. These foam plastics are extremely light and are used for heat insulation, packaging and model making.

BAKELITE

A hard phenolic thermosetting plastic which is very cheap and is used for electrical insulated parts, tool handles, bonding material for grinding wheels, etc.

TUFNOL

A laminated plastic, i.e., one containing fabric, paper, etc. Available in sheet, rod and tube, and used widely in engineering for bearings, gears, pulleys and insulated parts.

PTFE (POLYTETRAFLUORETHYLENE)

Marketed under the names Fluon and Teflon this is a plastic with high chemical inertness and heat resistance used for extremely low-friction bearings and non-stick surfaces.

EPOXY RESINS

Polymers such as Araldite are widely used for structural plastics, adhesives and for encapsulation.

GLASS FIBRE

Fine threads of glass are used as a reinforcement in synthetic resin mouldings for boat hulls, pump impellers, roof lights, etc., and also as a structural material.

CARBON

Amorphous carbon is used for fluid seals in pumps and steam turbines. *Carbon fibres* are extremely strong and can be used to increase greatly the strength of epoxy resin mouldings and metal components.

DIAMOND

A form of carbon used for the tips of oil-well drills etc., and as a dust on dressing tools for grinding wheels.

RUBBER

Natural latex combined with sulphur, carbon black and other materials is widely used in engineering where flexibility is required. Examples of its use are tyres, flexible couplings and anti-vibration mountings.

SYNTHETIC RUBBER

A wide range of synthetic rubbers, such as Neoprene, Buna and butyl, are used for flexible mountings and couplings and oil seals, etc. In their properties they are often superior to natural rubber.

CERAMICS

This is a general name for all non-metallic, non-organic materials but usually it refers to materials which will withstand very high temperatures. They are extremely hard and also wear- and corrosion-resistant and can be moulded into a variety of shapes before firing. They are used for burner nozzles, gas-turbine parts and electrical insulation.

ASBESTOS

A natural mineral material used for fireproofing. It can be woven into cloth or made into board. Sindanyo is the name of a form of asbestos board used for low voltage insulation.

PORTLAND CEMENT

A material made by burning a mixture of clay and lime. Mixing it with sand, aggregate and water produces concrete, and this is usually reinforced with steel bars to make structural columns and beams.

ABRASIVES

Materials such as carborundum and emery are used for making grinding wheels and sharpening stones.

WOOD

Wood is used in engineering in its natural form, and also in plywood, chipboard and blockboard.

Index

Abrasives, 104, 121
Absorption brake (dynamometer), 62
Acetylene gas (welding), 111
Acme power transmission thread, 14
Acrylic resin (Perspex), 120
Active flux, 108
Addendum/circle (gear), 19
Adjustable spanner (wrench), 94
Adjuster (brake), 61
Air bearing lubrication, 46
Air bellows spring, 18
Air (gas) bearings, 44
Air (pneumatic) spring, 18
Allen key (hexagon socket wrench), 3, 94
Alloy cast iron, 118
Alloy elements (steel), 118
Alloy metals, 118–120
Aluminium (aluminum), 119
Aluminium
  alloys, 119
  bar/tube, 59
  -copper-zinc alloys, 119
  gasket, 28
  oxide (abrasive), 104
  rivet, 10
  sealing washer, 28
Anchor bolt (Rawlbolt), 4
Angle of V (screw thread), 13–14
Angle milling, 97
Angle section steel bar, 58, 115
Angular contact bearing, 44
Angular tooth milling cutter, 97
Anti-friction bearings, 44
Anvils, 89, 114
Arbor, 96–97
Area (bottom of screw thread), 1, 13
Arc welding/plate/rod, 109
Argon gas (welding), 111
Asbestos gland packing, 24
Asbestos (Sindanyo), 121
Attachments, socket spanner, 94
Auto. brake, 61
Auto. disk brake calliper, 61
Auto. dynamo porous bearing, 43
Auto. friction clutch, 63
Auto-type clutch plate (disk), 63
Auto-type drum brake, 61
Auto-type poppet (mushroom) valve, 37
Auto-type universal joint, 69
Axial (face) cam, 81
BA/BSF/BSW bolt/screw threads, 1, 13
Babbitt (white) metal, 120
Bakelite, 121
Ball-bearing components, 44–45
Ball-bearing power screw, 15
Ball peen hammer, 86
Ball thrust bearing, 46
Ball-type non-return valve, 36
Ball-types of bearing, 44–46
Band/rope brake (dynamometer), 62–63
Bandsaws (power), 107
Band-type hose clip, 12
Bar, boring, 106
Bar handle, 94
Barrel (micrometer), 89
Barrel nuts, 7
Bar solder, 108
Bars/sections, 57–59, 115
Base circle (cam), 79
Bead chain/drive, 74
Beak (anvil), 114
Bearing lubrication, 46–47
Bearing materials, 44
Bearings/components, 42–47
Bed/bedplate (design feature), 47
Bed (horizontal borer), 106
Bed (lathe), 47, 102
Bell crank lever, 74
Bell crank lever (double block brake), 60
Belleville washer (diaphragm spring), 18
Bellows flexible pipe joint, 32
Bellows joint, hinged, 32
Bellows seal, carbon faced, 27
Belt conveyor, 72
Belt drives/pulleys, 70–72
Belt materials, 70–71
Bench drilling machine, 98
Bench grinder, 106
Bench/pedestal grinders, 106
Bench vice (vise), 92
Bending (presswork), 116
Bends, duct/pipe, 29–30, 32–34
Beryllium copper, 119
Bevel gears, 20–21
Billet (extrusion), 115
Bit, soldering iron, 107–108
Blacksmiths' anvil, 114
Blacksmiths' cold chisel, 83
Black steel bar, 58
Black steel bolts, 1

Blanking (presswork), 116
Blanks, 114, 116
Blind drilled hole, 52
Block-and-tackle, 72–73
Body (design feature), 47
Bolt dimensions, 1, 3
Bolted/flanged pipe joint, 30, 34
Bolts/bolt heads, 1–4
Bolt hole clearance, 2, 4
Bolt load/strength, 1–2
Bolt threads, 1, 13–15
Bolt tightening torque, 2
Bonded rubber flexible shaft coupling, 67
Bonded rubber spring, 18
Borax (brazing flux), 108
Bored hole, 52
Boring, 102, 106
Boring bar, 106
Boring lathe tool, 103
Boring machines, 106
Boring mill, 106
Boring tool, 103
Boss (design feature), 48
Bottom fuller (forging), 114
Box, core (casting), 113
Box/casing (design feature), 47–48
Box spanner (wrench), 93
Boxwood-head hammer, 86
Brace, 94
Bracket (design feature), 48
Brake components, 60–62, 65
Brakes, 60–63
Branch (ducting), 34
Brass, 119
Brasses (bearings), 42
Brass pipe joints/fittings, 31–32
Brazed cone pipe coupling, 31
Brazing (hard soldering), 108–109
Brazing torch, 108
Bright bar, 58
Bright bolt, 1
Bright steel bar, 58
Broach, 53
Broad-nosed facing tool, 103
Bronzes, 119
Brush, rotary wire, 105
Buffing (polishing) mop, 105
Buna, synthetic rubber, 121
Bush (design feature), 48
Bush (sleeve), bearing, 42, 48
Butane gas (welding), 111
Butterfly valve, 37
Butt joints, 10, 109–110
Button head socket bolt/screw, 3
Buttress power transmission screw thread, 14
Butyl, synthetic rubber, 121

C clamp, 91
C spanner (wrench), 94
Cable clip, 12
Cadmium/plating, 120
Cage, ball bearing, 44
Callipers, 61, 88–90
Cam details, 79
Cam followers, 80
Cams, 79–81
Camshaft, 39
Cantilever leaf spring, 17
Canvas belt, 70
Cap (crown/dome) nut, 6
Cap (design feature), 48
Cap head socket bolt/screw, 3
Capillary pipe fitting, 30
Cap, pipe fitting, 29
Captive nut, 7
Carbon, 121
Carbon face seals, 27
Carbon fibres/for sealing, 121
Carbon seals, 26–27
Carbon segmental seal, 26
Carbon steels, 118
Carborundum (abrasive), 121
Carriage (coach) bolt, 2–3
Carriage (laminated leaf) spring, 17–18
Casing/box (design feature), 47–48
Casting, 48, 112–114
Casting (design feature), 48
Casting dies, 113
Casting, lost wax (investment), 113
Casting methods, 112–114
Cast iron, 118
Castle nut, 7
Cast pulley, flat belt, 70
Cast steel gear, 23
Catch plate (lathe), 104
Cellophane, celluloid, cellulose, 120
Cement, 121
Centre distance (gear), 19
Centre/drill (lathe), 104
Centre (engine) lathe, 102–104
Centre finder (combination set), 88
Centre holes (shaft), 104
Centre punch, 84
Centres, turning between (lathe), 104
Centrifugal brake, 61
Centrifugal casting, 113–114
Centrifugal clutch, 65
Centrifugal dead-weight governor, 76–77
Ceramics, 121
Chain flexible shaft coupling, 69
Chain pulley, 74
Chains/chain drives, 73–74
Chain sprocket, 73–74
Chamfer (design feature), 48–49
Chamfer (shaft), 38
Channel bar/section, 58, 115
Check (non-return) valves, 35–36
Cheese-head bolt, 3–4
Cheese-head screw, 5
Chequer plate, 58
Chisels (sets), 83
Chromium (alloy element), 120
Chromium plating, 120
Chucks, 84, 102–104
Chuck with key, 99
Circlips (retaining rings), 13
Circlip groove (shaft), 39
Circular arc cam, 81
Circular pitch (gear), 19
Clamps, 91, 109
Clapper box (shaper), 100
Claw (dog) clutch, 64
Claw shaft coupling, 66

Clearance (bearings), 42
Clearance (bolt hole), 2, 4
Clearance (gears), 19
Clips, 12–13
Clutch components, 63–65
Clutches, 63–65
Coach (carriage) bolts, 2–3
Cobalt (alloy element), 118
Cold chisel, 83
Cold extrusion, 115
Cold-rolled steel sections, 58
Cold rolling, 115
Collars (shaft), 39, 43
Collet chuck (collet), 103
Column (drilling machines), 98–99
Column (milling machine), 95
Column (pillar) (design feature), 49, 54
Combination set, 88
Compression coupling (shaft), 66
Compression pipe couplings, 31
Compression piston ring, 27
Compression springs, 15, 17–18
Compression stop (spring lock) nut, 7
Concrete, 121
Cone clutch, 64
Coned pulley, 72
Conical head rivet, 10
Conical (upholstery) spring, 17
Connecting rod (crank-slider), 75
Constant acceleration/deceleration cam, 80
Constantan, 119
Constant-velocity cam, 80
Constant-velocity universal joint, 69
Contour grinding wheels, 104
Contour milling/cutter, 97
Conveyor belt, 72
Copper, 118–119
Copper-asbestos gasket, 28
Copper (capillary) pipe fittings, 30
Copper/fibre inserts (mallet), 86
Copper nickel alloys, 119
Copper rivet, 10
Copper sealing washer, 28
Core, core box/pins (die casting), 113
Cork gasket, 28
Corrugated sheet steel, 57
Cotter, 12, 42
Cottered joint (rods), 42
Cotter (split) pin, 12
Cotton belt, 70
Cotton gland packing, 24
Counterbored hole, 52
Counterboring, 100
Countersinking, 52, 85
Countersinking tool, 85
Countersunk head (flat) screw, 5
Countersunk hole, 52
Countersunk rivet, 10
Couplings (pipe fittings), 29–32
Cover/coverplate (design feature), 49
Crankpin, 39
Cranks, 39, 75
Crankshaft, 39–40
Crank-slider mechanism, 75
Crest (screw thread), 13
Crosscut cold chisel, 83
Crossed belt drive, 70
Crosshead, 76
Cross-head (Phillips) screw, 5
Cross-head (Phillips) screwdriver, 93
Cross peen hammer, 86
Crown (cap/dome) nut, 6
Cup seal, 25
Cutters, milling machine, 95–98
Cutters, wire, 92
Cylinder (design feature), 49
Cylinder (extrusion), 115
Cylindrical grinder, 105

Dashpot, 107
Dead mild (low) carbon steel, 118
Dead-weight safety valve, 35
Dedendum/circle (gear), 19
Deep drawing/dies, 116
Deep groove bearings, 45
Dial gauge (indicator), 90
Diametral pitch (gear), 19
Diamond (abrasive), 104
Diamond-pointed cold chisel, 83
Diamond tool tips, 121
Diaphragm spring, 18
Die casting, 113
Die casting core/ejector pins, 113
Dies, 85, 113–117
Die stock, 85
Disk brake, 60
Disk clutch, 63–64
Disk-type flexible shaft coupling, 67
Distance piece (spacer) (design feature), 49
Dividers (spring), 88–89
Dog (claw) clutch, 64
Dome (cap/crown) nut, 6
Double block brake, 60
Double butt weld, 110
Double cone pipe joint, 31
Double helical gear, 20
Double Michell thrust bearing, 44
Double reduction gear train, 23
Double riveted butt joint, 10
Double row ball bearings, 45
Dovetail milling/cutter, 97
Dowel/pin, 11
Drawing (presswork), 116
Drawing, wire, 117
Drifts, 84
Drill chuck/key, 99
Drilled holes, 52
Drilling head, 99
Drilling (lathe), 102
Drilling machine operations, 100
Drilling machines (drill presses), 84, 98–99
Drills, 84, 104
Drive chains, 73–74
Drive screw, 5–6
Driving dog/pin (lathe), 104
Drop forging machine/dies/blank, 114
Drum brake, 61
Drum, wire drawing, 117
Dry fluid clutch, 65
Duct/pipe materials/fittings, 29–34
Duplex lip seal, 25
Duralumin sheet, 119
Dwell (cam), 79
Dynamometer (absorption brake), 62

Earthing clamp (welding), 109
Eccentric, 75
Eccentric circle cam, 80
Eccentric-crank and slider mechanism, 75
Efficiency of screw threads, 15
Effort on levers, 74
Ejector pin (die casting), 113
Elastic stop (Nyloc) nut, 8
Elbow pipe fittings, 29–32
Electrical contact (cantilever leaf) spring, 18
Electric power hand drill, 84
Electric soldering iron, 108
Electrode/holder (welding), 109
Electromagnetic friction clutch, 65
Elliptical cross-section lever, 74
Elongated hole, 52
Emery (abrasive), 121
Endmilling/cutter, 97
Engine (centre) lathe, 102–104
Engineers' rules, 86–87
Engineers' vice (vise), 92
Epicyclic gear, 22
Epoxy resins, 121
Ermeto pipe joint, 31
Expanded plastics, 121
Expanded polystyrene, 121
Expansion joints/bends, 32
Explosive rivet, 11
Extension bar (socket spanner), 94
External circlip, 13
External involute shaft splines, 40
Externally serrated (tooth) lock washer, 9
External screw-cutting lathe tool, 103
Extruded sections, 115
Extrusion billet/cylinder/dies/mandrel, 115
Extrusion, cold/hot, 115
Eye bolt, 4, 49
Eye (design feature), 49
Eye, wire, 49

Fabric belt, 70
Face (axial) cam, 81
Face (design feature), 49
Face milling/cutter, 97
Face plate (lathe), 103
Face spanner (wrench), 94
Facing (lathe), 102
Faucet (recess) (design feature), 50
Feather key (shaft), 40–41
Feeler (thickness) gauge, 87
Felt sealing rings, 26
Fibre sealing washer, 28
File handle, 82
Files, hand, 82
Filler rod (welding), 111
Fillet (design feature), 50
Fillet (shaft), 38
Fillet weld, 109
Fillister screw head, 5
Fin (design feature), 49–50
First order lever, 74
Fitted bolt, 4
Flame cutting, 112
Flange (coupling), 66–69
Flange (design feature), 50
Flanged pipe bend, 30
Flanged pipe joints, 30–34
Flanged shaft coupling, 66
Flange/washer screwed brass pipe coupling, 31
Flanging (presswork), 116
Flap non-return valve, 36
Flash welding, 110–111
Flat belt drive, 70
Flat-bottomed hole, 52
Flat cam follower, 80
Flat circlip, 13
Flat cold chisel, 83
Flat file, 82
Flat fillister screw head, 5
Flat head rivet, 10
Flat (plain) washer, 8
Flat scraper, 83
Flat sheet steel, 57
Flexible bellows pipe joint, 32
Flexible expansion pipe bends, 33
Flexible hoses/pipes/fittings, 33
Flexible shaft couplings, 67–69
(*see* Shaft couplings)
Fluid flywheel (fluid coupling), 65
Fluid seals, 23
Flush rivet, 10
Fluxes, 108
Fly cutting/cutter, 98
Flywheel (design feature), 50
Foamed plastics, 121
Folding (presswork), 116
Folding rule, 87
Followers (cam), 79–80
Foot (design feature), 50–51
Foot-operated shearing machine, 116
Footstep thrust bearing, 43
Forging (design feature), 51
Forging dies/hammer/methods, 114
Fork/fork end (design feature), 51
Former/forming tool (spinning), 117
Foundation bolts, 4
Four-bar chain, 75
Four-jaw independent chuck, 103
Freewheeling (over-running) clutches, 64
Friction clutches, 63–65
Friction coefficient, 60, 65
Friction disk/lining, 61, 63–65
Friction materials (brakes/clutches), 65
Friction pad, 60
Friction plate (clutch), 64
Friction-welded poppet (mushroom) valve, 112
Friction welding, 112
Fulcrum (lever), 74
Fullers (forging), 114
Fusible alloys, 120

Ganged milling cutters, 96
Garter spring, 25–26
Gas (air) bearing, 44
Gas bearing lubricant, 46
Gas bottle, 111
Gaskets (seals), materials, 28
Gas pressure control valve (welding), 111
Gas shielded metal arc welding, 112
Gas welding/torch, 111
Gate (sluice) valve, 36
Gauges, 87–88, 90

Gearbox, 22
Gear changing, 23
Gear flexible shaft coupling, 68
Gear layshaft, 22
Gear materials, 23
Gears, 19–23
Gear shaft, splined, 23
Gears in mesh, 20
Gear teeth data, 19
Gear-tooth callipers, 89
Gear train, 22–23
Geneva wheel mechanism, 76
Gib head key (shaft), 40–41
Gland packings, 23–24
Gland-ring, 23
Gland (seal), 23
Glass fibre, 121
Glass pipe, 29
Globe valve, 34
Globoid cam, 81
Governors, 76–77
Grease bearing lubrication, 46
Grease nipple, 46
Greaser, screw-down, bearing lubrication, 46
Grinding machines (grinders), 104–106
Grinding wheels/materials/motor, 104–106
Grooved pin, 11
Grooves in shafts, 39
Grub screw, 5
Gunmetal, 119

HT (high tensile) bolt, 1
Hacksaws, 83
Half nut, 6, 7
Half-round chisel, 83
Half-round file, 82
Half-round scraper, 83
Halved (split) pedestal bearing, 42
Hammers, 86, 114
Hand/electric power drills, 84
Hand files, 82
Hand forging tools, 114
Handle, bar, 94
Handle (design feature), 51
Handle, file, 82
Handle, ratchet, 94
Hand reaming/tapping, 85
Handwheel (design feature), 51
Hardie/Hardie hole (hand forging), 114
Hard solder/soldering (brazing), 108
Hartnell spring-loaded governor, 77
Hatchet-type soldering iron, 108
Hat packing (seal), 25
Headstock (lathe), 102
Hearth, brazing, 108–109
Heavy-duty band saw, 107
Heavy-duty pedestal grinder, 106
Heavy-duty pipe joint, 30
Heavy screwdriver, 93
Helical coil spring, 15
Helical compression springs, 15, 17
Helical gears, 20
Helical reamer, 85
Helical rectangular-section spring, 15
Helical spring data/materials, 16
Helical spring lock washer, 9
Helical tension/torsion springs, 16–17
Hemp (gland packing), 24
Hermaphrodite callipers, 89
Herringbone gear, 20
Hexagonal bar, 58–59
Hexagonal head bolt, 1–2
Hexagon nut, 6–8
Hexagon socket head screw (bolt), 3
Hexagon socket wrench (Allen key), 3, 94
Hide-head hammer, 86
High carbon steel, 118
High-pressure hydraulic hose, 33
High tensile (HT) bolt, 1
Hinged bellows expansion pipe joint, 32
Hinged flap non-return valve, 36
Holes, 52–53, 104, 114
Holes (design feature), 52–53
Hollow rectangular/round sections, 58/59
Hollow shaft, 38
Hollow steel sections, 58
Hooke's-type universal joint, 69
Horizontal axis centrifugal casting, 113–114
Horizontal boring machine, 106
Horizontal milling machine, 95
Horizontal milling, up/down cuts, 96
Hose clips, 12
Hose pipe fittings, 33
Hot chisel, 83
Hot extrusion/extruded sections, 115
Hot-rolled bar, 115
Hot-rolled steel sections, 58
Hot rolling. 115
Housing (bearing), 46, 53
Housing (design feature), 53
Hub (design feature), 53
Hub, pulley, 53
Hydraulic brake system, 62
Hydraulic cylinder, 26, 61–62
Hydraulic hose/fittings, 33
Hydraulic jack, 77
Hydraulic pipe joint, 30
Hydraulic relief (safety) valve, 35
Hydraulic shock absorbers, 78
Hydrogen gas (welding), 111
Hypoid gears, 21

IC engine piston rings, 27
I-section hot-rolled bar, 115
I-section lever, 75
I-section steel bar/beam, 58, 115
ISO metric precision hexagon nuts, 6
Impact extrusion tools, 116
Indented foundation bolt, 4
Independent four-jaw chuck, 103
Indicator (dial) gauge, 90
Inserted tooth milling cutter, 98
Inside callipers, 89
Inside micrometer, 90
Instrument makers' screwdriver, 93
Instrument screw thread, 5
Integral collar (shaft), 39
Intermittent weld, 109–110
Internal circlip, 13
Internal expanding shoe brake, 61
Internal gear, 22
Internally serrated (tooth) lock washer, 9

Internal shaft splines, 40
Investment (lost wax) casting, 113
Involute gears, 19–23
Iron, 118
Iron pipe, 29

Jacks, 77–78
Jam (locked) nuts, 7
Jenny callipers, 89
Jet bearing lubrication, 46–47
Joints/gaskets, 28
Journal/bearing/shell, 42
Jubilee hose clip, 12

Keys/keyways (shafts), 40–41
Killed spirit (zinc chloride) (flux), 108
Knifed (spotfaced) hole, 53
Knife-edge cam follower, 80
Knuckle (pin) joint (tie rods), 41
Knurling (design feature), 53

Labyrinth gland (steam turbine), 27
Labyrinth seal (ball bearing), 27–28
Laminated leaf (carriage) spring, 17–18
Laminated plastics, 121
Laminations (*see* Metaflex flexible shaft coupling)
Lap joint, riveted, 10
Lathe, centre/engine, 102–104
Lathe components/operations/tools, 102–104
Layshaft (gear), 22
Lead/lead alloys, 120
Lead bronze, 119
Lead-head hammer, 86
Leadscrew (lathe), 102
Lead, screw thread, 14
Leaf spring, 17–18
Leather belt, 70
Leather sealing washer, 28–29
Left-hand screw thread, 13
Leftward welding, 111
Levers, 74–75
Lift (cam), 79
Light-duty bandsaw, 107
Light gauge tube, 59
Line of action (gear), 19
Linkages (mechanisms), 75–76
Link belt chain/drive, 74
Lip seal with garter spring, 25
Loads on components
  Belleville washer, 18
  block-and-tackle, 72–73
  bolt/bolt tightening, 1–2
  buttress thread, 14
  cell (brake), 62
  conical spring, 17
  helical gear, 20
  jacks, 77–78
  leaf spring, 17–18
  lever, 74
  ring spring, 18
  roller bearing, 45–46
  shock absorber, 78
  spring design, 16
  strut, 56
Locked (jam) nut, 7
Lock washers, 8–9
Long-nose (needlenose) pliers, 92
Loose collar (shaft), 39
Lost wax (investment) casting, 113
Low carbon steel, 118
Low melting point alloys, 120
Lubricants/lubricators (bearings), 46
Lubrication (bearings), 47
Lug (design feature), 54
Lyre flexible expansion pipe bend, 33

Machine reaming/tapping, 100
Machine screw, 5
Machine tools, 95–107
Machine-tool tables
  auxiliary drilling, 99
  bandsaw, 107
  borers, 106
  drilling machine, 98–99
  milling machines, 95
  shaper, 100–101
  surface grinder, 104
  vertical shaper, 106
Machine vice (vise), 92
Magnesium alloys, 119
Magnetic base test set, 90
Magnetic chuck (surface grinder), 104
Major diameter (thread), 1, 14
Male/female coupling (pipe fitting), 32
Malleable cast iron, 118
Malleable iron screwed pipe fittings, 29
Mallets (soft hammers), 86
Mandrel (extrusion), 115
Manganese (alloy element), 118
Manganese bronze, 119
Manilla rope, 72
Marking-off, 87
Masonry twist drill, 84
Master cylinder (brake), 62
Maul (sledge hammer), 86
Mechanical friction damper, 78
Mechanisms (linkages), 73–81
Medium carbon steel, 118
Mesh (gears), 19–20
Mesh, wire, 58
Metaflex flexible shaft coupling, 69
Metal alloys, 118–120
Metal inert gas (MIG) welding, 112
Metallic gasket, 28
Metallic packing seal, 24
Metal spring flexible shaft coupling, 68
Metric bolt/screw threads, 1, 13
Michell thrust bearing/pad, 43
Micrometer head, 90
Micrometer components, 89–90
Mild carbon steel, 118
Milling cutter nomenclature, 96
Milling cutters, 96–98
Milling machine components/operations, 95–98
Milling machines, 95–96
Minor diameter (thread), 1, 14
Misalignment (shafts), 67–68
Mist bearing lubrication, 47
Module (gear), 19
Molybdenum (alloy element), 118

Monel metal, 119
Mop, buffing/polishing, 105
Morse taper (twist drill), 84
Motor, grinding wheel, 105
Mould (casting), 113
Moulded rubber insert shaft coupling, 67
Moulding box components (casting), 113
Moulding sand (casting), 113
Muff shaft coupling, 66
Multi-plate (disk) brake, 61
Multi-plate (disk) friction clutch, 64
Multiple V belt drive, 71
Multiple V pulley, 71
Multi-start power screw thread, 14
Multi-start worm gear, 21
Mushroom (poppet) valve, 37, 112

Natural rubber, 121
Needlenose (long-nose) pliers, 92
Needle (pattern) files, 82
Needle roller/bearing, 44–45
Needle screw-down valve, 34
Needle-type non-return valve, 36
Neoprene, 121
Nickel (alloy element), 118–119
Nickel-chrome steel, 118
Nimonic alloys, 119
Non-ferrous metals, 59, 118–120
Non-metallic materials, 120–121
Non-return (check) valves, 35–36
Nose (cam), 79
Notching (presswork), 116
Nut-and-sleeve pipe joint, 31
Nuts, 6–8
Nyloc (elastic stop) nut, 8
Nylon, 120
Nylon cords (belt), 71

O-ring seal, 26
Odd leg callipers, 89
Off-hand grinder, 106
Oil lubrication, 47
Oil grooves (shaft), 39
Oil jet/mist/splash bearing lubrication, 47
Oil scraper piston ring, 27
Oil seals (*see* Seals)
Oilways (shafts), 40
Oldham flexible shaft coupling, 68
Open-ended (open-jaws) spanner (wrench), 93
Opposed taper roller bearings, 45
Orders of levers, 74
Oscillating crank mechanism, 76
Outside callipers, 88–89
Overhung crank, 39
Over-running (freewheeling) clutches, 64
Oxygen (welding), 111

PTFE (plastic), 121
PVC (plastic), 120
Packing (seals), 23–28
Pan head taper neck rivet, 10
Paper gasket, 28
Parallel-face gate valve, 36
Parallel motion mechanism, 75
Parallel roller (bearing), 44
Parallel sleeve compression pipe joint, 31
Parting-off (lathe), 102
Parting-off lathe tool, 103
Passive flux, 108
Pattern (casting), 113
Pattern (needle) files, 82
Pedestal bearing, 42
Pedestal/bench grinders, 106
Pedestal casting, 48
Pedestal (design feature), 54
Perspex (acrylic resin), 120
Phillips recess (cross-head) screw, 5
Phillips cross-head screwdriver, 93
Phosphor bronze, 119
Piercing (presswork), 116
Pillar (column) (design feature), 49, 54
Pin drift, 84
Pin hammer, 86
Pinion (gear), 21, 79
Pin (knuckle) joint (tie rods), 41
Pins
- crank-, 39
- core (die casting), 113
- dowel, 11
- driving (lathe), 104
- ejector (die casting), 113
- grooved, 11
- plain, 11
- roll, 11
- split (cotter), 12
- taper, 11

Pipe bends, 30, 33
Pipe casting, centrifugal, 113–114
Pipe clip, 13
Pipe couplings/fittings, 29–33
Pipe/duct joints (couplings), 29–34
Pipe/duct materials/fittings, 29–34
Pipe expansion joints, 32
Pipes, 29–34
Pipe (Stillson) wrench, 95
Pipe vice (vise), 92
Piston (design feature), 54
Piston (hydraulic) shock absorber, 78
Piston rings, 26–27
Piston rod, 26
Piston-type non-return valve, 36
Pitch circle/point (gear), 19
Pitch (screwthread), 1, 13–14
Pivoted segment (Michell) bearing, 43
Plain (flat) washer, 8
Plain/plain journal bearings, 42
Plain pin, 11
Plain thrust bearing, 43
Planet (epicyclic) gear, 22
Plastic-head mallet, 86
Plastic pipes, 31
Plastics, 120–121
Plate (design feature), 54
Plate (radial) cam, 79
Plates
- arc welded, 109
- bed, 47
- brake friction, 60–61
- catch (lathe), 104
- clutch friction, 63–64
- clutch pressure, 64

Plates *continued*
cover-, 49
deep drawn, 116
flame cut, 112
gas welded, 111
non-ferrous metal, 59
pressure (clutch), 64
presswork on, 116
ribbed, 55
steel, 57
steel chequer, 58
surface, 91
welded, 109–112
Plating, cadmium/chromium, 120
Pliers, 92
Plug cock valve, 38
Plug (pipe fitting), 29
Plug weld, 110
Plunger (design feature), 54
Pneumatic (air bellows) spring, 18
Polishing (buffing) mop, 105
Polyethylene, 120
Polypropylene, 120
Polystyrene, 120
Polytetrafluorethylene (PTFE), 121
Polythene, 120
Polyurethane, 121
Polyvinylchloride (PVC), 120
Poppet (mushroom) valve, 37, 112
Pop rivet, 11
Porous bearing, 43
Port (design feature), 55
Ports, 36–37, 55
Positive return cam, 81
Power absorption brakes (dynamometers), 62
Power saws, 107
Power tapping/attachment, 100
Power transmission screw threads, 14–15
Precision grinders, 104–105
Press/presswork, 116
Pressure angle (gear), 19
Pressure plate (clutch), 64
Pressure regulator valve (gas welding), 111
Profile (cam), 79
Prony brake, 62–63
Propane gas (welding), 111
Protractor (combination set), 88
Pulley block, 72–73
Pulley drive (drilling machine), 98
Pulley hub, 53
Pulleys, 70–74
Punch, centre, 84
Punched hole, 52
Punch (impact extrusion), 116
Punching (presswork), 116
Pure copper, 118

Quick-return mechanism, 76

Races (bearing), 44
Rack-and-pinion gear, 21
Rack-and-pinion steering, 79
Radial (plate) cam, 79
Radial-arm drilling machine, 99
Radius (design feature), 55
Rag (foundation) bolt, 4
Ram (die casting), 113
Ram (slotter), 101
Rasp, 83
Rasp (Surform-type), 83
Ratchet handle, 94
Ratchet mechanism, 76
Ratchet screwdriver, 93
Rawlbolt (anchor bolt), 4
Rayon, 120
Reamed hole, 53
Reamers/reaming, 85, 100
Recessed socket-head screw, 3, 55
Recess (faucet) (design feature), 50
Reciprocating power hacksaw, 107
Reciprocating surface-grinder table, 104
Rectangular bar, 58–59
Rectangular key (shaft), 40
Rectangular-section lever, 75
Rectangular-section spring, 15–16
Reducers (pipe fittings), 29, 32
Resin, acrylic (Perspex), 120
Resin-cored wire solder, 108
Resin flux, 108
Resistance seam weld, 110–111
Resistance welding, 110–111
Resistance wire, 119
Retainer (bearing), 44
Retaining rings (circlips), 13
Ribbed belt/drive, 71
Ribbed neck coach bolt, 2–3
Ribbed plate, 55
Rib (design feature), 55
Right-hand screw thread, 13
Rightward welding, 111
Ring (epicyclic) gear, 22
Ring oiler bearing, 43
Ring (round) nut, 6
Ring spanner (box wrench), 93
Ring spring, 18
Riser (casting), 113
Riveted joints, 10
Rivet materials, 10
Rivets, 9–11
Rods
arc welding, 109
brazing, 108
connecting, 75
cottered joint for, 42
filler, 111
pin (knuckle) joint for, 41
piston, 26
screwed, 2
sealing of, 26
tie, 41
Rolled steel sections, 115
Roller and rocker arm cam follower, 80
Roller bearings, 45–46
Roller cam follower, 80
Roller chain/sprocket drive, 73–74
Roller forming tool (spinning), 117
Roller freewheeling clutch, 64
Rolling-contact bearing, 44
Rolling/rolling mill, 115
Rolling (slab) milling/cutter, 97
Roll pin, 11
Rolls for I section, 115

Root (screw thread), 13
Rope (band) brake (dynamometer), 62–63
Rope drive/pulley, 72–73
Ropes, 72–73
Rotary files, 82
Rotary wire brush, 105
Rotating machine-tool table, 106
Rotor (design feature), 55
Round bar, 58–59
Round file, 82
Round head countersunk rivet, 10
Round head screw, 5
Round key (shaft), 41
Round-nose pliers, 92
Round (ring) nut, 6
Round-section circlip, 13
Rubber belt, 70
Rubber-bushed pin-type flexible shaft coupling, 67
Rubber gasket, 28
Rubber hose (auto), 33
Rubber insert sealing washer, 28
Rubber, natural/synthetic, 121
Rubber, pipe, 29, 33
Rubber springs, 18
Rubber-tyre-type flexible shaft coupling, 68
Rules, 86–87
Runner (casting), 113

Saddle key (shaft), 41
Saddle (lathe), 102
Safety valves, 35
Sand casting/equipment, 112–113
Saunders valve, 37
Sawing machines, 107
Scissors jack, 78
Scotch yoke mechanism, 76
Scrapers, 82–83
Screw-and-nut steering, 79
Screw-cutting /die (hand), 85
Screw-cutting (lathe), 102
Screw-cutting tool setting gauge, 87
Screw-down bearing greaser, 46
Screwdrivers, 93
Screwed brass pipe couplings/fittings, 31–32
Screwed iron pipe fittings, 29
Screwed rod, 2
Screwed shaft, 39
Screw heads, 5
Screw jack, 77
Screw pitch (thread) gauge, 87
Screws, 4–6
Screw shut-down (globe) valve, 34
Screw taps, 85
Screw threads/details/dimensions, 1, 13–15
Scribers, 87
Scriber with surface gauge, 88
Sealed ball bearing, 45
Sealing (rods), 26
Sealing washers, 28–29
Seals/joints/gaskets, 23–29
Seam weld, 110
Second order lever, 74
Segmental carbon ring seal, 26
Self-aligning ball bearing, 45
Self-centring three-jaw chuck, 103
Self-oiling bearing, 43
Self-tapping screws, 5
Sensitive drilling machine, 99
Serrated lock washer, 9
Serrated neck coach bolt, 2–3
Set screws, 5
Set (*see* Chisels)
Shaft collars, 39, 43
Shaft couplings, 66 (*see* Flexible shaft couplings)
Shafts (types/details), 22–23, 38–41, 43
Shaping machine/components/tools (shaper), 100–101
Shearing/machine, 116
Shears (snips/tinsnips), 93
Shear/tension rubber spring, 18
Sheaves (pulleys), 72–73
Sheet metals
  duralumin, 119
  non-ferrous metal, 59
  steel, flat/corrugated, 57
Shell endmilling/cutter, 97
Shells (journal bearing), 42
Shock absorbers, 78
Shoe (brake), 61–62
Shoulder (shaft), 38
Shoulder socket bolt/screw, 3
Side and face milling/cutter, 97
Side-cutting (knife) tool, 103
Sight feed drop oiler (bearings), 46
Silicon (alloy element), 118
Silicon carbide (abrasive), 104
Silver solder (soldering), 108
Silver steel, 118
Simple harmonic motion cam, 80
Simple square drift, 84
Sindanyo (asbestos), 121
Single block brake, 60
Single helical gear, 20
Single plate (disk) friction clutch, 63
Single row ball bearing, 44
Single-start worm gear, 21
Skew bevel gear, 21
Slab (rolling) milling/cutter, 97
Sledge hammer (maul), 86
Sleeve (bush) (bearing), 42
Sleeve (design feature), 56
Sleeve shaft coupling, 66
Sleeve valve, 37
Slider, 75
Slideway (lathe), 102
Sliding contact bearing, 42
Sliding expansion pipe joint, 32
Slot (design feature), 56
Slot milling/cutter, 96–97
Slotted head screw, 5
Slotted nut, 7
Slotter (vertical shaper), 101
Slotting machine, 101
Slot weld, 110
Slow bend pipe fitting, 29
Sluide (gate) valve, 36
Snap head rivet, 10
Snips (tinsnips/shears), 93
Snug (pin), 3–4
Socket head screws/bolts, 3, 5
Socket pipe fitting, 29
Socket screw wrench (Allen key), 3, 94
Socket spanner (wrench)/attachment, 94
Soft hammers, 86

Soft solder/soldering methods, 107–108
Soldered copper (capillary) pipe fittings, 30
Soldering iron bit, 107
Soldering irons, 107–108
Soldering torch, 107
Solders, 107–108
Solid bolted flanged coupling, 66
Solid shaft, 38
Spacer (distance piece) (design feature), 49
Spanners (wrenchers), 2–3, 93–95
Spelter (brazing), 108
Spherical plug cock valve, 38
Spigot (design feature), 56
Spindle, machine tool, 95–99
Spindle nose (lathe), 104
Spindle (small shaft), 38
Spinning/equipment, 117
Spiral bevel gear, 20
Spiral torsion spring, 16–17
Splash bearing lubrication, 47
Splined gear shaft, 23
Splines (shaft), 40
Split (cotter) pin, 12
Split (halved) pedestal bearing, 42
Split but, 7
Spool valve, 37
Spotfaced (knifed) hole, 53
Spotfacing, 100
Spot weld, 110
Sprag/over-running clutch, 64
Spring collet (chuck), 103
Spring data, 16
Spring dividers, 89
Spring-joint callipers, 88
Spring-loaded carbon face seal, 27
Spring-loaded safety valve, 35
Spring (compression stop) lock nut, 7
Springs, 15–18
Spring set brake, 61
Spring tape rule, 87
Spring washer, 9
Spring wire hose clip, 12
Sprocket (chain drive), 73–74
Sprue (lost wax casting), 113
Spur gear, 19–23
Square bar, 58–59
Square (combination set), 88
Square head bolt, 1
Square hole, 53
Square neck coach bolt, 2–3
Square nut, 6
Square power transmission screw threads, 13–14
Square shaft splines, 40
Square (try square), 88
Stainless steel, 118
Stamped spring nut, 8
Standard ball bearing, 44
Standard grinding wheel, 105
Standard lip seal, 25
Standard pliers, 92
Steam safety valve, 35
Steel angle section, 58, 115
Steel bar, 57–58
Steel chequer plate, 58
Steel grinding wheel (abrasive coated), 105
Steel I section, 58, 115
Steel pipe, 31
Steel rivet, 10
Steels, 118
Steel sealing washer (rubber insert), 28
Steel sections, 58
Steel sheet, 57
Steel strip, 57
Steering mechanisms, 79
Stepped pulley drives, 70–71
Stillson (pipe) wrench, 95
Straight bevel gear, 20
Straight peen hammer, 86
Straight pipe coupling, 29, 32
Straight reamer, 85
Straight shank twist drill, 84
Straight shaper tool, 101
Straight soldering iron, 108
Stock, die, 85
Stop valve, 34
Strap clamp, 91
Strip (steel), 57
Strut (design feature), 56
Stud brass pipe coupling, 32
Stud/stud bolt/box, studding, 2
Stuffing box (gland), 23–24
Sun (epicyclic) gear, 22
Surface finish, shaft, 38
Surface gauge with scriber, 88
Surface grinder, 104
Surface plate, 91
Surface table, 91
Surform rasp, 83
Swage (forging), 114
Swan neck shaper tool, 101
Sweating (joints), 107
Swivel adjustment (shaper), 100
Synthetic rubbers, 121

T bolt, 3
T-section bar, 115
T slot, 3, 56
T-joint pipe fitting, 29–30, 32
Tab washer, 9
Tables, 91, 95, 98, 104, 106, 109
Tack weld, 110
Tailstock (lathe), 102
Tangent cam, 81
Tap bolt, 2
Taper neck pan head rivet, 10
Taper pin, 11
Taper reamer, 85
Taper roller (bearings), 44–46
Taper (shaft), 38–39
Taper shank twist drill, 84
Taper washer, 8
Tapped/through blind holes, 53
Tapping, 85, 100
Tapping attachment, 100
Taps, 85
Tap wrench, 85
Telescopic hydraulic shock absorber, 78
Tensioner, chain drive, 73
Tension/shear rubber spring, 18
Thermoplastic/thermosetting, 120
Thickness (feeler) gauge, 87
Thimble (micrometer), 89
Thin nuts, 6
Third order lever, 74